Advances in

OPTICAL *and* ELECTRON
MICROSCOPY

Advances in

OPTICAL *and* ELECTRON MICROSCOPY

Volume 7

Edited by

V. E. COSSLETT

Department of Physics,
Cavendish Laboratory, University of Cambridge,
England

AND

R. BARER

Department of Human Biology and Anatomy,
University of Sheffield, England

ACADEMIC PRESS · 1978
LONDON, NEW YORK AND SAN FRANCISCO
A Subsidiary of Harcourt Brace Jovanovich, Publishers

ACADEMIC PRESS INC. (LONDON) LTD.
24/28 Oval Road,
London NW1

United States Edition published by
ACADEMIC PRESS INC.
111 Fifth Avenue
New York, New York 10003

Library of Congress Catalog Card Number: 65–25134
ISBN: 0–12–029907–0

PRINTED IN GREAT BRITAIN BY
THE WHITEFRIARS PRESS LTD.
LONDON AND TONBRIDGE

Contributors List

H. C. BERG, *Department of Molecular, Cellular and Developmental Biology, University of Colorado, Boulder, Colorado 80309, U.S.A.*

A. CASTENHOLZ, *Department of Human Biology, University of Kassel, Germany.*

P. W. HAWKES, *Laboratoire d'Optique électronique du CNRS, 29, rue Jeanne Marvig, 31055 Toulouse Cedex, France.*

D. L. MISELL, *Biophysics Division, National Institute for Medical Research, Mill Hill, London NW7 1AA, England. (Present address: Institution of Metallurgists, Northway House, Whetstone, London N20, 9LW, England).*

H. J. PINCUS, *Department of Geological Sciences, The University of Wisconsin-Milwaukee, Milwaukee, Wisconsin 53201, U.S.A.*

B. K. VAINSHTEIN, *Institute of Crystallography, Academy of Sciences, Moscow, U.S.S.R.*

Preface

In the Preface to the first volume in this series (1966) we excused its appearance on the grounds of a need for informative reviews "in a subject like microscopy which is not only advancing rapidly but impinges on so many branches of science and technology". That we had identified a real need in our chosen field has been confirmed by the reception accorded to successive volumes by readers and reviewers. Volume 7 continues the aim of wide-ranging coverage without, we hope, sacrificing depth for breadth.

Two of the articles on optical microscopy deal with problems arising from the study of moving objects. Berg offers a solution to the frustrating problem of keeping a motile organism, moving randomly in three dimensions, both in view and in focus. The construction of a microscope capable of doing this automatically would have seemed impossible at one time, but modern technology has provided several solutions. Castenholz applies a principle well known in radiology but little used in microscopy to the recording and quantitative evaluation of certain types of movement of microscopic objects. Pincus discusses optical diffraction analysis in some detail. Similar techniques have been used to analyse electron micrographs but the method has been less widely used in optical microscopy. Pincus' examples are mainly geological but there may be many suitable problems in biology and materials science.

In electron microscopy the emphasis on this occasion is on physical principles of image formation and interpretation rather than on aspects of instrumentation. Hawkes treats at length the subject of coherence and partial coherence. Although there is a considerable literature on the related problem in light optics, this is the first thorough treatment for electron optics. Misell deals with the phase problem in similar detail. Here the literature has been quite extensive, on the experimental as well as the theoretical side, partly because of the related (but more difficult) situation in X-ray structure research. Misell brings it all together, including the prospects for imaging single atoms. Finally Vainshtein describes recent progress at the next level of analysis, the determination of the three dimensional structure of macro-molecules.

As previously, we believe it will be of interest to list the topics on which articles for future volumes are being commissioned. The editors will be grateful for suggestions for, and especially offers of, articles on other subjects of current importance in microscopy.

Use of lasers in microscopy
Microscopy with polarized light
Reflection interference microscopy
Reflectance microscopy
New methods of investigating chromosome structure
High resolution electron microscopy
Cryomicroscopy
Image intensifiers for electron microscopy
Optimisation of conditions for very high resolution
Phase contrast electron microscopy
Characteristics of electron guns
Radiation damage and image resolution

V. E. COSSLETT

August, 1978   R. BARER

Contents

Microkymography and Related Techniques
A. CASTENHOLZ

Coherence in Electron Optics
P. W. HAWKES

The Phase Problem in Electron Microscopy

D. L. MISELL

Electron Microscopical Analysis of the Three-Dimensional Structure of Biological Macromolecules

B. K. VAINSHTEIN

The Tracking Microscope

HOWARD C. BERG

Department of Molecular, Cellular and Developmental Biology,
University of Colorado,
Boulder, Colorado 80309, U.S.A.

I. Motivation

Many bacteria swim. Cells of diameter 10^{-4} cm may move steadily at speeds of the order of 30×10^{-4} cm/sec, then abruptly reverse or choose new directions at random. If able to respond to sensory inputs, they bias the probability of the occurrence of these all-or-none events and migrate to regions that are hot or cold, light or dark, or of favourable chemical content.‡ How is one to study such behaviour? At magnifications high enough for close observation, the cells move out of focus in a fraction of a second; when confined to a thin chamber, their motion is perturbed by its walls. These difficulties have been overcome by the development of a microscope that automatically follows the motion of individual cells in three dimensions (Berg, 1971). The design and operation of this instrument are reviewed here.

II. Rationale

If a chamber containing a suspension of bacteria is moved so that the position of a given organism remains fixed, the displacement of the chamber will provide a measure of the motion of that organism relative to the medium

‡ For recent reviews on bacterial behaviour, see Adler (1975, 1976), Berg (1975a,b,c), and Koshland (1976).

in which it is suspended. Since the propulsion of a micro-organism is governed by viscous rather than inertial forces (Ludwig, 1930; Taylor, 1952; Purcell, 1976), the displacement of the chamber will not affect the motile behaviour of the bacterium in any way (Berg, 1971). One needs a microscope with a detector that monitors changes in the position of the image of the bacterium and an electro-mechanical transducer that drives the chamber so that the image moves back toward the centre of the detector. If the bacterium swims 30 diameters/sec and its image is about the size of the detector, the signals generated by the detector will change appreciably in 1/30 sec. The transducer must be able to move in the right direction in times shorter than this. It can do so only if its resonant frequencies exceed 30 Hz; the mass and moments of inertia of the moving parts of the transducer must be small and their suspension stiff. If the transducer is driven at frequencies higher than its resonant frequencies, the system will oscillate; the gains of the servo-loops must be attenuated at high frequencies. The filter of choice is an RC circuit, since its phase shift is at most $\pi/2$.

III. Design

A system embodying these principles is shown schematically in Fig. 1 (Berg, 1971). The chamber containing the bacteria is mounted between a long-working distance phase-contrast condenser and a bright contrast phase objective.‡ The beam emerging at the top of the trinocular is split so that three images of the organism being tracked fall on six fibre-optics fibres, each leading to its own photomultiplier. The diameters of the fibres are all the same, about the width of the image of the bacterium. One image is focused on the ends of the set x_1, x_2, y_1, y_2, the second in front of z_1, the third behind z_2. When the bacterium moves in the $+X$ direction, the image moves so that more light falls on x_1 than x_2; when it moves in the $+Y$ direction, more light falls on y_1 than y_2; when it moves in the $+Z$ direction, more light falls on z_1 than z_2 (because the image focuses more sharply on z_1 and less sharply on z_2). Signals proportional to the errors in displacement are obtained from the differences in the photomultiplier outputs $x_1 - x_2$, $y_1 - y_2$, and $z_1 - z_2$. They are amplified, filtered ($RC = 8$ sec) and used in current-injection circuits to drive the coils in the electromagnetic transducer. Each coil is mounted in the annular gap of a cylindrical magnet. Its equilibrium position is determined by the balance between the electro-

---

‡ A dark-contrast phase objective also can be used, provided that the error signals are inverted. Success depends on the absolute difference between the intensity of the image and that of the background, not on the image contrast. Images obtained with dark-field microscopes look brighter, but they may not be suitable.

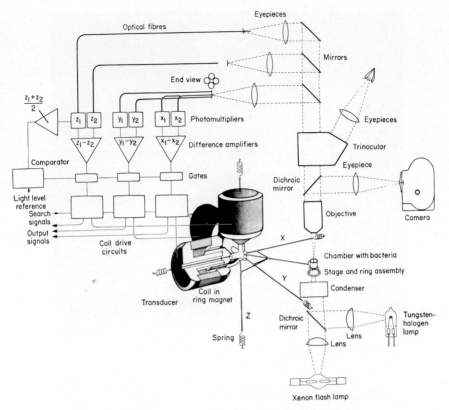

FIG. 1. Schematic diagram of the tracking microscope.

magnetic force, due to the current, and the net elastic force, due to the difference in the lengths of a pair of springs. The currents are bipolar; when the power is off, the stage rests at its centre position; when the power is on, it can be driven about 5×10^{-2} cm in any direction. The servo loop is closed by a comparator when the amount of light falling on the detector exceeds a predetermined value (Fig. 1).

The system is built around a Nikon S-Ke microscope and a Zeiss Optovar (Fig. 2). The transducer is demountable (Fig. 3). The ends of the drive coils can be seen when the transducer is viewed obliquely from below (Fig. 4). Since the springs can move sideways as well as lengthwise, the coils can rotate as well as translate; there are six degrees of freedom. The translational modes have resonant frequencies of about 80 Hz, the rotational modes about 120 Hz. The translational modes are damped electrically, the rotational ones by a ring immersed in an annular pool of oil (Berg, 1971).

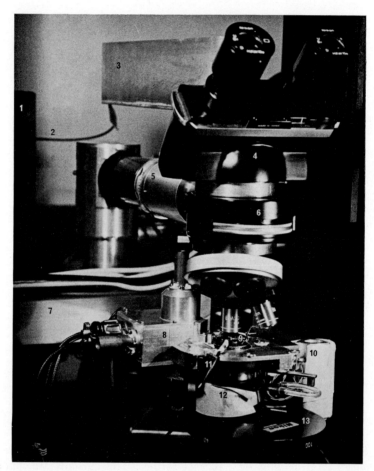

FIG. 2. Optical system: (1) Photomultiplier housing (mostly out of view, standing with the microscope on a vibration-isolation table, Barry Controls Serva Bench Mark III-1). (2) Fibre optics bundle. (3) Detector housing (contains mirrors, eye-pieces, and input ends of fibre-optics fibres). (4) Trinocular beam splitter. (5) Camera relay lens. (6) Zeiss Optovar (lenses of magnification 1·6 and 2·0 replaced by dichroic mirrors that reflect part of the light to the camera). (7) Beam that supports camera (bolted to the frame of the vibration-isolation table). (8) Transducer. (9) Tempera-ture-controlled housing (for the tracking chamber). (10) Temperature-controlled bucket (for fluids to be transferred to the tracking chamber). (11) Thermistor cable. (12) Condenser cooling coil (covered with tape). (13) Condenser turret. Light sources (not shown): for tracking, a tungsten-halogen lamp, Sylvania FCR, run DC; for photography, a xenon flash lamp, Illumination Industries X-80-2084-6.

The ring is mounted under the stage on three struts and is concentric with the optical axis (Fig. 3). The stage and ring assembly are enclosed by a temperature-controlled housing (Fig. 5) that also holds the pool of oil (oil not shown). The housing is fastened to the top of the condenser via a thin stainless-steel sleeve. Its temperature is sensed by a thermistor and changed

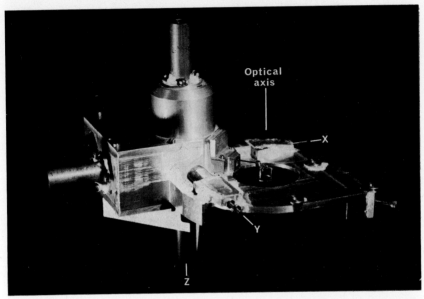

FIG. 3. Transducer. The axes are labeled X, Y, and Z. The stage is mounted on the optical axis at the end of a tungsten strut. The tracking chamber (not shown) sits on the stage. The ring below the stage is immersed in an annular pool of oil (not shown).

by a small heating coil (non-inductively wound). For work below ambient temperature, the body of the condenser is water cooled (see Fig. 2). The chambers (Fig. 6) either sit on the stage or clip on to it. They are made of tantalum, because tantalum has a high thermal conductivity and is chemically inert. They are small, partly for reasons of mass, partly to inhibit convective flow (see below).

IV. OPERATION

A. *Manipulating Bacteria*

The chambers shown in Fig. 6 have been used in studies of the motion of bacteria in spatial (Berg and Brown, 1972) and temporal (Brown and Berg, 1974) gradients of chemical attractants. The spatial gradients are generated

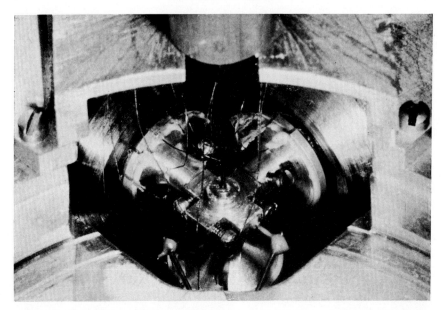

Fɪɢ. 4. Transducer drive coils seen projecting from the cylindrical magnets (Z bottom, X left, Y right). The transducer is viewed obliquely from below.

by the diffusion of the chemical from the capillary tube into the chamber (Futrelle and Berg, 1972; Adler, 1973).‡ The chamber is filled with a suspension of bacteria, the capillary tube with a solution of the chemical; the capillary tube is inserted, and the top window is sealed on. The gradient changes with time, but not rapidly; the bacteria are stimulated as they swim from place to place. The temporal gradients are generated by enzymatic reaction. The inlet pipe (Fig. 6) is connected with polyethylene tubing to a vial containing a suspension of bacteria and substrates for the reaction; the outlet pipe is connected to a valve on a vacuum line; the chamber is purged of air, and the top window is sealed on. Enzyme is added to the vial, and the mixture is drawn into the chamber. Subsequent changes in concentration are strictly temporal; the bacteria are stimulated regardless of how they swim.

Convective flow can introduce serious errors, particularly with cells that swim slowly. This is not a problem with the chambers shown in Fig. 6 (flow rates 10^{-5} cm/sec or less), but it is with chambers that have four windows (additional windows in front and back) used for stimulation of cells that respond to light (flow rates 10^{-4} cm/sec or more, higher when the

‡ In the former reference, for $\sqrt{Dt}$ read $\sqrt{(Dt)}$; for γ^2 in the argument of *erfc* read 2γ. For a solution of the diffusion equation with different boundary conditions, see Brokaw (1958).

stimulus light is on). The convection can be eliminated as follows: First, a suspension of bacteria is drawn into the chamber (via inlet and outlet pipes, as in Fig. 6). Then the lower fourth of this suspension is displaced by an identical one containing, in addition, 0·1 M stachyose. The diffusion constant and specific gravity of this tetrasaccharide are such that a vertical density gradient is established in a few minutes that stabilizes the fluid against convective flow for an hour or more. A procedure of this kind is required in any study of the motion of inert particles.

The motile behaviour of bacteria can be monitored in another rather novel way. The helical filaments that propel bacteria are driven at their base by rotary motors (Berg and Anderson, 1973). A cell tethered to a glass

Fig. 5. Stage and ring assembly and temperature-controlled housing (expanded view; oil and thermistor not shown).

slide by one of these filaments rotates, now clockwise, now counter-clockwise (Silverman and Simon, 1974; the filament is linked to the glass with anti-filament antibodies). The tracking microscope can follow this motion (Berg, 1974; see below). A suspension of cells is mixed with a solution of antibody, and the mixture is allowed to settle over a chamber window. The chamber

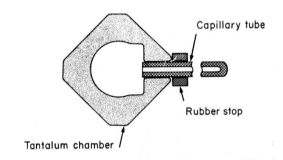

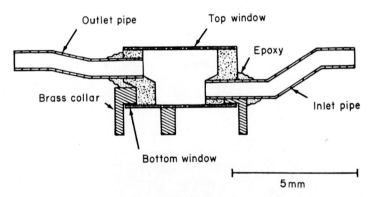

FIG. 6. Scale drawings of two tracking chambers, one (top) shown in horizontal section, the other (bottom) in vertical section. The bodies are tantalum, the windows glass. The bottom windows are attached with a silicone rubber cement (GE RTV-102), the top windows with a hydrocarbon vacuum grease (Apiezon L). The brass prongs (bottom) are used to clip the chamber to the stage.

(Fig. 6, bottom) is filled to overflowing with cell-free medium, and the window is inverted and sealed on. The cells are stimulated by displacing this medium with solutions containing chemical attractants at different concentrations (see Macnab and Koshland, 1972; Larsen et al., 1974). A single cell can be studied for several hours.

B. *Collecting and Analysing Data*

The signals that provide a measure of the position of the bacterium (voltages proportional to the currents in the drive coils) are amplified and filtered (by simple RC circuits or Butterworth four-pole filters), displayed by an analogue monitor, and converted to digital form for on-line computer analysis or storage on computer-compatible magnetic tape (see Berg and Brown, 1974).‡ Factors for converting the X, Y, and Z scales from volts to micrometres are determined empirically; displacements along the Y and Z axes depend linearly on the voltages; the X axis requires a small quadratic correction (for reasons unknown). The Z axis is a special case, because motion in this direction changes the thickness of the medium between the objective and the bacterium being tracked; the displacement of the bacterium is n times larger than the displacement of the chamber, where n is the index of the refraction of the medium. Organisms are manoeuvred to the sensitive region of the field by search signals (Fig. 1) generated by a three-axis joy-stick designed for model aeroplane control. The data acquisition system is turned on by the comparator. At concentrations of order 10^7 cells/ml, bacteria are easy to find but collisions are rare. The experiments are monitored visually in order to rule out such events.

The coordinates X, Y, Z and/or their time derivatives (generated by analogue circuits) are digitized. A string of data points is obtained that represents the position and/or the velocity of the organism as a function of time. The data load is far smaller than that encountered in a scanning microscope. With a scanning microscope, one would have to examine some 10^5 points to locate a single organism (assuming 10^4 bacteria, each of volume 10^{-12} ml, in 1 mm^3). Once found, the organism would be easier to find again, but some form of image analysis would be required. Although the tracking microscope follows one cell at a time, as many as 100 cells can be sampled in a single experiment.

One of the most useful techniques for preliminary analysis is stereo display. One asks the computer to project and plot the X, Y, Z data on a plane as it might appear in front of either eye. If this is done on microfilm, the film can be examined with a stereo viewer. Enlargements of two such slides are shown in Fig. 7.

The computational methods used with the bacterium *Escherichia coli* to distinguish intervals during which changes in direction are gradual ("runs") from those in which they are abrupt ("twiddles") are described in detail elsewhere (Berg and Brown, 1974).

A camera (Fig. 1) has been added for work on the alga *Chlamydomonas*

‡ This is a reprint of Berg and Brown (1972) with an addendum that adds technical and mathematical detail.

reinhardtii (Fig. 7), an organism that is able to sense the *direction* of a beam of light. In order to analyse this sensory process, one needs to know the orientation of the cell as well as its position. The tracking data are used to trigger the camera to record specific events.

If the image of a cell is larger than the detector, the tracker follows one

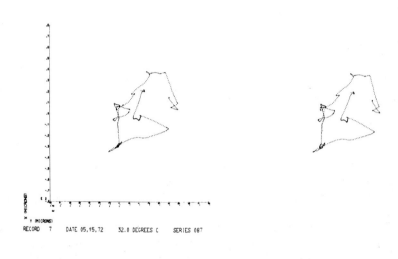

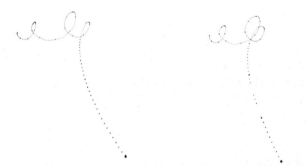

Fig. 7. Stereo pairs of tracks of the bacterium *Escherichia coli* (top) and the alga *Chlamydomonas reinhardtii* (bottom). The plots will fuse and appear in stereo if viewed with two magnifying lenses. *E. coli:* A random walk in an isotropic medium. Strain AW405, 32°C, 272 data points, 12·6 data points per sec, mean speed 21 μm/sec, 26 runs. *C. reinhardtii:* Movement along a right-handed helical path, tracked at wavelengths greater than 610 nm. Strain 120c(+), 27°C, 211 data points, 48·6 data points per sec, mean speed 35 μm/sec, mean yaw 2·3 rad/sec, mean roll 3·9 rad/sec (data courtesy of Robert Smyth). The scales are 1·6 × 10^{-2} cm long.

edge.‡ The currents that move the transducer are proportional to error signals that, in turn, depend on the offset of the image on the detector. The offset is large when the transducer is working near the limits of its range, small when it is working near the centre of its range: the offset increases as the organism moves away from the centre of the chamber. This is possible only if the edge of the cell closest to the centre of the chamber is imaged on the detector (for the Z axis, if the edge of the cell closest to the centre of the chamber is the more out of focus). Given this fact, one can show that the transducer will execute a nearly circular path on following a tethered rod-shaped cell (a cell rotating about an axis normal to the axis of the rod). If the cell spins clockwise, the transducer executes a clockwise path. If the axis of rotation is near one end, the transducer and the cell move at the same frequency; if it is at the centre of the cell, the transducer moves at twice the frequency. The X and Y velocities of the tracked point of one such cell are shown in Fig. 8. Data of this kind are of use in studies

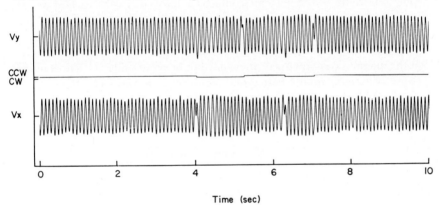

Time (sec)

FIG. 8. A strip-chart record of the X and Y velocities (Vx and Vy) of the tracked point of a tethered cell. An event marker sensitive to the difference in phase between the two signals also is shown. The cell was spinning at 11 Hz, now clockwise (CW), now counter-clockwise (CCW).

of bacterial chemotaxis (Berg and Tedesco, 1975). They are not of much use, however, in studies of the fine structure of the rotary motion, because the transducer will not respond faithfully at high frequencies. One can, instead, allow the rotating image to sweep across a pinhole and monitor the intensity of the transmitted light (Berg, 1976). A technique of this kind has been used by Rikmenspoel (1965) to measure the velocities of spermatozoa.

‡ The situation is more complicated if the image has structure, as is the case for *Chlamydomonas*. The tracker tends to follow first one part of such an image and then another. The discontinuities tend to occur along the Z axis.

V. Possible Improvements

The range and/or resonance frequencies of the transducer could be increased. With Alnico V, fields of 5000 gauss should be possible (instead of 2200 gauss; Berg, 1971); the ring magnets are too short, and the ratio of the coil diameter to the axial gap length is too small (R. J. Parker, private communication). One could do even better with ring magnets of cobalt–rare earth (Nesbitt and Wernick, 1973); these were not available when the tracker was developed. If the coils were impregnated with a silicone compound rather than epoxy, they could be run at higher currents (higher temperatures). Note that the resonance frequencies are determined by the mass of the moving parts of the transducer and the spring constants. Once the spring constants are set, the range is limited by the available applied force. The force is proportional to the product of the intensity of the magnetic field and the current.

The sensitivity of the detector could be improved. In the earliest design, photomultipliers with comparatively large dark currents were used (RCA 6217), so ceramic ring magnets were taped to their faces (see Berg, 1971). The photomultipliers now in use have smaller dark currents (RCA C7164R), but the magnets were retained; they may not be required (P. C. Thonemann, private communication). Better photomultipliers are available; the choice was limited for reasons of economy.

VI. Related Systems

Other tracking schemes are possible. If one were willing to deal with objects in a single field of view, the X and Y tracking could be done with a computer-controlled image dissecting tube (or equivalent), the Z tracking by servo-control. The Z-axis error signal could be generated from out-of-focus scans (see Preston, 1973; Wayland, 1975). Construction of a stage that could move rapidly along the Z axis should be comparatively easy. A computer-linked video system has been developed for analysing the motion of micro-organisms in two-dimensional projection (Davenport et al., 1970), but a television raster scan may not be the most efficient for use in a tracker.

A manually operated device has been developed for following the motion of bacteria over comparatively large distances (Lovely et al., 1974). The bacteria are suspended in a cuvette mounted on a micromanipulator driven by three stepping motors. The stepping rates are controlled by potentiometers. The operator views the suspension with a horizontally mounted dark-field microscope and tries to keep the image of a given cell in focus in the centre of the field. He does this by moving the potentiometers with hand and foot.

An automated three-dimensional tracking system has been built for following the motion of the sporangium of *Phycomyces*, a spherical object about 5×10^{-2} cm in diameter borne by an aerial stalk (Foster, 1972). The stalk elongates at rates of order 10^{-4} cm/sec and reaches lengths of several centimetres. Optical systems parallel to the X and Y axes project contours of the sporangium on three sets of edge detectors. Error signals control DC servo-motors that drive pistons in hydraulic systems that, in turn, move a heavy-duty ball-bearing X, Y, Z stage. The position of the sporangium is held fixed; the growth of the stalk is measured in microscopic detail.

For references to papers dealing with more conventional methods of measuring bacterial motility, see Berg (1971, 1975b). For techniques developed for measuring the velocity of blood cells, see Monro (1966).

Acknowledgements

The tracking microscope was developed at Harvard University (1968–70) with funds obtained in part from a PHS Biomedical Sciences Support Grant. Work at the University of Colorado has been supported by the Research Corporation, the National Science Foundation, and the National Eye Institute.

References

Adler, J. (1973). A method for measuring chemotaxis and use of the method to determine optimum conditions for chemotaxis by *Escherichia coli*. *J. gen. Microbiol.* **74**, 77–91.

Adler, J. (1975). Chemotaxis in bacteria. *A. Rev. Biochem.* **44**, 341–356.

Adler, J. (1976). The sensing of chemicals by bacteria. *Scient. Am.* **234**, 4, 40–47.

Berg, H. C. (1971). How to track bacteria. *Rev. scient. Instrum.* **42**, 868–871.

Berg, H. C. (1974). Dynamic properties of bacterial flagellar motors. *Nature, Lond.* **249**, 77–79.

Berg, H. C. (1975a). Bacterial behaviour. *Nature, Lond.* **254**, 389–392.

Berg, H. C. (1975b). Chemotaxis in bacteria. *A. Rev. Biophys. Bioeng.* **4**, 119–136.

Berg, H. C. (1975c). How bacteria swim. *Scient. Am.* **233**, 2, 36–44.

Berg, H. C. (1976). Does the flagellar rotary motor step? *In* "Cell Motility" (R. Goldman, T. Pollard and J. Rosenbaum, eds), Cold Spring Harbor Conferences on Cell Proliferation, Vol. 3, pp. A47–A56. Cold Spring Harbor Laboratory, Cold Spring Harbor.

Berg, H. C. and Anderson, R. A. (1973). Bacteria swim by rotating their flagellar filaments. *Nature, Lond.* **245**, 380–382.

Berg, H. C. and Brown, D. A. (1972). Chemotaxis in *Escherichia coli* analysed by three-dimensional tracking. *Nature, Lond.* **239**, 500–504.

Berg, H. C. and Brown, D. A. (1974). Chemotaxis in *Escherichia coli* analyzed by three-dimensional tracking. *In* "Chemotaxis: Its Biology and Biochemistry" (E. Sorkin, ed.), Antibiotics and Chemotherapy, Vol. 19, pp. 55–78. Karger, Basel.

Berg, H. C. and Tedesco, P. M. (1975). Transient response to chemotactic stimuli in *Escherichia coli*. *Proc. Natn. Acad. Sci. USA* **72**, 3235–3239.

Brokaw, C. J. (1958). Chemotaxis of bracken spermatozoids. *J. exp. Biol.* **35**, 197–212.

Brown, D. A. and Berg, H. C. (1974). Temporal stimulation of chemotaxis in *Escherichia coli*. *Proc. Natn. Acad. Sci. USA* **71**, 1388–1392 (1974).

Davenport, D., Culler, G. J., Greaves, J. O. B., Forward, R. B. and Hand, W. G. (1970). The investigation of the behavior of microorganisms by computerized television. *IEEE Trans. Bio-Med. Engr.* BME-17, 230–237.

Foster, K. W. (1972). The photoresponses of *Phycomyces*: Analysis using manual techniques and an automated machine which precisely tracks and measures growth during programmed stimuli. Ph.D. Thesis, California Institute of Technology.

Futrelle, R. P. and Berg, H. C. (1972). Specification of gradients used for studies of chemotaxis. *Nature, Lond.* **239**, 517–518.

Koshland, D. E. Jr. (1976). Bacterial chemotaxis as a simple model for a sensory system. *Trends biochem. Sci.* **1**, 1–3.

Larsen, S. H., Reader, R. W., Kort, E. N., Tso, W.-W. and Adler, J. (1974). Change in direction of flagellar rotation is the basis of the chemotactic response in *Escherichia coli*. *Nature, Lond.* **249**, 74–77.

Lovely, P., Dahlquist, F. W., Macnab. R. and Koshland, D. E. Jr. (1974). An instrument for recording the motions of microorganisms in chemical gradients. *Rev. scient. Instrum.* **45**, 683–686.

Ludwig, W. (1930). Zur Theorie der Flimmerbewegung (Dynamik, Nutzeffekt, Energiebilanz). *Z. vergl. Physiol.* **13**, 397–504.

Macnab, R. and Koshland, D. E. Jr. (1972). The gradient-sensing mechanism in bacterial chemotaxis. *Proc. Natn. Acad. Sci. USA* **69**, 2509–2512.

Monro, P. A. G. (1966). Methods for measuring the velocity of moving particles under the microscope. *In* "Advances in Optical and Electron Microscopy" (R. Barer and V. E. Cosslett, eds), Vol. 1, pp. 1–40. Academic Press, London and New York.

Nesbitt, E. A. and Wernick, J. H. (1973). "Rare Earth Permanent Magnets". Academic Press, New York and London.

Preston, K. (1973). Automated microscopy for cytological analysis. *In* "Advances in Optical and Electron Microscopy" (R. Barer and V. E. Cosslett, eds), Vol. 5, pp. 43–93. Academic Press, London and New York.

Purcell, E. M. (1976). Life at low Reynolds number. *In* "Physics and Our World; a Symposium in Honor of Victor Weisskopf" (K. Huang, ed.), American Institute of Physics Conference Proceedings, No. 28, pp. 49–64. American Institute of Physics, New York. Reprinted: (1977). *Am. J. Phys.* **45**, 3–11.

Rikmenspoel, R. (1965). Electronic analyzer for measuring velocities and the concentration of spermatozoa. *Rev. scient. Instrum.* **35**, 52–57.

Silverman, M. and Simon, M. (1974). Flagellar rotation and the mechanism of bacterial motility. *Nature, Lond.* **249**, 73–74.

Taylor, G. (1952). The action of waving cylindrical tails in propelling micro-organisms. *Proc. R. Soc.* A **211**, 225–239.
Wayland, H. (1975). Intravital microscopy. *In* "Advances in Optical and Electron Microscopy" (R. Barer and V. E. Cosslett, eds), Vol. 6, pp. 1–47. Academic Press, London and New York.

Additional References added in Proof

Greene, F. M. Jr. and Barnes, F. S. (1977). System for automatically tracking white blood cells. *Rev. scient. Instrum.* **48**, 602–604.
Kobayasi, S., Maeda, K. and Imae, Y. (1977). Apparatus for detecting rate and direction of rotation of tethered bacterial cells. *Rev. scient. Instrum.* **48**, 407–410.

Optical Diffraction Analysis in Microscopy

HOWARD J. PINCUS

Department of Geological Sciences,
The University of Wisconsin–Milwaukee,
Milwaukee, Wisconsin, U.S.A.

I. Introduction

Just over a century has passed since Abbe (1873) presented his explanation of microscope optics in terms of diffraction theory. In 56 pages of text, without equations or diagrams, the 33-year-old lecturer at Jena set forth a rational basis for the study of the limits of optical resolution. In Part III of his four-part paper, Abbe discussed the physical basis for the formation of images of fine structures. He worked with the images of a wide variety of objects, including butterfly scales, diatom shells, and striated muscle fibres, and man-made objects such as diamond-scribed graduations on glass and coarse powders.

Some 33 years after Abbe's paper appeared, Porter (1906) published his extremely lucid article, "On the Diffraction Theory of Microscopic Vision". Porter's use of some simple mathematics and several diagrams enabled him to cover a great deal of material in a mere 13 pages.

Porter's opening summary of Abbe's theory merits quoting:

> If a lens is to produce a truthful image of an illuminated object, it must have an aperture sufficient to transmit the whole of the diffraction pattern produced by the object; if but part of this diffraction pattern is transmitted, the image will not truthfully represent the object, but will correspond to another (virtual) object whose whole diffraction pattern is identical with that portion which passes through the lens; if the structure of the object is so fine, or if the aperture of the lens so narrow, that no part of the diffraction pattern due to the structure is transmitted by the lens, then the structure will be invisible no matter what magnification is used.

Porter then applied Fourier's theorem to optical transmission and, like Abbe, performed experiments to test his explanations.

Optical diffraction analysis as presented in this paper is an outgrowth of the Abbe–Porter treatment. Following the appearance of the laser in 1960, diffraction became a practical vehicle for data-processing. Details of the method have been described, with a variety of applications, by Dobrin *et al.* (1965), Jackson (1965), Taylor and Lipson (1965), Pincus and Dobrin (1966), Pincus (1966, 1969a, 1969b, 1972, 1973), Shulman (1966, 1970), and others. Applications to microscopy have been presented by Gall (1966), Power (1973), and Power and Pincus (1974).

By far the most comprehensive recent treatment of applications in microscopy is that of Power (1973), some of whose work is elucidated in this paper.

II. Fourier Optics

Abbe's (1873) theory states that variations in transparency in the plane of an illuminated aperture yield a diffraction pattern in the back focal plane of the objective lens. With a second lens, the rays of light forming this pattern can be focused to reconstruct the aperture image (Figs 1 and 2).

Abbe's aim was to understand and improve the image-forming capabilities of the microscope. The main concern of this paper, and of many of the papers to which it makes reference, is to use such optics to analyse the spatial information in the input.

The input may be a microscope slide, or a reduced transparent replica of a photograph, drawing, or map. The input functions as a diffraction grating with unknown spatial properties. The source of illumination has known spectral properties; a laser radiates coherent, monochromatic illumination, and the resulting diffraction pattern is the two-dimensional Fourier transform of the input image. This transform is a graph of the distribution of orientations and spacings of the elements in the input.

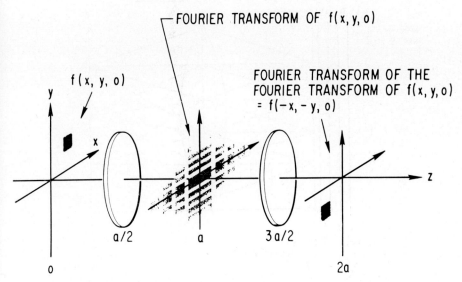

FIG. 1. Production of Fourier transform (diffraction pattern) and reconstructed image by lens system. Light travels from left to right along Z-axis. Front and back focal lengths of each lens are $a/2$. Input image is black square, represented by transmission function $f(x,y,o)$. Reconstructed image at $2a$ is the Fourier transform of the Fourier transform. (Sherman, 1967.)

As indicated earlier, an additional lens can reconstruct the input image from the light rays that form the diffraction pattern or transform. A spatially filtered reconstruction of the input image can be produced by blocking out selected rays in the transform plane (Figs 3 and 4).

A. *Transforms and Filtered Images*

Figures 5 and 6(a) and (b) show basic relations between input and transform. Figure 6(c)–(e) shows also how filtering can be accomplished to remove a specified directional or spatial frequency component of the input image. Obscure features can thus be detected more easily, and complicated spatial information can be studied by systematically removing some components in the input.

Transforms of images and related subjects have been treated very competently and in detail by Taylor and Lipson (1965), Parrent and Thompson (1969), Sherman (1967), Shulman (1966, 1970), Yu (1973), and in the series in which this paper appears, by Hanszen (1971) and Erickson (1973). Power (1973) has applied these concepts to microscopy of specimens with refractive index and optical density varying as a function of position in the input aperture. Accordingly, the treatment that follows is brief.

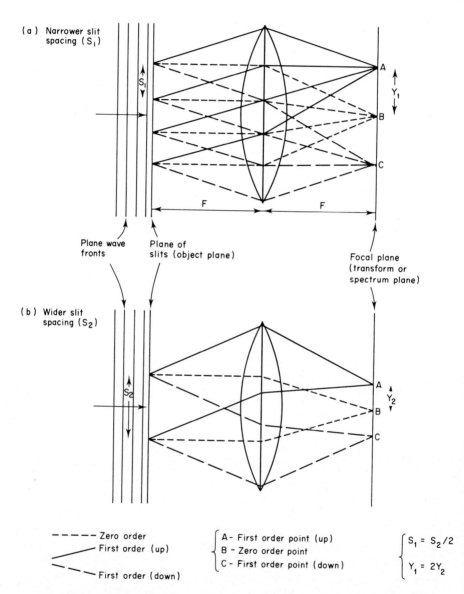

FIG. 2. Fraunhofer diffraction with a lens. Y in the transform plane varies with $1/S$ (spatial frequency) in the input (object) plane. Only zero and first-order diffractions are shown. (Pincus *et al.*, 1973; after Shulman, 1970.)

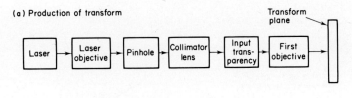

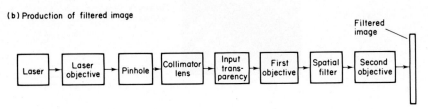

Fig. 3. Flow charts for production of Fourier transform (a) and (b) reconstructed, filtered image. Spatial filter is inserted in the transform plane. (Pincus, 1969a.)

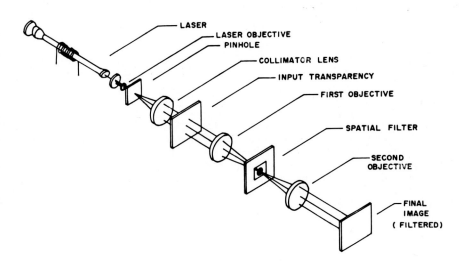

Fig. 4. Schematic diagram of bench-mounted system for optical diffraction analysis. The spatial filter is located in the plane of the diffraction pattern (Fourier transform). (Dobrin *et al.*, 1965.)

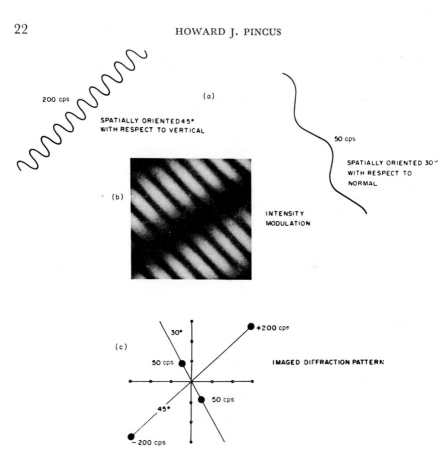

FIG. 5. Basic properties of optical transforms. (a) Two sinusoidal input signals, 200 Hz (cps) and 50 Hz, to an oscilloscope, and (b) their combined image, via intensity modulation, on the oscilloscope. (The input signals are analogous to the constituent transmission functions of a transparency of (b).) (c) Diffraction pattern (transform) of (b). The radial coordinate of each dot-pair is proportional to the spatial frequency of the corresponding input signal; the radii of each dot-pair are perpendicular to their respective input bands; the transform of the composite of the two input functions is the sum of the transforms of the individual input functions. (The vertical and horizontal axes in (c) provide a calibration scale; these can be generated from rectangular coordinate paper.) (Shulman, 1966.)

A general expression for the two-dimensional Fourier transform, as applied in optics, is as follows:

$$F(u, v) = A \int\limits_{-\infty}^{\infty}\!\!\int \mathscr{F}(x, y) \exp\left[- 2\pi i(ux + vy)/\lambda f\right] \mathrm{d}x\mathrm{d}y \qquad (1)$$

where

$\mathscr{F}(x,y)$ = input function as a function of position coordinates x, y in the object plane (front focal plane)

$F(u, v)$ = complex amplitude as a function of position coordinates u, v in the transform plane (back focal plane)

f = focal length of lens

λ = wavelength of the incident light

A = a constant depending in part on the amplitude of the incident light to the input.

The input function, or complex modulating function

$$\mathscr{F}(x,y) = f(x,y) \exp\left[i\phi(x,y)\right] \tag{2}$$

in which

$f(x,y)$ = amplitude modulation

and

$\phi(x,y)$ = phase modulation

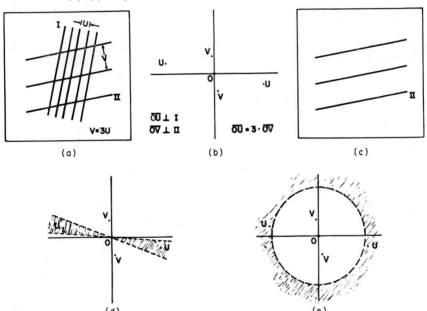

FIG. 6. Line-pattern input and its outputs. (a) Input: spatial frequency of Set I is $3\times$ that of Set II. (b) Transform of (a): first-order diffraction dot-pairs U and V are produced from Sets I and II, respectively. (c) Filtered output: Set I has been removed by filtering in the transform plane, as in (d) or (e). (d) Directional filtering: rays forming dot-pair U are blocked by wedges (shaded). (e) Frequency filtering: rays forming dot-pair U are blocked by high-cut filter (shaded). (Pincus, 1969a.)

are functions of the position coordinates x, y in the input plane. Amplitude modulation results from variations in transparency (or transmission) across the input aperture. Variations in refractive index account for phase modulation.

In processing black and white photographic transparencies as inputs the input function can be treated as consisting entirely of the amplitude modulation function. Most petrographic thin sections contribute both amplitude and phase terms.

Figures 7 and 8 illustrate some one-dimensional transform relations in which the input function is accounted for entirely by amplitude modulation.

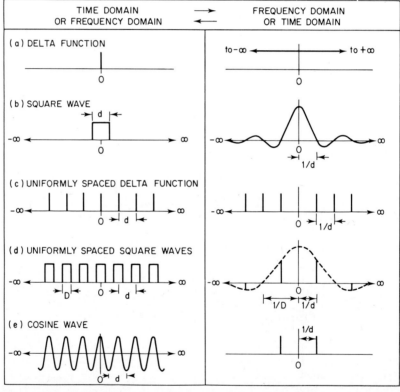

FIG. 7. Fourier transform pairs. The functions in each column are the transforms of the adjoining functions in the other column. The transmission curve for a white line on a black background is a square wave (b). Note that (c), (d), and (e), with the same fundamental frequency, yield identical first-order spectra (right-hand column). (The diffraction pattern that is seen photographed or mapped by photodetector is actually proportional to the square of the transform function, hence negative transform values are sensed as positive.) (Peterson and Dobrin, 1966.)

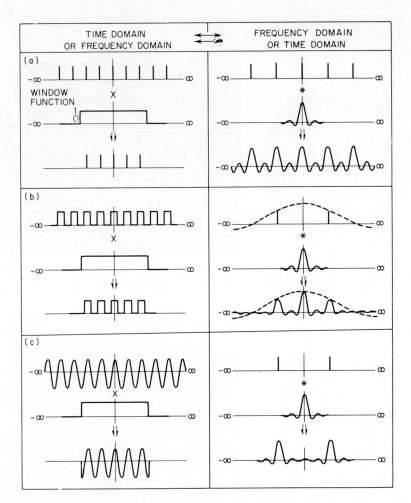

FIG. 8. Fourier transforms of truncated functions. The infinite functions on line with (a), (b), (c) in the left-hand column correspond to (c), (d), (e) in Fig. 7. The window function, equal to unity within the window and zero outside, yields the truncated function immediately below it when multiplied by the infinite functions. The transform equivalents of the left-hand column are the adjoining functions in the right-hand column, as in Fig. 7. The symbol * denotes convolution, the process by which the transform of the truncated function is obtained from the functions above. (Peterson and Dobrin, 1966.)

The squares of Fourier transform values yield the intensity or power spectrum; however, when the power spectrum is so obtained, phase information is lost.

Figures 9–11 illustrate some binary inputs and their transforms. (What are referred to as transforms in these figures, and in figures that follow, are

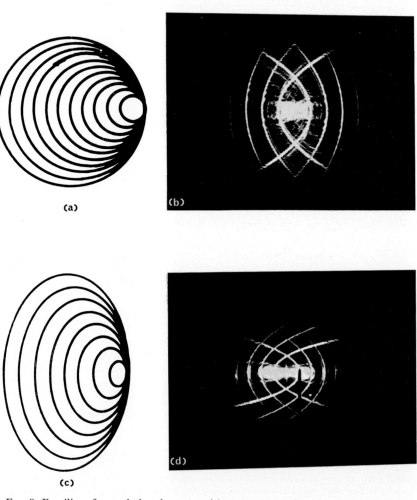

Fɪɢ. 9. Families of nested closed curves with a common point of tangency ((a) circles; (c) ellipses) and their transforms ((b) and (d) respectively). The upper end of the vertical black line in (d) is tangent to one of two first-order diffraction curves at the point denoting minimum spatial frequency; this point corresponds to the spatial frequency in (c) measured horizontally toward the left. (Note that the vertical elongation in (c) as compared to (a) is associated with greater horizontal elongation in (d) as compared to (b).) (Pincus *et al.*, 1973.)

not actually Fourier transforms, because photographic emulsions are sensitive to intensity, or amplitude squared.)

It is standard practice to produce calibration transforms (Figs 11(d) and 5(c)) in order to read spatial frequencies directly from the photographic record of the transform. This is accomplished with inputs of rectangular coordinate paper, knowing the relative scales of the coordinate paper and the inputs being studied.

As indicated earlier (Figs 1, 3, 7, and 8), the input image can be reconstructed through operations yielding the Fourier transform of the Fourier transform. Strictly speaking, this is not equivalent to obtaining the inverse Fourier transform, which cannot be accomplished optically (Shulman, 1970). The Fourier transform of the Fourier transform yields an inverted image, as indicated in Fig. 1. The only changes in the image, then, are in the signs of coordinates, and in scale (depending on the relative focal lengths of the two lenses).

(a)

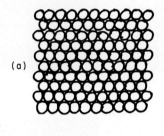

(b)

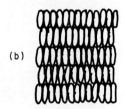

(c)

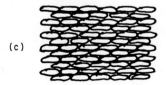

FIG. 10. Rhombic stacking of ovals. (a), 1·0; (b) and (c), 3·0. (Pincus, 1969b, Part I.)

Spatial filtering, some examples of which are presented in Section VII, and which is also indicated in Figs 3, 4, and 6, can be accomplished by inserting masks or patterns in the transform plane. In effect, the filter is a modulating function $G(u, v)$ which is multiplied by the light arriving at the filter, $F(u, v)$ (Eqn (1)). The product $G(u, v)F(u, v)$ is Fourier-transformed to yield the filtered, reconstructed image. In the examples given in this paper, $G(u, v)$ consists only of amplitude-modulation components.

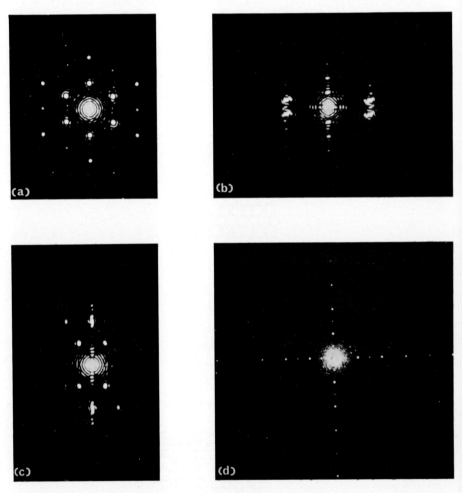

Fig. 11. (a)–(c), Transforms of oval-stacks (a)–(c) in Fig. 10. (d), Transform of calibration grid; spacing between more intense dots corresponds to average diameter in Fig. 10(a) and to radial spacing of more intense dots in transform (a). (Pincus, 1969b, Part I.)

It is of historical interest that Abbe (1873) was actually concerned, in part, with high-cut frequency filtering (Fig. 6(c)) and Porter (1906) achieved useful results from directional filtering (Fig. 6(d)).

B. *Applications to Microscopy*

Gall (1966) has generated diffraction patterns with the microscope, inserting photographic inputs above the objective. Power (1973) has produced optical transforms with a microscope from a variety of inputs; his instrumental set-up is described in Section VB of this paper. In effect, what Gall and Power have done, in part, is to make directly available to the microscopist's eye or camera the diffraction pattern about which Abbe (1873) had written a century earlier.

Figures 12 and 13, which appeared in Power's thesis (1973), present transforms, generated by transparent photographic inputs, utilizing, first, a microscope (microtransform) and, second, a large optical bench set-up (macrotransform). Note that the radial coordinates denoting equivalent spatial frequencies are smaller in the macrotransforms than in the micro-transforms, but the macrotransforms generally show more details even with a relatively compressed scale. The greater detail results from differences in type and level of illumination, in lens parameters, and in optical set-ups; it should also be pointed out that the microtransforms show all of the information required in the study for which they were produced, and the cost of the microscope set-up was but a small fraction of the cost of the optical bench set-up.

It should be noted that the inputs in both Figs 12 and 13 are entirely amplitude modulated. We turn now to the treatment of phase modulation. Although the discussion is concerned explicitly with crystals in petrographic thin sections, it applies as well to other slide-mounted materials in which the diffracting elements are planar, the specimen modulates phase and ampli-tude, and illumination is coherent (or partially coherent).

To analyse diffraction by crystals of different refractive index, Power (1973) started with Sommerfeld's (1954) phase grating of the rectangular laminary type (Fig. 14(a)). The model of a crystal array is shown in Fig. 14(b), in which the grooves in material of refractive index η_1 are filled with material of refractive index η_2. The amplitude distribution in the transform plane generated by an element d from an array such as that in Fig. 14(b) is

$$f(\beta) = \frac{\sin\{\phi(\mathrm{d}/2) + \theta\} - \sin\theta}{\phi(\mathrm{d}/2)} \tag{3}$$

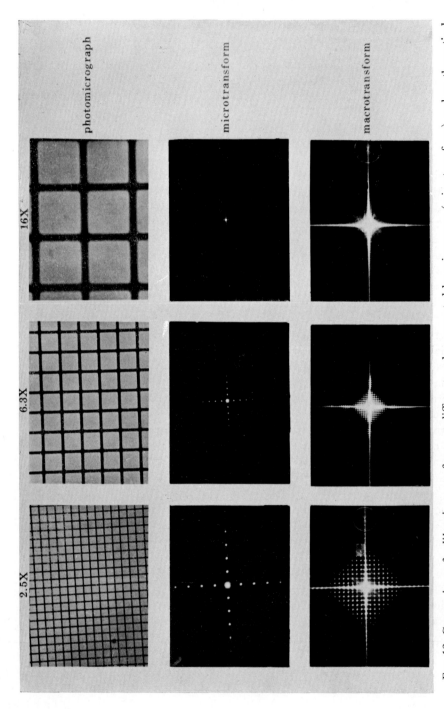

Fig. 12. Comparison of calibration transforms at different scales generated by microscope (microtransform) and on the optical bench (macrotransform). Spacing of input grid is 0·1 mm (spatial frequency is 10 lines/mm). (Power, 1973.)

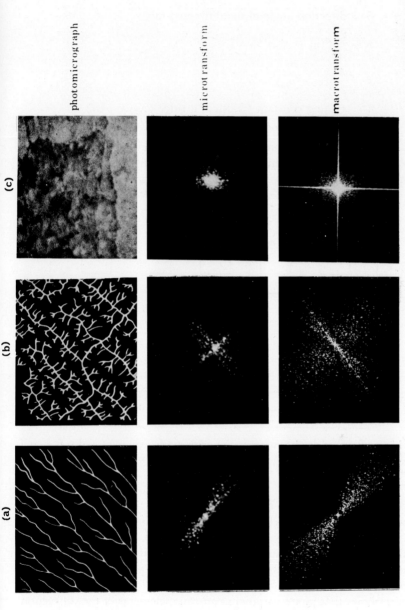

FIG. 13. Photographic inputs and their transforms generated by microscope (microtransform) and on the optical bench (macrotransform). Inputs (a) and (b) (high contrast) are idealized drainage patterns. Input (c) (variable tone) depicts a rock surface; its microtransform is sensitive to both the fuzzy patterning of the surface and the film grain. The cross in its macrotransform was generated by a rectangular aperture. The ratio of equivalent radial coordinates (denoting the same spatial frequency) between macro- and microtransforms is 0·31. (Power, 1973.)

where

β = direction angle of the diffracted ray

$$\phi = \frac{2\pi}{\lambda}\beta(\eta_1 - \eta_2)$$

$$\theta = \frac{\pi}{\lambda}\,\delta(\eta_1 - \eta_2)$$

d = grating constant (width of a ridge-groove pair)

δ = depth of grooves.

Figure 15 shows the function $f^2(\beta)$, the distribution of amplitude squared, or intensity, in the transform plane, for an element d. Although this is asymmetrical about the zero-order ($h = 0$), the composite term for the entire grating is symmetrical about the zero-order.

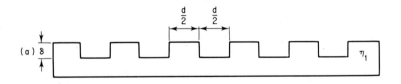

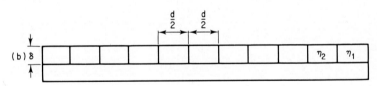

Fig. 14. (a) Rectangular laminary grating with grating constant d, depth δ, and refractive index η_1. (b) Thin-section model in which grooves of (a) have been filled with material of refractive index η_2. (Power, 1973.)

Power points out that the model in Fig. 14(b) is not realistic for many petrographic thin sections, which are more typically composites of many single element gratings with different grating constants and indices of refraction. The more abundant and irregular the single-element gratings, the more asymmetric and diffuse will be the pattern produced in the transform plane.

He also shows that phase variations can cause elements of the diffraction pattern to be displaced with respect to each other, resulting in smearing of the pattern. The zero-order diffraction spot, normally a bright circular spot, may then be elongated. Such smearing is associated with fine-grained

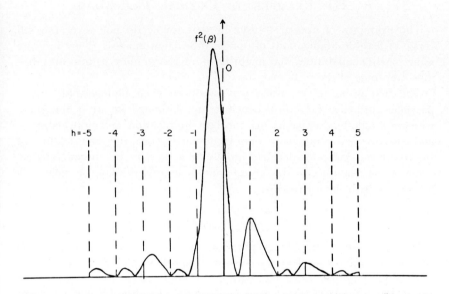

FIG. 15. Distribution of light intensity in the Fraunhofer plane for a single element (d) grating. Spectral order is denoted by h. Note that the curve is asymmetrical. (Sommerfeld, 1954; Power, 1973.)

or largely glassy, optically heterogeneous material. The heterogeneity in non-glassy materials can be reduced by increasing the power of the objectives; of course there are practical limits on objective power.

The components of a diffraction pattern generated at a grain boundary will also be shifted if the boundary is not perpendicular to the planar surfaces of the specimen. The magnitude of the shift depends on the departure from perpendicularity and the direction of shift depends on the relative magnitudes of refractive indices across the grain boundary. As can be expected, the diffraction pattern is also affected by curvature of surfaces between grains. As the grain size decreases, or as the number of grains in the field of view increases, the complexities introduced into the composite diffraction pattern increase.

Turning to the other extreme, diffraction by a single crystal, Power (1973) shows that shifts or blurring from birefringence are negligible in the diffraction patterns of standard thin sections of single crystals. Opaque elements within or adjoining a crystal simply contribute amplitude modulation components.

III. Examples of Optical Transforms

The examples of optical transforms that follow do not cover the full range of feasible applications of optical diffraction analysis. They indicate some types of capabilities that might be of interest to microscopists and they illustrate some of the principles discussed earlier.

The first group of examples was produced from photographic transparencies, utilizing the optical bench set-up. Although we are dealing here with amplitude-modulated inputs, coherent illumination, and more elaborate and costly optical components than in the microscope, the main features of the transforms indicate what can usually be achieved with the microscope. Most of the examples in this group were generated prior to or separately from work with the microscope.

A. *Optical Bench Products*

We have processed photographs from the scale of satellite imagery to that of the scanning electron microscope. Inputs have included sets of multi-spectral photographs, radar photographs (crossed and parallel polarization), aerial photographs of waterwaves and clouds, photographs of hand specimens and outcrops of rock, photographs of skulls and other bones, contact photographs of acetate peel replicas of rock surfaces, contour maps, geologic maps, line drawings, many test patterns and other artificial inputs, a few colour transparencies, and of course, photomicrographs of petrographic thin sections and thin sections directly. Many of these results have been published in references listed at the end of this paper.

Figures 16–21, all optical bench products, indicate a variety of transform relationships, some of which are elucidated in the figure captions.

Figure 16 illustrates a large variety of rock textures and their transforms. The inputs are photographs of line drawings; high-contrast photography yields results much like those from line drawings. The central crosses in the transforms were generated by rectangular apertures in the input plane.

An important property of optical transforms, not previously discussed in this paper, is illustrated here. The location of input elements within the input does not affect the transform. Thus the large crystals in Fig. 16(e) and (j) could be translated (without rotation) within the input without affecting the transform.

Note also the usefulness of the transforms in recovering information on preferred orientation and concentration of spatial frequencies. For example, compare the preferred orientation in Fig. 16(i) and (a), and the frequency banding in Fig. 16(b) and (a).

These inputs and their transforms, part of an extensive library of reference inputs and transforms, can be used to demonstrate a useful operating procedure. By studying the transform and its input together, one can often detect spatial details in the input that might otherwise have been over-looked.

Figure 17 demonstrates the systematic relationship between elongation in the input and in the transform. Figures 10 and 11 illustrate the same relationship, and also the sensitivity of the transform to stacking geometry. Transforms are most sensitive to elongation when the long axes of grains are parallel, or nearly so.

Figures 18 and 19 illustrate some early results to determine the capabilities for discriminating variations in grain size. Figures 18 and 19 differ mainly in that the inputs in the former are line drawings and in the latter are half-tones and some of the grains are twinned.

There are three main categories of spatial frequencies in Fig. 19. From lowest to highest these are grain boundaries (grain size), twinning, and the half-tone, which functions as a carrier frequency the diffraction pattern of which falls outside the transform images in the figure. In both figures, the transforms become larger with decreasing grain size, as is to be expected.

Figure 20 has been included to illustrate that useful results may be obtained from coloured displays, and that variation in directions of trends in the input show up as directional dispersion in the transform.

Figure 21 indicates that systematic changes in particle shapes are accompanied by systematic changes in the transforms. It is important to note that the transforms (c) were generated from assemblages of particles (b), the orientations of which have been varied, that is, the transforms are not the products of the single particles in (a).

B. *Microscope Products*

Figures 22–25 (from Power, 1973) illustrate some results using petrographic thin sections (amplitude and phase modulation) as inputs. They also illustrate approximately equivalent processing of photomicrographs using the optical bench (amplitude modulation).

In a series of experiments conducted by Power (1973), an increase in objective power from $6 \cdot 3 \times$ to higher power is accompanied by a decrease both in transform size and in smearing of the transform image, as is to be expected. An increase in objective power from $2 \cdot 5 \times$ to $6 \cdot 3 \times$ is accompanied by an increase in the number of diffraction dots which is manifested as an increase in the size of the transform. By comparing his data from these experiments, Power concludes that this increase from $2 \cdot 5 \times$ to $6 \cdot 3 \times$ is real, that is, the $6 \cdot 3 \times$ objective is resolving high spatial frequencies beyond the resolution of the $2 \cdot 5 \times$ objective. Figure 22 illustrates such changes in

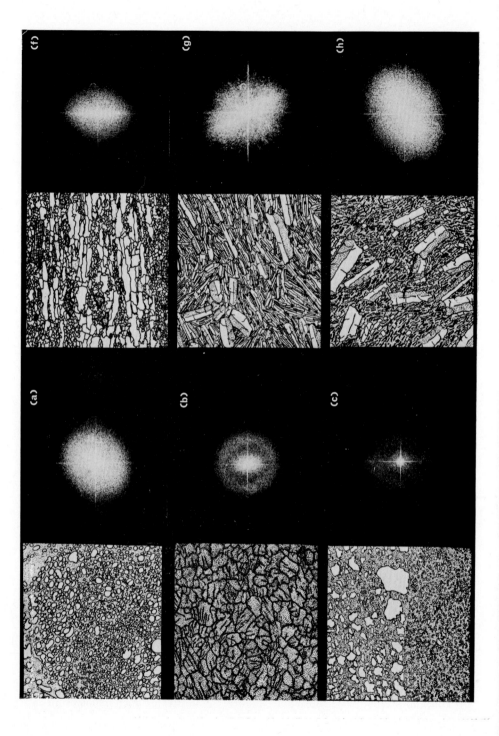

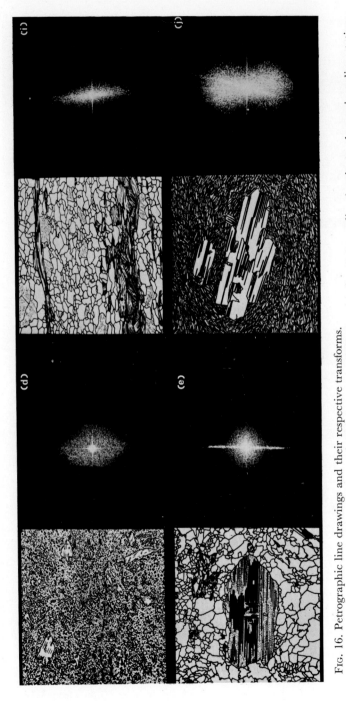

Fig. 16. Petrographic line drawings and their respective transforms.
(a) Vesicular structure in pumice. (b) Granoblastic texture in epidotite. (c) Quarteoze pelite showing a change in sedimentation.
(d) Micaceous pelite. (e) Oligoclase porphyroblast in a matrix of quartz (predominantly), plagioclase, and biotite. (f) Fine grained
granulite, crudely layered, with lenses of quartz. (g) Trachyte with some fan-shaped clumps of sanidine. (h) Phonolite with trachytic
structure; sanidine phenocrysts. (i) Mica gneiss with quartz and feldspar bands. (j) Microlitic, porphyritic andesite with plagioclase
phenocrysts. (Pincus, 1973; inputs from Jung, 1969.)

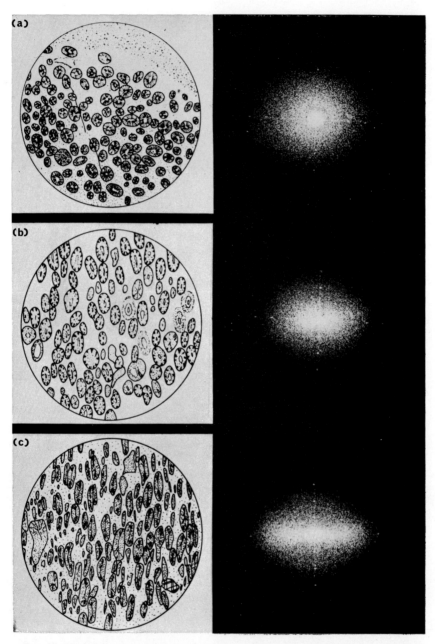

Fig. 17. Undeformed and deformed oolites and their transforms. (a) Undeformed. (b) Ooliths deformed 24%. (c) Ooliths deformed 50%. Diameter of each input approximately 8 mm. Note progressive elongation of transforms, both in outline and more prominently in the shape of the inner bright area. (Inputs from Whitten, 1966; after Cloos, 1943.)

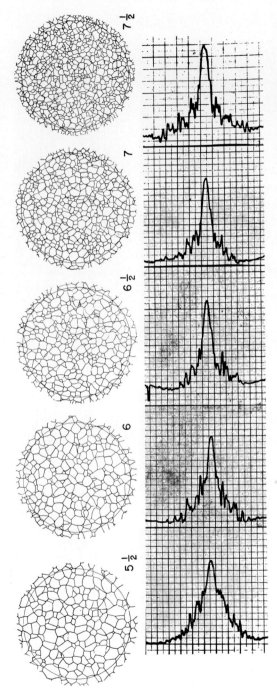

Fig. 18. Upper row: Part of ASTM Plate I, E112–68, showing ASTM size no. $5\frac{1}{2}$–$7\frac{1}{2}$ in $\frac{1}{2}$ number steps. Originals are 9 cm in diameter, published at $100\times$ magnification; the five grain sizes represented are 0·055, 0·045, 0·035, 0·030, and 0·026 mm. Lower row: Microdensitometer profiles of photographs of transforms of $5\frac{1}{2}$–$7\frac{1}{2}$. Optical transmission increases from left to right. The large spike locates the transform centre.

Note that the flanks of the spikes are displaced downward and outward from $5\frac{1}{2}$–$7\frac{1}{2}$, indicating the transition from lower to higher spatial frequency. (From Pincus, 1969b, Part II.)

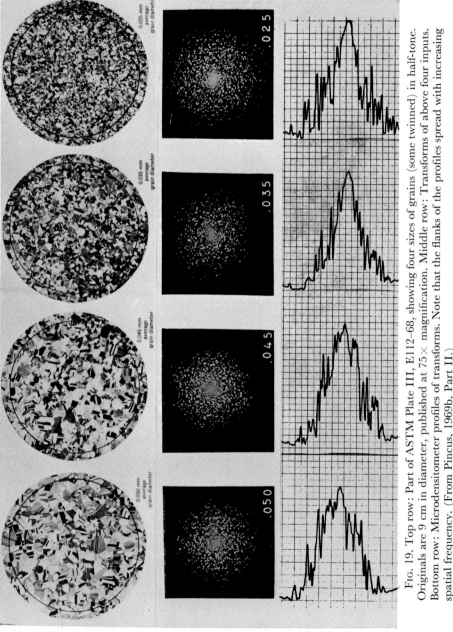

FIG. 19. Top row: Part of ASTM Plate III, E112–68, showing four sizes of grains (some twinned) in half-tone. Originals are 9 cm in diameter, published at 75 × magnification. Middle row: Transforms of above four inputs. Bottom row: Microdensitometer profiles of transforms. Note that the flanks of the profiles spread with increasing spatial frequency. (From Pincus, 1969b, Part II.)

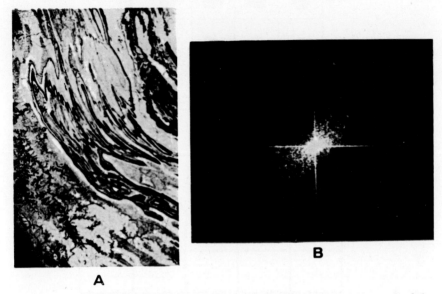

FIG. 20. (a) Geologic map of a portion of Pennsylvania. North is to the left; Harrisburg is in the centre of the lower right quarter. The area shown is approximately 169 × 267 km. (Original map, in colour, published by Pennsylvania Department of Internal Affairs). (b) Transform of A. The spread in the band running from upper right to lower left results from the change in direction of the grain of the rock structure. (Appalachian folded belt.) (Pincus *et al.*, 1973.)

transforms, for objectives of 2·5 ×, 6·3 ×, 16 × and 40 ×. The corresponding macrotransforms show much the same orientation information. The pinhole to which reference is made is part of the illumination system (Fig. 29(b)).

Figure 23 does not show the same progression, with magnifications, as in Fig. 22, because exposure times were varied. The sharpness of the microtransforms increases, in general, with increasing objective power. Note the asymmetry of the microtransforms for 16 ×, 40 ×, and 100 ×.

Figure 24(b) illustrates a smeared microtransform. Power (1973) reports that the diffraction dots in this and other instances of smearing could not be brought to a sharp focus. Of approximately 300 petrographic thin sections studied, eleven yielded grossly smeared transforms and twenty-five had areas that yielded smeared transforms and other areas that generated sharp transforms. The smearing is not photographic; in fact, photographs of smeared transforms show less smearing than was directly observed.

Figure 25 illustrates an important result which is consistent with the earlier treatment (Section IIB) of phase gratings. Microtransforms generated directly from thin sections of twinned crystals are more similar to macro-

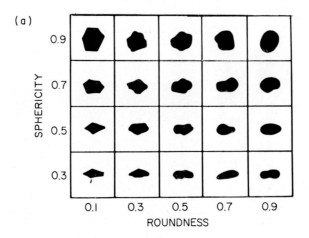

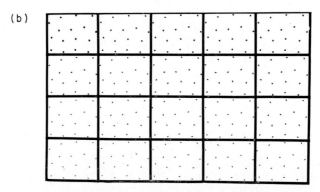

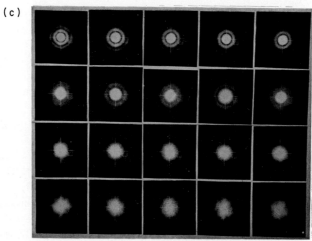

FIG. 21. Idealized particulate shapes and their transforms.
(a) Sphericity and roundness chart. (b) Assemblages of particles such as those in (a).
(c) Transforms of (b). (Larson, 1973; input from Krumbein, 1941.)

transforms of crossed-polarizer photomicrographs than to macrotransforms of uncrossed-polarizer photomicrographs. Thus regular twinning acts as a multiple-element phase grating, as is to be expected.

Many more illustrations of transforms produced directly from thin sections have been assembled by Power (1973).

IV. Spatial Analysis

Optical diffraction analysis, as described in this paper, is but one approach to the analysis of spatial data. Spatial analysis, a burgeoning tool in many disciplines, is concerned with the description and analysis of variables that assume different values at different locations (Davis and McCullagh, 1975). The spatial analysis of distributions composed of line elements, or of features that can be resolved into line elements by Fourier resolution and other methods, can be treated in terms of the three variables, spatial frequency, orientation, and location.

Optical diffraction analysis, as presented in this paper, is sensitive to spatial frequency and orientation, but not to location. Other optical methods, not treated here, are in fact sensitive to location; these employ holographic methods to process location information (Pincus, 1973).

Spatial frequency, or density, is an attribute of both rectilinear and curvilinear elements. It is expressed in terms of lines per unit distance, measured perpendicular to the lines. Bands, zones, and changes in greyness can all be treated as composites of line-sets of different spatial frequencies and orientation. Elongation ratios and size distributions can be expressed in terms of spatial frequencies.

Orientation applies to rectilinear features, straight-line segments of or approximations to curvilinear features, and axes of elongation. Often the degree and direction of preferred orientation are of interest in characterizing spatial distributions.

Optical transforms provide the means for convenient and concurrent analysis of spatial frequencies and orientations. Co-variations between spatial frequencies and orientations may be detected. Spatial frequencies and orientations from different inputs and at different scales may be compared by studying optical transforms, with suitable calibration.

It must be noted that the analyses dealt with in this paper are two-dimensional, that is, they treat spatial features as distributed in planes or as projected on planes. However, the reality is that most of the physical systems we wish to study spatially are three-dimensional, and two-dimensional interpretations can lead to serious error. Figures 26 and 27 illustrate how projection on a plane can cause error.

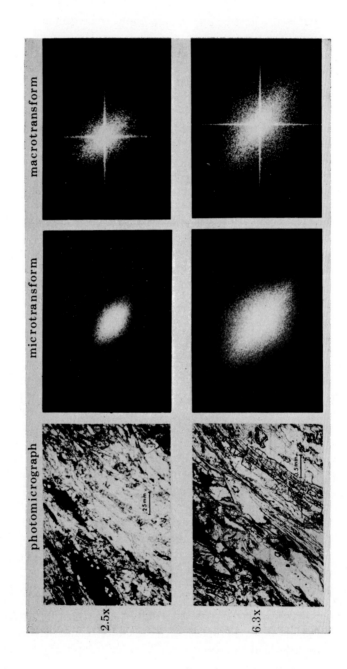

photomicrograph   microtransform   macrotransform

2.5mm.

0.5mm.

2.5x

6.3x

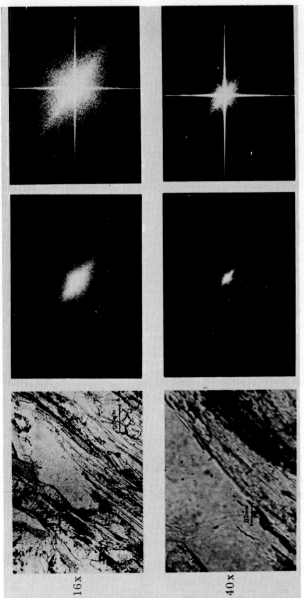

Fig. 22. Photomicrographs of a schist and their microtransforms and macrotransforms. Photomicrographs (top to bottom) were recorded with objectives of $2 \cdot 5 \times$, $6 \cdot 3 \times$, $16 \times$ and $40 \times$. Macrotransforms were produced from the corresponding photomicrographs. The ratios of equivalent radial coordinates (denoting the same spatial frequency) between macro- and microtransforms are $0 \cdot 31$, $0 \cdot 32$, $0 \cdot 56$, $0 \cdot 41$ and $0 \cdot 33$, in order of increasing objective power. A $0 \cdot 025$ mm pinhole was used with the $2 \cdot 5 \times$ objective and a $0 \cdot 050$ mm pinhole was used with the other objectives. Exposure times were constant in each transform series. Note the increase in high frequency components from $6 \cdot 3 \times$ to $40 \times$.

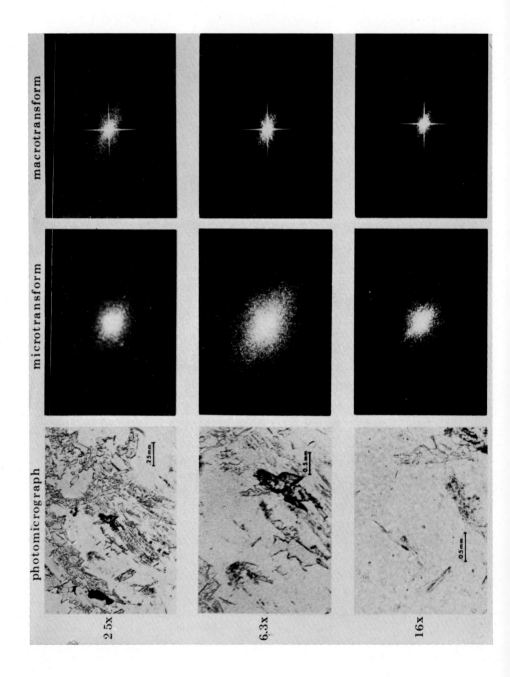

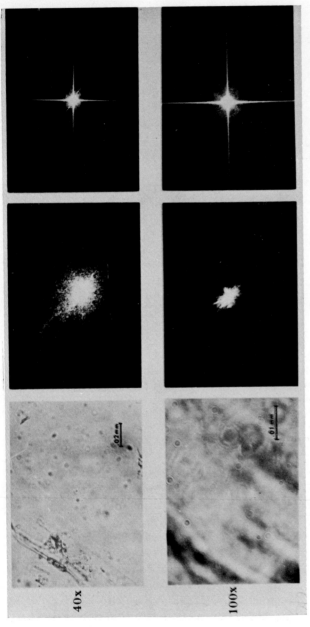

Fig. 23. Photomicrographs of Mount Airy Granite (North Carolina) and their microtransforms and macrotransforms. Photomicrographs (top to bottom) were recorded with objectives of 2·5×, 6·3×, 16×, 40× and 100×. Macrotransforms were produced from the corresponding photomicrographs. The ratios of equivalent radial coordinates (denoting the same spatial frequency) between macro- and microtransforms are 0·31, 0·32, 0·54, 0·41 and 0·33 in order of increasing objective power. A 0·025 mm pinhole was used with all objectives. Exposure times were varied to yield transform photographs of the best quality. (Compare with Fig. 22.) (Power, 1973.)

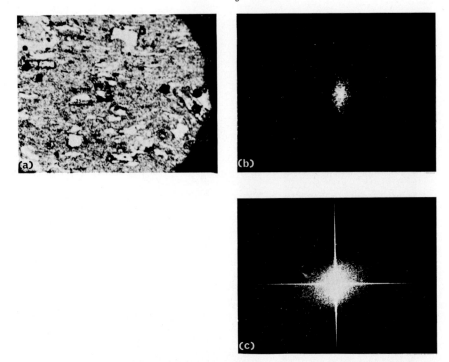

Fig. 24. Example of smearing in a microtransform.

(a) Photomicrograph of a thin section of dacite from Devil's Lake, Oregon; plagioclase laths in a fine-grained groundmass. (b) Microtransform, exhibiting smearing. Note elongated D.C. (central) spot which should have the same shape as the circular pinhole. (c) Macrotransform. The ratio of equivalent radial coordinates (denoting the same spatial frequency) between macro- and microtransform is 0·79. (Power, 1973.)

The field of stereology is concerned with extrapolation from two to three dimensions (Underwood, 1970) and accordingly provides some extremely important insights into problems involving shape, size distribution, particle characteristics, orientation, sampling, and the like.

In studying, for example, the deformation fabrics of rocks in three dimensions, it may be necessary to deform anisotropic rocks in three mutually perpendicular directions, to prepare optical transforms of rock surfaces in three mutually perpendicular directions for each of the three sets of deformation directions, and to profile each transform (Section VI) in at least several directions (Pincus, 1972, 1973). This is not intended to discourage the prospective user of optical transforms, because in fact it is often quite feasible, through symmetry and other considerations, to reduce the number

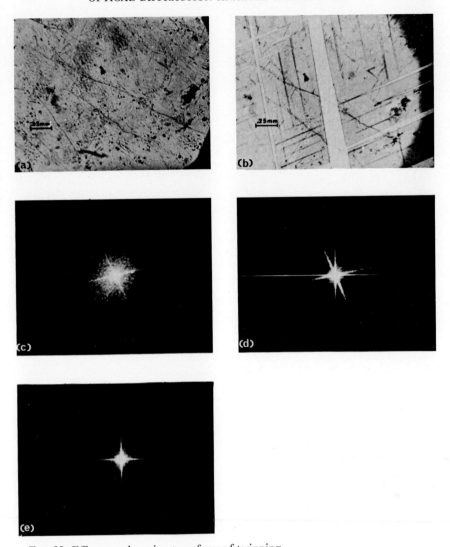

FIG. 25. Effects on the microtransform of twinning.
(a) Photomicrograph of a feldspar grain in a thin section of Duluth Gabbro (Minnesota). Uncrossed polarizers. (b) Same as (a), with crossed polarizers. (c) Microtransform produced directly from thin section. (d) Macrotransform produced from photomicrograph (b). (e) Macrotransform produced from photomicrograph (a). The ratio of equivalent radial coordinates (denoting the same spatial frequency) between macro- and microtransforms is 0·79.

Note that the microtransform is sensitive to the orientation of the twins even though the twins are visible only with crossed polarizers. The twins act as phase gratings. (Power, 1973.)

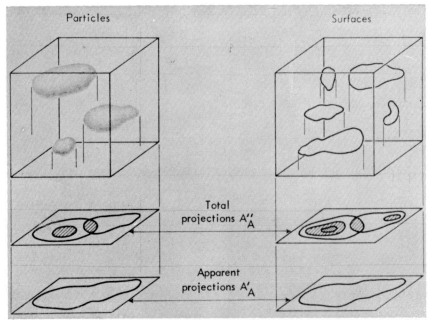

FIG. 26. Ambiguities in the projection of particles and surfaces. (Underwood, 1970.)

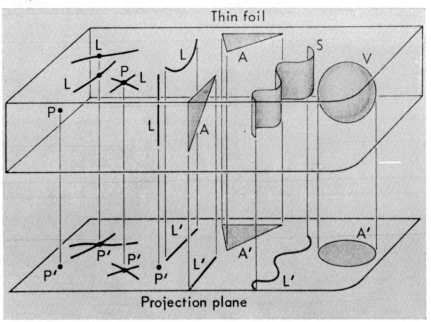

FIG. 27. A set of idealized objects in space and their projections on a plane. (Underwood, 1970.)

of transforms and transform profiles needed. It is intended, however, to convey the urgency of avoiding confusion between two- and three-dimensional representations.

V. OPTICAL SYSTEMS HARDWARE AND PROCEDURES

The hardware for both optical bench and microscope set-ups in optical diffraction analysis conforms to the layouts in Figs 3 and 4, except that filtering in the transform plane with the microscope has not yet been attempted by us.

A. *Production of Inputs*

Photographic inputs have been prepared in sizes from 35 mm to 4 × 5 in. (102 × 127 mm). We have used a variety of cameras and copy equipment to generate suitable photographic transparencies as inputs, including 35 mm and 120 cameras, 4 × 5 in. view camera, view camera equipped with 120 and 35 mm backs, Polaroid cameras and camera backs, Illumitran copier with 35 mm camera, 135 mm telemicroscope and 35 mm camera, and microscope with 35 mm camera. Many of these units are also used to prepare photographs of transforms and spatially filtered images.

On the optical bench, the input is typically a 35 mm black-and-white frame; 70 mm film and glass plates of several sizes have also been processed. Size and shape of inputs for the microscope depend in part on the geometry of the instrument.

To achieve effective diffraction by the elements of interest in an input, we have controlled the size of the input so that the spacing between elements is 0·25–0·02 mm.

In preparing a reduced photographic transparency from a photograph, drawing, or map, we commonly insert a patch of coordinate paper and a standard grey scale in corners of the subject frame, and photograph these and the image together. The coordinate paper is used either to generate a separate calibration transform (Fig. 11(d)) or a combined transform of the calibration grid and the image (Fig. 5(c)). The grey scale is used to check for uniformity of processing of input transparencies from suites of inputs (Fig. 19) the transforms of which are to be compared; with an optical microdensitometer we compare grey-scale densities in the reduced transparencies.

Although positive and negative renditions of an image, whether binary or continuous tone, yield the same basic transform, it is preferable to use the one that transmits less unnecessary light. This practice leads to cleaner transforms. Thus, if we are interested chiefly in grain boundaries, it is better to use the transparency in which these appear as light lines on a dark background than vice versa. If a photomicrograph shows some light and some dark grain boundaries, the rendition in which more grain boundaries (or greater length of grain boundaries) are light than dark is preferable. The input transparencies for Fig. 18 were negatives of the upper row; for inputs such as those in Fig. 19, positives and negatives yield about the same quality transforms.

When the input is to consist of a petrographic thin section, the normal requirements for petrographic study suffice. That is, the ordinary requirements for uniformity of thickness and smoothness of surfaces are adequate. The rock slice must be embedded in a medium with refractive index close to those of most minerals in the section, and there must be optical continuity between the slice, the embedding medium, and the parallel, bounding, glass flats (slide and cover glass). Equivalent requirements apply to materials other than rocks.

It is of interest that the slide mounts described above play the same role optically as the combination of the photographic transparency and its enclosing, liquid-filled optical gate in the optical bench set-up described below.

B. *Optical Bench Equipment*

The core of the optical bench equipment is a modified Conductron laser scan C120 system. Figure 28 shows the components most commonly used in this set-up.

Illumination is provided by a 3 mW He-Ne laser (Fig. 28(a)). The beam of light leaving the collimator (c) illuminates the input in the optical gate (e). The intervening mask (d) provides variable rectangular framing of the input; this may be replaced by a circular aperture or an iris diaphragm. The first and second objectives (f and i) and most other lenses in the system have short focal lengths; even so, the length of the bench is almost 4 m. The spatial filter (h) shown is for directional filtering; wedges with different angles may be inserted and rotated. Frequency filters, consisting of circular holes, discs, and annuli can be placed at (h) or in several other positions along the optical path at which the transform is reproduced by auxiliary lenses.

Other items regularly used but not shown in Fig. 28 are an electronic shutter, light attenuators, laser power meter, rotatable and translatable optical gates, and spot-scanner and strip-chart recorder. We have also constructed a wide variety of spatial filters appropriate to specialized projects.

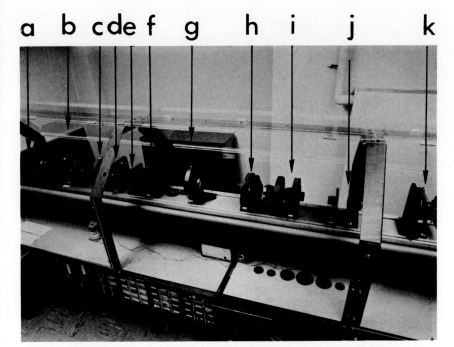

a b cdef g h i j k

FIG. 28. Bench set-up for optical diffraction analysis. (Refer to Figs. 3 and 4.) a, Laser; b, laser objective and pinhole; c, collimator; d, adjustable mask; e, optical gate for input; f, first objective (transform lens); g, transform enlarging lens; h, spatial filter (in transform plane); i, second objective (image reconstruction lens pair); j, auxiliary lenses (for control of size and location of reconstructed image); k, camera assembly (plane of reconstructed, filtered image).

(Note: To arrive at optimal configurations, a television monitor is used to view transforms, filter alignments, and reconstructed images.)

C. *Microscope Equipment*

The microscope equipment used to produce the microtransforms illustrated in this paper is shown in Fig. 29. A less expensive microscope can be used, provided it has a focusable Bertrand lens and there is the capability for adequate alignment of the illuminating system.

A laser source was not used with the microscope because petrographic thin sections illuminated with light with a high degree of coherence produce much noise. Parrent and Thompson (1969) have presented an informative discussion of the characteristics of light of different degrees of coherence.

The source used was mercury vapour light, filtered chromatically and spatially (Fig. 29(a) and (b)) to yield quasi-monochromatic light with sufficient coherence.

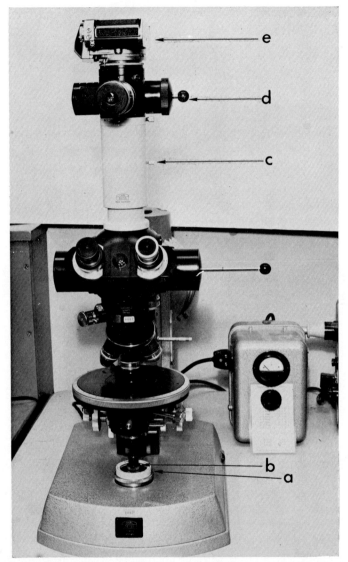

Fig. 29. Microscope system used to produce and record optical diffraction patterns (transforms) directly from petrographic thin sections. Optovar-equipped Zeiss standard universal microscope and mercury vapour illuminator.
a, Interference filter (5461A, 100A band-pass); b, spatial filter (0·025 mm pinhole); c, monocular photo tube; d, Basic Body II, with focusing eyepiece; e, 35 mm camera (Nikon). (Power, 1973.)

Power's (1973) procedures for producing consistent microtransforms of good quality are as follows:

(1) remove polarizer and analyser from the optical path;
(2) adjust for Köhler illumination;
(3) open condenser diaphragm fully;
(4) insert interference and spatial filters into the light path, as in Fig. 29;
(5) insert and focus the Bertrand lens until the diffraction pattern is sharp;
(6) centre the diffraction pattern by moving the filter assembly;
(7) place beam-splitting slide in Basic Body II in middle position, view transform through focusing eyepiece, and focus eyepiece precisely;
(8) finely focus transform;
(9) push beam-splitting slide (Basic Body II) all the way in and photograph.

D. *Processing and Other Details*

Determination of scales of inputs, filtered images, and transforms is often critical in optical diffraction analysis. Calibration transforms have been discussed elsewhere in this paper (Section IIA). Scaling equations can easily be calculated for objectives of different powers to relate spatial frequencies in a suite of inputs to the radial coordinates in their respective transforms.

Table I (from Pincus, 1973) summarizes some basic scaling relationships applicable to optical diffraction analysis.

Photographic materials and procedures are also important in this work. Tables II and III, from the same source as Table I, give relevant details.

VI. Mapping and Analysis of Transforms

The newcomer to optical diffraction analysis frequently reacts to photographs of optical transforms as "just so many clouds of dots". Although many optical transforms are distinctive, there are also others that are not easily interpreted by the unaided, if experienced, eye. Further, there are many situations in which the transforms are not really helpful until they have been quantified in some way.

Figures 18 and 19 present profiles made some years ago (Pincus, 1969b, Part II) by photographing the transforms and scanning them with a recording microdensitometer that produced both the profiles in these figures and contour maps (not reproduced here). The photographic processing for recording the transforms was both non-linear and somewhat noisy, and accordingly the profiles and maps are less effective than they should be.

TABLE I

Reduction, enlargement, and scaling relationships via measurements on inputs and outputs (Pincus, 1973)

(See notation index below double line on next page)

	Corresponding distances, intervals	Reduction (enlargement)	Scale	Remarks
Original (ground distance, distance on peel, micro-slide etc.)	X_o			Same scale as input for direct processing of thin section or 1:1 photocopy of acetate peel
Photo, map, line drawing of original. ("Record".) (Calibration grid included at this stage)	X_i	$\dfrac{X_o}{X_i}$	$\dfrac{X_i}{X_o}$	Often the display "of record", in publication, etc. Work back from calibration grid to original as well as forward to outputs
Input (reduced transparency)	X_t	$\dfrac{X_o}{X_t} = \dfrac{X_o}{X_i} \cdot \dfrac{X_i}{X_t}$ $\dfrac{X_i}{X_t}$ (from preceding step)	$\dfrac{X_t}{X_o}$	This is the "original" in direct processing of thin section ($X_t = X_o$); for contact or 1:1 copy of acetate peel, X_t also $= X_o$
Transform generated by input	r_1		$\dfrac{K(X_t)}{K'X_t}$	$K = X_t^2 K'$

Photo, map or profile of transform; TV	r_i'	$e_1 r_1 = \dfrac{e_1 K_1}{X_t} = e_1 K_1 X_t$ = enlargement of print or TV display of transform	$\dfrac{r_i'}{r_1} = e_1$	$\dfrac{r_i'}{X_f} = \dfrac{e_1}{e_2} \cdot K_2'$
Reconstructed (filtered) image	X_f	$\dfrac{X_o}{X_f} = \dfrac{X_i}{X_t} \cdot \dfrac{X_t}{X_f}$	$\dfrac{X_f}{X_o}$ $\dfrac{X_f}{X_t}$ = enlargement of output with respect to input $= \dfrac{K_1}{K_2}$ $= \dfrac{K_2}{K_1}$ $\dfrac{X_f}{X_i}$ = relative scale of output with respect to "record"	
Photo (enlarged) of reconstructed image; TV	X_f'	$\dfrac{X_f'}{X_f}$ = enlargement of print or TV display of reconstructed image $(= e_2)$	$\dfrac{X_f'}{X_o}$ = scale of print or TV display or reconstructed image $= e_2 \cdot \dfrac{X_f}{X_o} = e_2 \dfrac{K_1'}{K_2'} \cdot \dfrac{X_t}{X_o}$	See r_i' entry above

Notation:

X's are corresponding distances in input and output images.

r's are corresponding distances in transforms, from centre of D.C. spot to first order diffraction.

K is transform scaling factor for spacing in the input.

K_1', $1/K$ are transform scaling factors for spatial frequency in the input.

$\begin{cases} K_1 = K \text{ for } X_t, \text{ input to transform plane} \\ K_2 = K \text{ for } X_f, \text{ output from transform plane} \end{cases} \begin{cases} \text{Ditto } K_1' \text{ for } K' \\ \text{Ditto } K_2' \text{ for } K' \end{cases}$

e = enlargement factors (e_1, transforms, e_2 reconstructed image; enlargement with respect to preceding step).

TABLE II

Some characteristics of film used in optical diffraction analysis (Pincus, 1973)

Film	Size	ASA	Inputs	Outputs	Remarks
Panatomic X	35 mm	32	Good contrast. Good resolution. Fine grain. Best film for normal contrast subjects	Good contrast. Good resolution. Fine grain. Currently used for all transforms	Used in most of our applications as inputs and outputs
Panatomic X	120	32	Same as above	Too large format for continuing use	Most commonly used film and format for photographing specimens under load in rock mechanics experiments
Plus X	35 mm	125	Good contrast. Good resolution. moderate grain	Good contrast. Good resolution; moderate grain	More grainy than Pan X, therefore not used

Film	Format	ASA	Input/Use	Characteristics	Comments
Tri X	35 mm	400	Continuous tone inputs; grainy	Microtransforms; grainy	Useful where light levels are low, as in microscopy
SO 410	35 mm	160	Used only slightly so far	High red sensitivity; good resolution and speed	New Kodak film—may be very useful in future applications
Kodalith	35 mm 4 × 5 in	6	Good for line drawings (binary inputs)	Not red sensitive; binary spatial filters	Pinholes are produced in developing; must be retouched
High contrast copy	35 mm	25	Good for line drawings (binary inputs)	Too much contrast for most applications	Difficult to determine proper ASA. Thin base leads to problems in gate
Agfa Gevaert 10E75	35 mm 2 × 3 in. plates	?	Very high resolution; very high contrast	Slow; poor transforms; good for holography	Difficult to determine proper exposure
Polaroid 55 p/n	4 × 5 in	50		Good for spot checks	
Polaroid 57	4 × 5 in.	3000		Good for spot checks; very fast	

TABLE III

Darkroom procedures (Pincus, 1973)

Film	ASA	Developer	Temp.	Mixture	Time
Panatomic X/35 mm	32	D76	20°C	1:1	8½ min
Panatomic X/120	32	D76	20°C	1:1	10 min
Plus X/35 mm	125	D76	20°C	1:1	9 min
Tri X/35 mm	400	D76	20°C	1:1	10 min
Tri X/35 mm	1200	Acufine	24°C	Stock	3¾ min
Kodalith/4 × 5 in.	6	Kodalith A + B	24°C	Stock	2 min
High contrast copy/35 mm	25	D19	24°C	Stock	4 min
SO 410/35 mm	160	HC110	20°C	1:19 Dilution F	8 min
Agfa Gevaert 10E75	(?)	HRP	20°C	1:4	1·5 min

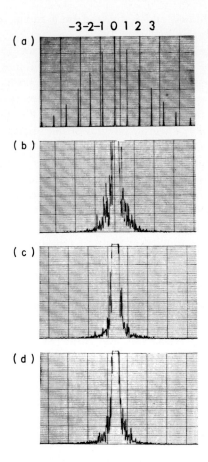

FIG. 30. Profiles of transforms from deformation experiment. Uniaxial compression of cylinder of Tennessee marble. Surface fabric recorded under load with acetate peel.
(a) Calibration transform showing D.C. spike (0-order) and six orders of diffraction (first three are labelled). The 0–1 interval represents 2·5 lines/mm in the input.
(b) No-load transform. (c) Transform of loaded specimen at 7220 psi (49·78 MN/m²).
(d) Transform of loaded specimen at 13540 psi (93·36 MN/m²). (Profiles (b), (c), (d) are parallel to the cylinder axis and the direction of compression.) The changes from (b) to (c) are consistent with the closing of cracks under initial loading, and from (c) to (d) with the onset of new fracturing. (Pincus, 1973.)

Figure 30 illustrates profiles made with a spot-scanner placed on the optical bench in the transform plane. The scanner senses light intensities as it traverses a horizontal path, and its output is fed to a strip-chart recorder. By rotating the input in equal angular increments after each scan, the transform is also rotated and is covered by a radial assembly of profiles, called a "spoke diagram" (Pincus, 1972).

Comparable profiles of a suite of transforms can be analysed quantitatively by measuring changes in area under the profiles in specified spatial frequency bands and changes in roughness of the profiles (Pincus, 1973).

More recently, we have inserted an analogue processor between the spot-scanner and strip-chart recorder; this provides for direct plotting of the intensity's square root, integral, integral of the square root, or square root of the integral. The square root has the dimensions of amplitude and also makes for easier study of fine structure by suppressing large magnitudes; the integral smooths out noisy parts of the profile.

Davis's (1970) maps of photographs of transforms are presented in Fig. 31. With these maps and calibration data, quantitative statements about size distributions and degrees of preferred orientation can be developed.

We have not as yet profiled or mapped microtransforms. This will probably be done first by photographing the transforms and scanning them with a recording microdensitometer. Linear low-noise photography is now within our capability. Direct scanning of the microtransform, which will come later, requires additional hardware.

VII. Analysis by Spatial Filtering

Spatial filtering provides a means for dissecting the information in a two-dimensional input according to spatial frequency or direction. Figures 32 and 33, produced on the optical bench, are examples of spatial filtering. Compare the results of processing a photograph and its tracing. The photograph gives cleaner results, but both sets of outputs are quite comparable. Many other examples of spatial filtering are available (Pincus and Dobrin, 1966; Pincus, 1969a and b; Pincus et al., 1973). Such filtering is routinely accomplished in real time on the optical bench with a TV monitor, to search for optimum filter configurations and combinations; only the most useful results are photographed.

Figure 34 illustrates detection of a defect by filtering, plus some important principles in filtering as elucidated by Parrent and Thompson (1969). It is of interest that (d) and (e) are based on much earlier experiments by Porter (1906).

We have not attempted spatial filtering with the microscope, but plan to do so. Wherever the transform is produced along the optical path, filters may be inserted. At this time, it appears that the most practical approach with our equipment is to work with the transform external to the eyepiece.

All of the filtering described above is amplitude or "real" filtering. "Complex" filters, which operate on both phase and amplitude information,

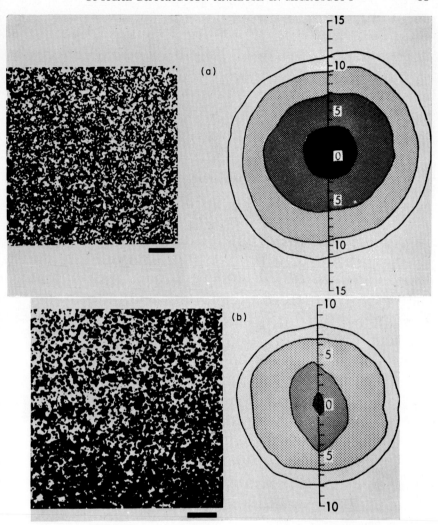

FIG. 31. Pore patterns and their contoured transforms. Images were produced by high-contrast contact-printing thin sections of rock impregnated with red plastic; pore areas are white. Bar with each image represents 1·0 mm. Contours indicate relative intensity; scale divisions represent 1/N mm. Mapping was accomplished by IDECS processor.

(a) Muddy sandstone (Wyoming). The circular pattern indicates no preferred orientation. The finer the spacings, the smaller are the contributions to total porosity.

(b) Dakota sandstone (Kansas). The pattern is elongated for sizes larger than 0·3 mm, but circular for smaller sizes. This results from horizontal elongation of some of the larger pores. (Davis, 1970.)

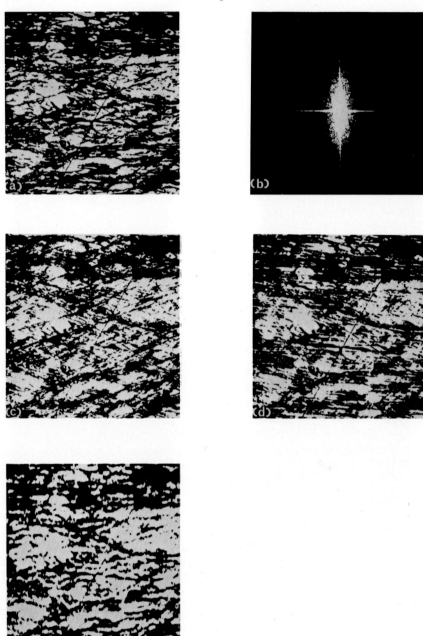

Fig. 32.

can be used, for example, to produce difference images (such as growth increments in crack patterns) and to obtain measures of correlation between two images (such as between a test pathological specimen and a control specimen (Bond *et al.*, 1973)). Such filters are not within the scope of this paper.

Following the completion of this paper, L. K. Lepley (8841 N. Calle Loma Linda, Tucson, Arizona 85704) informed the author that he had accomplished spatial filtering with a microscope set-up like that described here. His filters are inserted in the accessories slot above the objective of a polarizing microscope, where the quartz wedge, mica plate, or gypsum plate are normally inserted.

VIII. Other Types of Analysis

Many other approaches to the study of spatial information in images are feasible and appropriate, and have been amply discussed. One need only consult the series in which this paper appears to find an abundance of such information (Allen *et al.*, 1966; Mendelsohn *et al.*, 1968; Humphries, 1969; Beadle, 1971; Billingsley, 1971; Nathan, 1971; Gahm, 1973; Piller, 1973; Preston, 1973). Underwood's (1970) book on quantitative stereology, cited in Section IV, presents a variety of relevant practical techniques.

Digital analysis of images, covered in some of the foregoing references, has some ardent advocates, particularly in the study of satellite-based imagery. Hybrid digital-optical approaches to image analysis hold much promise; for example, the digital treatment of transform profiles discussed in Section VI will yield additional quantitative measures not practically attainable by the methods we have used so far.

Relatively simple techniques, applied in combination with others described earlier in this paper, can expedite interpretation of results. For example, we have constructed a comparator to delineate differences between similar optical transforms (Pincus, 1972, 1973). The images of the two transforms are projected, each in a different colour, on a back-lighted screen. The size, orientation, and location of each image can be varied; the most common configuration is that of equal scale and exact superimposition.

FIG. 32. Filtering of photomicrograph of quartzite (Raintal, Bozen Province). Side of input represents about 20 mm in the specimen.
(a) Input. (b) Transform of input. (c) Directionally filtered image; horizontal linears removed (10° wedge). (d) Directionally filtered image; linears sloping 15° toward the left removed (20° wedge). (e) High-cut filtered image. (Pincus and Dobrin, 1966.)

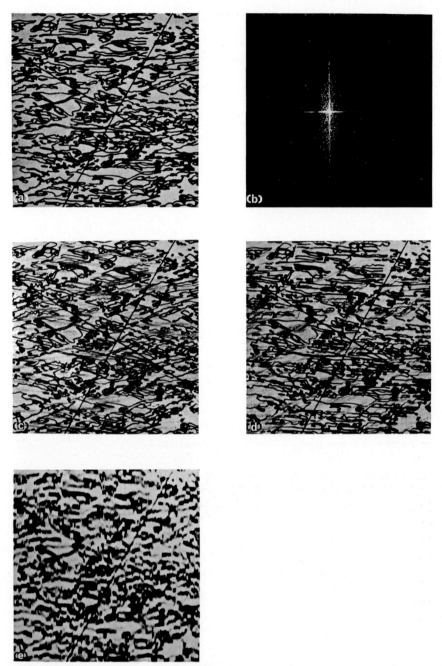

Fig. 33. Input (a) is the tracing of Fig. 32a. (b)–(e) have been produced by the same processing as in Fig. 32b–e, except that the transform (b) is larger (hence less intense) than the transform in Fig. 32b. (Pincus, 1969b, Part III.)

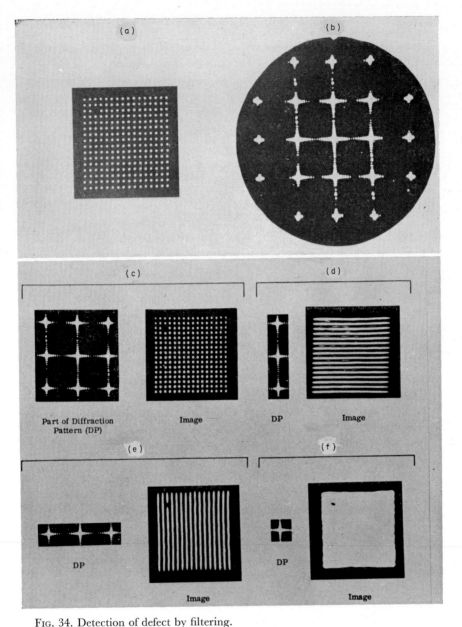

FIG. 34. Detection of defect by filtering.
(a) Original image. One dot in periodic structure is missing. (b) Transform of (a).
(c) Central nine peaks from (b) and the image reconstructed by allowing them to
pass through the optical system. (d) Three peaks in central vertical band from (b)
and the image reconstructed from them. (e) Three peaks in central horizontal band
from (b) and the image reconstructed from them. (The defect is indicated.) (f) Central peak and the image reconstructed from it. The resulting information consists of
the envelope of (a) and the defect. (Parrent and Thompson, 1969.)

Another feasible arrangement is that of processing large numbers of inputs on film strips, using a motorized optical gate now available commercially. (The processing of microscope slides can also be automated.) With suitable photodetection hardware and masks in the transform plane, inputs could be screened on the basis of degree and direction of preferred orientation, and on the basis of spatial frequencies (within a range of spatial frequencies at specified concentrations).

IX. Concluding Remarks

It is practical to produce optical transforms with a microscope. These transforms are useful in interpreting the images from which they are generated, and in making comparisons between such images.

The quality of optical transforms generated with the microscope (microtransforms) has been checked against equivalent transforms (macrotransforms) produced with a high-quality optical bench set-up, and it is clear that the microtransforms are valid.

Microtransforms have been generated directly from slide-mounted material. Clean transforms can be produced from many birefringent, heterogeneous materials. The theoretical basis for generating such transforms has been elucidated by Power (1973), with explanations of conditions affecting the quality of transforms.

The production of optical transforms with a microscope is attractive because it is a relatively inexpensive data-processing tool that utilizes an instrument already available where people are likely to find use for transforms; additional equipment costs are minor. The straight-through optical approach described throughout much of this paper is a clean, hands-on, do-it-yourself technique. Additional analytical capabilities, such as transform mapping and spatial filtering can be acquired as needed without disturbing the original set-up.

The microscope can also be used effectively to generate optical transforms from photomicrographs. Thus, if a slide-mounted specimen is too heterogeneous optically to yield a useful transform directly, a photograph of the slide may serve adequately as an input; accentuating the contrast in such inputs is often helpful. The microscope can, of course, be used to process other two-dimensional displays, provided that the scaling and photographic processing of the input are adequate.

Acknowledgements

This paper draws upon research by the author and his students in the Department of Geological Sciences, University of Wisconsin-Milwaukee.

This research has been supported directly or indirectly by the University of Wisconsin-Milwaukee, the US Bureau of Mines, and the Advanced Research Projects Agency of the US Department of Defense. The views and conclusions in this paper should not be interpreted as necessarily representing the official policies, expressed or implied, of any of the foregoing agencies or of the United States Government.

The experimental and theoretical work in microscopy was carried out by P. C. Power, Jr., as his thesis project, under the author's supervision.

The technical assistance of K. Scheibengraber, R.Wipf, D. Schmitt, and J. Awald is much appreciated.

REFERENCES

Abbe, E. (1873). *Arch. mikrosk. Anat. Entw Mech.* **9,** 413–468.

Allen, R. D., Brault, J. W. and Zeh, R. M. (1966). *In* "Advances in Optical and Electron Microscopy" (R. Barer and V. E. Cosslett, eds), Vol. 1, pp. 77–114. Academic Press, London and New York.

American Society for Testing and Materials (1963). "Estimating the Average Grain Size of Metals", ASTM Designation E112–63, Plates I and III.

Beadle, C. (1971). *In* "Advances in Optical and Electron Microscopy" (R. Barer and V. E. Cosslett, eds), Vol. 4, pp. 362–383. Academic Press, London and New York.

Billingsley, F. C. (1971). *In* "Advances in Optical and Electron Microscopy" (R. Barer and V. E. Cosslett, eds), Vol. 4, pp. 127–159. Academic Press, London and New York.

Bond, R. L., Mazumder, M. K., Testerman, M. K. and Hsieh, D. (1973). *Science* **179,** 571–573.

Bracewell, R. (1965). "The Fourier Transform and Its Applications". McGraw-Hill, New York.

Cloos, E. (1943). *Trans. Am. Geophys. Un.* **24,** 273–280.

Davis, J. C. (1970). *In* "Data Processing in Biology and Geology" (J. L. Cutbill, ed.), Vol. 3, pp. 69–87. Systematics Association.

Davis, J. C. and McCullagh, M. J., eds (1975). "Display and Analysis of Spatial Data", NATO Adv. Study Inst. Wiley, London and New York.

Dobrin, M. B., Ingalls, A. L. and Long, J. A. (1965). *Geophysics* **30,** 1144–1178.

Erickson, H. P. (1973). *In* "Advances in Optical and Electron Microscopy" (R. Barer and V. E. Cosslett, eds), Vol. 5, pp. 163–199. Academic Press, London and New York.

Gahm, J. (1973). *In* "Advances in Optical and Electron Microscopy" (R. Barer and V. E. Cosslett, eds), Vol. 5, pp. 115–161. Academic Press, London and New York.

Gall, J. G. (1966). *J. Cell Biol.* **31,** 130A.

Hanszen, K.-J. (1971). *In* "Advances in Optical and Electron Microscopy" (R. Barer and V. E. Cosslett, eds), Vol. 4, pp. 1–84. Academic Press, London and New York.

Humphries, D. W. (1969). *In* "Advances in Optical and Electron Microscopy" (R. Barer and V. E. Cosslett, eds), Vol. 3, pp. 33–98. Academic Press, London and New York.

Jackson, P. L. (1965). *Geophysics* **30,** 5–23.

Jennison, R. C. (1961). "Fourier Transforms and Convolutions for the Experimentalist". Pergamon Press, Oxford.

Jung, J. (1969). "Précis de Pétrographie". Masson, Paris.

Krumbein, W. C. (1941). *J. Sedim. Petrol* **11,** 64–72

Larson, W. C. (1973). M.Sc. thesis, University of Wisconsin-Milwaukee.

Martin, L. C. (1966). "The Theory of the Microscope". Elsevier, New York.

Mendelsohn, M. L., Mayall, B. H., Prewitt, J. M. S., Bostrom, R. C. and Holcomb, W. G. (1968). *In* "Advances in Optical and Electron Microscopy" (R. Barer and V. E. Cosslett, eds), Vol. 2, pp. 77–150. Academic Press, London and New York.

Nathan, R. (1971). *In* "Advances in Optical and Electron Microscopy" (R. Barer and V. E. Cosslett, eds), Vol. 4, pp. 85–125. Academic Press, London and New York.

Packham, G. H. (1955). *J. Geol.* **63,** 50–58.

Parrent, G. B., Jr. and Thompson, B. J. (1969). "Physical Optics Notebook". Soc. Photo-Opt. Instrum. Engrs., Redondo Beach, California.

Peterson, R. A. and Dobrin, M. B. (1966). "A Pictorial Digital Atlas". United Geophysical Corp., Pasadena, California.

Piller, H. (1973). *In* "Advances in Optical and Electron Microscopy" (R. Barer and V. E. Cosslett, eds), Vol. 5, pp. 95–114. Academic Press, London and New York.

Pincus, H. J. (1966). *In* "Proceedings of the First International Congress on Rock Mechanics", Vol. 1, pp. 173–177. Int. Soc. Rock Mech., Lisbon.

Pincus, H. J. (1969a). *In* "Proceedings of the Sixth Symposium on Remote Sensing of Environment", pp. 261–274. Inst. Sci. and Tech., Ann Arbor, Michigan.

Pincus, H. J. (1969b). *Int. J. Rock Mech. Min. Sci.* **6,** 259–276.

Pincus, H. J. (1972, 1973). "Development of Capabilities of Optical Diffraction Analysis for Quantitatively Comparing and Correlating Rock Fabrics and Fabric Changes—Annual Technical Reports". Adv. Res. Proj. Agency and US Bur. Mines, ARPA Order No. 1579, Program Codes 1F10 and 2F10.

Pincus, H. J. and Dobrin, M. B. (1966). *J. Geophys. Res.* **71,** 4861–4870.

Pincus, H. J., Power, P. C., Jr. and Woodzick, T. (1973). *Geoforum* **14**/73, 39–52.

Porter, A. B. (1906). *Proc. Phil. Mag.* **11,** 154–166.

Power, P. C., Jr. (1973). M.S. thesis, University of Wisconsin-Milwaukee.

Power, P. C., Jr. and Pincus, H. J. (1974). *Science* **186,** 234–239.

Preston, K., Jr. (1973). *In* "Advances in Optical and Electron Microscopy" (R. Barer and V. E. Cosslett, eds), Vol. 5, pp. 43–93. Academic Press, London and New York.

Sander, B. (1970). "An Introduction to the Study of Fabrics of Geological Bodies" (F. C. Phillips and G. Windsor, trans.). Pergamon Press, Oxford.

Sherman, G. C. (1967). "Integral-Transform Formulation of Diffraction Theory". Air Force Report No. SAMSO-TR-67-101; Aerospace Report No. TR-0158 (3230-25)-1; AD-663231.

Shulman, A. R. (1966). "Principles of Optical Data Processing for Engineers". GSFC X-DOCUMENT, 521-66-434, Goddard Space Flight Center, Greenbelt, Maryland.

Shulman, A. R. (1970). "Optical Data Processing". Wiley, New York and London.

Sommerfeld, A. (1954). "Lectures on Theoretical Physics", Vol. 4. Academic Press, New York and London.

Taylor, C. A. and Lipson, H. (1965). "Optical Transforms". Cornell University Press, Ithaca, New York.

Underwood, E. E. (1970). "Quantitative Stereology". Addison-Wesley, Reading, Massachusetts.

Whitten, E. H. T. (1966). "Structural Geology of Folded Rocks". Rand McNally, Chicago.

Yu, T. S. (1973). "Introduction to Diffraction, Information Processing, and Holography". MIT Press, Cambridge, Mass. and London.

Microkymography and Related Techniques

A. CASTENHOLZ

Department of Human Biology,
University of Kassel, Germany

I. INTRODUCTION

In intravital microscopy the various phenomena of movement, as obvious indications of life function in cells, tissues and organs, have always stimulated interest comparable to that in static form and structural relationships. Whereas with new optical methods of microscopy, especially phase contrast and interference contrast methods, morphological details can be recognized even in unstained living preparations while fully exploiting the capacity of the light microscope, observation and recording of movement still presents some difficult problems. Only certain object movements which occur within a limited time range can be directly recognized by the observer. Others occur either too slowly or too fast so that their dynamics can neither be established nor analysed by the human eye.

Over the last 50 years the main method for studying movement processes under the microscope has been cinematography. In particular the time-lapse technique (serial photography) has been widely used. In this method the movement process is split into a series of single steps taken at a given time interval. On projection at normal speed, a subjective impression of continuous movement is created. However, for quantitative analysis this indirect method has the serious disadvantage of requiring a time-consuming examination of each individual picture.

The *direct* registration of movement in the form of curves has long been used in technology and medicine, in the form of *kymography*. In medicine it has been mainly used in the field of radiology. In relation to microscopy this method was first applied to the determination of the speed of blood flow by Basler (1917). A wider field of application for kymography at the microscopic level became available with the introduction of various technical modifications by Castenholz (1967, 1968a, 1973a); these enabled the method to be adapted to the special dynamic relationships in specimens ranging from whole organs down to individual cells. Although in general the term *"microkymography"* has been introduced for photokymographical registration through the microscope, different techniques are included within this title. These techniques have in common the recording of movements in curve form with the simultaneous reproduction of structural characteristics. Thus, depending upon the type of photographic technique, either the morphology or the function of the object will be accentuated in the record.

The kymographical principle was already used in the last century for the registration of pupil movements (Bellarminoff, 1885), and has found a place in the modern investigation of the pupil as infrared pupillokymography (Castenholz, 1968b). The recently developed modification of photographic registration known as *"stripe photomicrography"* (Castenholz, 1974a) is a bridge to customary photomicrography. This modification allows the advantages of complete photographic reproduction of the object, similar to photomicrography, to be combined in a special way with those of a functional kymographic representation.

At this point it should be emphasized, however, that the technique of microkymography has certain limitations. Unfortunately, suitable equipment is not yet commercially available. The interested microscopist is dependent upon the assembly and development of individually designed apparatus and consequently the quality of the photographic reproduction depends on the technical sophistication of the equipment. In addition, as a result of the limited depth of field of the microscope in the microkymograph, many movements of biological objects which occur in three dimensions can only be reproduced in a two-dimensional form. By analogy with the development of X-ray kymography one can hardly imagine microkymography as a routine procedure; as in every special technique for quantitative microscopy, its efficiency largely depends on the experience and patience of the individual investigator.

II. Principles of Microkymography (MKG)

In general, by kymography one understands a technique of registration, in which the process of movement is recorded in the form of a graph by means of a device which moves at a uniform speed. In technology and physiology a simple arrangement of this type consisting of a rotating soot-coated cylinder or drum ("kymograph"), to which the movements were transferred by a stylus attached to a mechanical lever, has been used for a long time. In *photokymography*, in place of the soot-coated cylinder, there is a corresponding moving system with light-sensitive paper or film on which the processes of movement are photographically recorded by means of a light beam. For most purposes a slit diaphragm is placed directly in front of the film to narrow the light beam. In radiology there is a similar principle that goes by the well-known name of *X-ray kymography*. Here movements of the internal organs can be recorded on film using an X-ray beam. Various kymographical modifications have been developed using different types of diaphragm (single slit and multiple slit or screen diaphragm) and a selective transport of either film or diaphragm (Gött and Rosenthal, 1912; Stumpf *et al.*, 1936). The kymographic principle of registration can be adapted to the special morphological and dynamic conditions of specific organs.

The principles of registration of X-ray kymography, with its various modifications, can be transferred by means of *microkymography* to the level of light microscopy. The optical system of the microscope replaces the X-ray beam and the enlarged image of the object under the microscope appears in total or sectional areas on the film (Figs 1, 2, 3). As in X-ray kymography the type of transport system (film or diaphragm movement) and the type of slit diaphragm (single or multiple) are of fundamental importance in relation to the type of record obtained. Examples of several possible records are shown in Fig. 3. The "slit window" corresponding to the single or multiple narrow zone or zones of the image determines the area of the object recorded on the film at any given moment (Fig. 2). Procedures using a stationary slit and stage involve a corresponding fixed zone on the object slide. When the slit or stage is moved this zone is spread out as a rectangular band across the field of view and the whole of the object is scanned (Figs 2, 3).

A. *Recording with Moving Film*

1. *Single-slit method (stripe MKG)*

The principle of registration with moving film and single-slit diaphragm is shown in Fig. 1 (1). The slit in the diaphragm lies perpendicular to the long axis of the film and has a fixed position relative to the picture frame of the camera. Consequently, the slit window is located on a certain cross-section of the image of the microscopical object. During registration the film moves at a constant speed and records all structures which reach the film through the slit in the diaphragm, in the form of a striated picture (Figs 3, 14 (1, 2). For this reason the technique is called *"stripe"* or *"streak image"* *microkymography*. Moving structures appear in stripe MKG as wavy

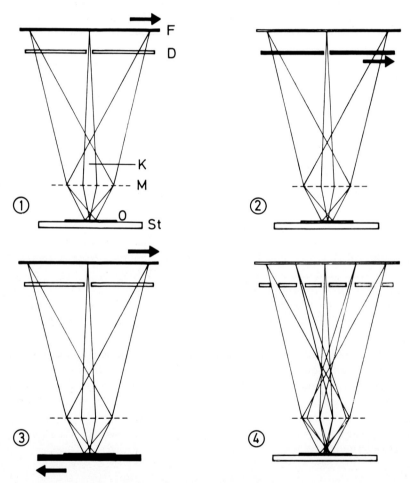

FIG. 1. Diagram showing the registration principles of (1) stripe MKG, (2) area MKG, (3) stripe MG, (4) the general arrangement for methods using a multiple-slit diaphragm (step and screen MKG, and screen MG).

St, stage; O, object; M, optical system of the microscope; K, section of the light beam which is recorded by the camera; D, slit diaphragm; F, film. Arrow indicates component which is moved during exposure.

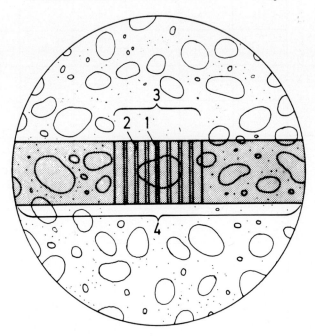

Fig. 2. Diagram illustrating single object zones ("slit windows") which are re-corded from the field of the microscope with microkymographical and stripe-photomicrographical procedures.

1, A single narrow zone: stripe MKG. 2, Several individual narrow zones: step MKG. 3, Area corresponding to the picture format of the camera: area MKG and screen MKG (in the latter, the area is divided into segments). 4, An unlimited wide zone running across the preparation: stripe MG.

or serrated lines; motionless structures on the other hand appear as straight striae running parallel to the film edge. Since the registration time is not limited, the length of the individual record can be chosen at will.

2. *Multiple-slit method (step MKG)*

If instead of the single-slit diaphragm a multiple-slit diaphragm is used for the registration technique described above, one obtains a picture which is composed of several partial kymographs corresponding to the number of slits (Fig. 1 (4)). The more slits a diaphragm has, the more cross-sections are recorded at the same time, so that the surface dimensions of an object are also outlined (Fig. 2 (2)). For this reason such a procedure is classified under "area kymography" in X-ray kymography. As in the single-slit method, the dynamics of movement of the object cross-sections involved

method of registration	picture representation and format of the record	recorded object area	technical features							
			film		diaphragm				stage	
			moved	fixed	moved	fixed	single slit	screen	moved	fixed
stripe microkymography	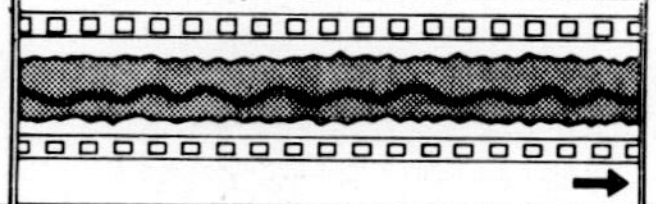	one narrow zone	+			+	+			+
step microkymography	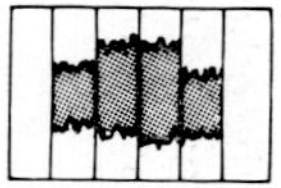	several narrow zones	+			+		+		+
area microkymography	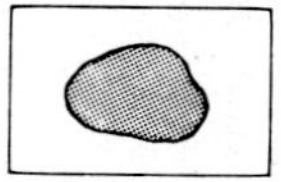	the whole object		+	+		+			+
screen microkymography		the whole object divided into several sections		+	+			+		+
stripe photomicrography		the whole object	+			+	+		+	
screen photomicrography	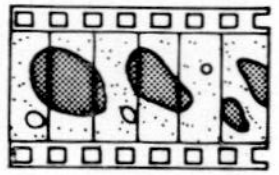	the whole object divided into several sections	+			+		+	+	

Fig. 3. Survey of registration principles and techniques; types of records obtained by various modifications of MKG and SMG.

are directly expressed in the strial structure of the individual image field. Striae and curved lines which run from one image field to the next are always offset from one another due to their parallel alignment to the film edge (Figs 3, 13 (2)). Thus a round or oval-shaped object appears with jagged margins with this type of registration. Because of this the technique has been called *"step microkymography"*. The format of the single record corresponds to that of an ordinary photomicrograph.

B. *Recording with Moving Slit Diaphragm*

1. *Single-slit method (area MKG)*

In this procedure a single slit diaphragm is moved, instead of transporting the film. The diaphragm travels from one end to the other of the image field in the camera, so that the object is photographically recorded in a sequential exposure and can be portrayed in its entirety (Fig. 1 (2)). With a static object one obtains a pictorial record similar to that of an ordinary photomicrograph. A characteristic record develops from areas of the object that contain moving structures. As with the stripe kymograph, this record expresses the dynamics of movement (Figs 3, 13(4)). This procedure has been designated as "area microkymography", since the total photographic representation of the object is always superimposed on the kymographic record. The length of exposure in the area MKG depends on the speed of slit movement and on the distance through which the slit moves. This is limited by the picture format of the camera.

2. *Multiple-slit method (screen (area) MKG)*

If a multiple-slit diaphragm or screen is used for the area MKG (Fig. 1(4) moving diaphragm and stationary film), one obtains a picture, which like a step MKG is divided into different pictorial zones corresponding to the number of diaphragm slits. The individual parts of the picture, however, fit together to give a total image of the object.

This procedure, known as "screen microkymography", corresponds in principle to a picture characteristic of an area MKG. Thus the contours of an object which run from one pictorial zone into the next are not offset in a stepwise manner as in the step MKG. Instead they are reproduced in their normal uninterrupted outline (Fig. 3). Moving objects are displayed in the form of curves, whereas non-moving objects appear similar to a photo-micrograph. During each registration the diaphragm can only be transported through the distance between two slits, so that the width of the record is limited.

80 A. CASTENHOLZ

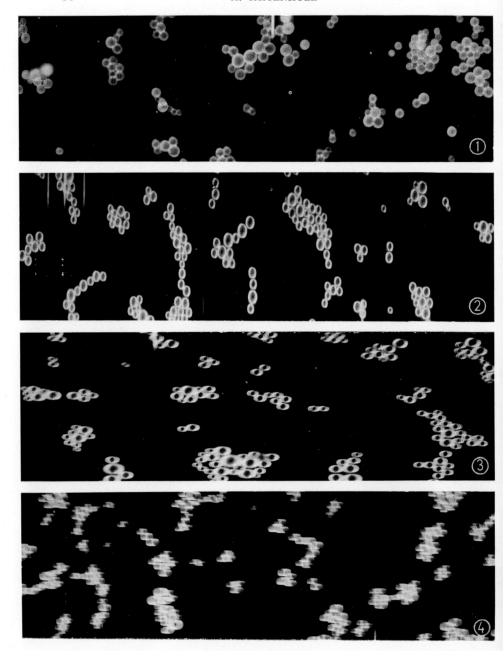

FIG. 4. (For legend see facing page)

III. The Principle of Stripe Photomicrography (SMG)

Continuous recording with both moving film *and* moving stage analogous to stripe microkymography makes the procedure of stripe photomicrography (SMG) feasible. Whereas in stripe microkymography an abstract graph derived from a narrow zone of the object is displayed, stripe photomicrography reveals the whole object complete with its structural details. Static segments of the object appear true to their form, so that the photographic record corresponds to a conventional photomicrograph (Fig. 3). In contrast, moving objects display an additional graphical presentation in the stripe micrograph. In this respect, stripe photomicrography shows certain similarities to area microkymography. In stripe photomicrography a microscopical object can be displayed in the form of a continuous record which may extend from one end of the specimen to the other. Differentiation between moving and non-moving objects is also possible for certain objects, e.g. cytological smear preparations of isolated living cells (Figs 9(3), 14(3)).

The principle of stripe photomicrography is as follows (Figs 1, 3): If in the stripe microkymographic method described in Section IIA1 (movement of the film with stationary single-slit diaphragm), the microscopic object is transported by the microscope stage in a direction opposite to the film motion, then the camera, as a result of reversal of the image in the microscope, records the movement of the film and the image of the object as being in the same direction. In addition, if the movement of the film and of the image are exactly synchronized by making the speed of the stage equal to the speed of the film divided by the optical magnification, the object is recorded as a non-moving and undistorted picture on the film. If the speeds of film and image do not correspond, the object is reproduced in either a lengthened or condensed form compared to its original shape (Fig. 4). The length of the record is unlimited. The slit diaphragm prevents the production of a blurred picture and makes the graphical registration of moving parts of an object feasible.

The idea of recording moving objects with a slit diaphragm and movement of the film was first applied in the form of a special technique of aerial

Fig. 4. Stripe photomicrograph of a spherical test object (latex particles, 12–35 μm diameter) to demonstrate the effects of speed and direction of movement of the film and the image.

(1) Correct reproduction of the object shape when the speed is uniform and the movements of film and image are in the same direction. (2) Distorted representation (vertically elongated figures) when the movement of the film is slower than that of the image. (3) Distorted representation (horizontally stretched figures) when the film moves faster than the image. (4) Picture with double contours. Here the image and the film have the same speed but are moving in opposite directions.

photography (Sonne, 1940). The photographic conditions for this procedure were basically similar to those of the stripe photomicrographic
recording principle. As a result of the flight movement objects moving over
the ground surface can be recorded continuously in a corresponding moving
film in a camera equipped with a slit diaphragm installed on the plane.

As for microkymography, different types of diaphragms can be used for
stripe photomicrography. Only the procedure with a single-slit diaphragm
is of practical value at present. The use of a multiple-slit diaphragm leads
to a partitioning of the record into several picture sections, so that by
analogy with the screen MKG one could speak of *screen photomicrography*.
The duration of exposure is thus limited to the time which a wandering
object needs to get from one slit diaphragm window to the next. It is only
possible to use the normal film format.

IV. Apparatus

A. *The Microscope*

Basically any type of microscope equipped with a phototube and certain
other standard accessories is suitable for microkymographical recording. An
Ortholux research microscope (E. Leitz, Wetzlar, Germany) with a unit for
recording MKG and SMG is shown in Fig. 5. To avoid vibrations from the
surroundings, a stable assembly of the microscope together with the recording equipment should be mounted on a solid common base plate. The
supporting device should be equipped with a vertical column, to which the
camera can be securely attached. All vibrations which are transferred to the
object are recorded along with the object's intrinsic movement and impair
the quality of the kymographical picture.

Only continuously running light sources with high brightness and no
appreciable fluctuation in intensity can be used. Modern halogen and
xenon lamps have proved suitable for kymography. Special optical systems
for phase contrast, interference contrast, dark-field, and fluorescence
microscopy may be employed, depending on the specific problem and the
optical properties of the object. It is almost impossible to do without such
equipment for work on unstained objects. An adjustable square stage is
essential for rapid and accurate location and focusing of the region of the
object to be registered. Special problems, such as stripe kymographical
and stripe photomicrographical registration of a certain cross-section of the
object, can only be solved with the aid of an additional rotatable mechanical
stage. For stripe photomicrography the microscope stage must be motorized
to move at least along either the x or y axis.

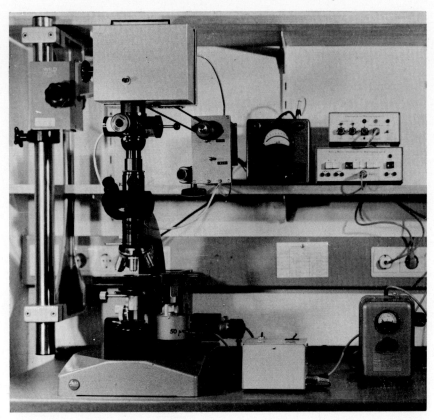

FIG. 5. Photograph of assembled equipment consisting of an Ortholux research microscope and a recording system, which is suitable for the registration not only of stripe microkymographs and stripe photomicrographs but also of ordinary photomicrographs.

The ability to vary the speed of the stage movement is desirable but not absolutely essential (see Section V). During the recording the object must remain visible to the observer, so that the location and focus of the region under study can be checked continuously and corrected when necessary. This can be done by means of a body for conventional photomicrography attached to the phototube of the microscope, which is furnished with a special focusing or seeker eyepiece and a beam-splitting prism which directs light to both the eye of the observer and to the camera. More light should be deflected to the camera (about 80%) than to the eye. This type of photomicrographic body often contains a shutter and a photometer unit for measuring exposure time.

B. *Equipment for MKG and SMG*

All procedures for MKG and SMG which have been discussed in Section II can be carried out with the help of two attachments for the camera and a transport system for the film or the diaphragm. Since at the moment there is no complete apparatus of this type for registration which is commercially available, the camera attachments which we have developed will be described. For economy it is best if a camera with 35 mm film and a large film magazine is used for stripe MKG and stripe MG when longer recordings are made. For other procedures which have a limited print size (step and

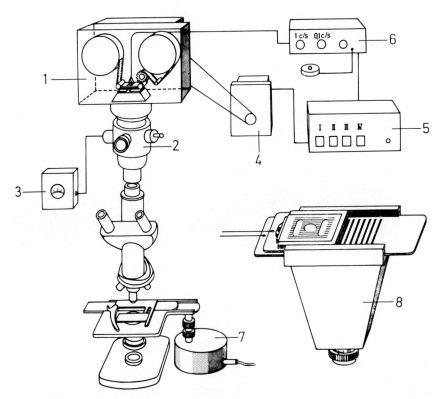

Fig. 6. Diagram of the equipment shown in Fig. 5.

1, Camera with large 35 mm film magazine, special system for continuous film transport, and a film guide plate furnished with three film marking systems (light-emitting diodes). 2, Body with focusing eyepiece and photocell. 3, Galvanometer. 4, Electric motor. 5, Power supply and control unit for motorized operation. 6, Impulse generator for light-emitting diodes. 7, Electric motor unit for automatic stage movement. 8, Special camera attachment for large film format with devices for transport of the filmpack holder and the slit diaphragm.

area MKG and screen MKG) a camera for larger prints in which a 9 × 12 cm filmpack holder can be used is recommended (Fig. 6(8)).

1. *35 mm camera attachment*

The registration equipment consists of a camera housing containing a magazine with 30 m of 35 mm film, a special film stage and a film transport system. The latter consists of a geared drive connected to various film spools. The film stage contains the diaphragm which is attached directly in front of the film. The width of the slit of the diaphragm can be adjusted to all values between 0 and 24 mm. For taking single photographs (without film movement), the slit diaphragm can be removed from the film stage, so that the camera attachment is suitable for ordinary photomicrography.

The film pressure plate contains three small light-emitting diodes aligned with fine slit windows, through which the light can be transmitted onto the back of the film. These serve to mark the film, for example for time registration, numbering, and denoting certain experimental conditions. A power supply unit yields regular repeated (1 or 0·1 Hz) or single short impulses at any desired time interval. The film drive is accomplished by an external synchronous motor coupled to the camera by a rubber belt. By means of the motor control unit, film can be driven at selected speeds. With the driving gears in both the motor and the camera attachment the speed can be further adjusted mechanically. Thus the final speed of transportation can be varied between 0·1 and 20 mm/sec. The motor unit provides a very smooth film or diaphragm movement and the danger of transferring vibration from the motor to the microscope is minimal.

2. *Large format attachment*

This attachment, which is easily exchanged with the 35 mm camera system, is designed to traverse a 9 × 12 cm filmpack holder and a slit diaphragm insert at right angles to the optical axis of the microscope. This is done by means of a separate motor unit coupled to a geared or belt drive system. The transportation speed can be varied, as with the 35 mm attachment, over a wide range. A rapid switch from the transport of the film holder to that of the slit diaphragm, that is, an interchange between stripe- and area-microkymographical types of registration, is easily accomplished. Various diaphragm inserts with single- or multiple-slit pattern are available.

The large format attachment can be used with or without a seeker eyepiece. In the latter case a special mirror housing for the optical inspection of the picture can be incorporated (Castenholz, 1967). For the proper selection of exposure time (particularly in screen and step MKG) a variable speed camera shutter is desirable.

V. Procedure and Recording Technique

In principle any film (black-white or colour emulsion), which can be used for photomicrography is suitable for MKG and SMG. The exposure time is not determined by the length of time during which the camera shutter is open, as in ordinary photomicrography, but on the speed with which the film is transported and the width of the diaphragm.

$$\text{Exposure time (sec)} = \frac{\text{width of slit (mm)}}{\text{film speed (mm/sec)}}$$

The values for the width of the diaphragm and speed of film transport can be read from the diagram of Fig. 7 for the standard exposure times between 1 and 1/125 sec which are usual in photography. Commercial microscope photometers can be utilized without special calibration.

For the choice of recording conditions one has to consider the special dynamics of the object movement which is to be registered. Rapid and rhythmical motions require a higher transport speed of the film or the diaphragm than do slow and non-rhythmical processes. If the width of the slit is too large, the registration is not well defined. This means that in the place of fine graphs there are broad bands, in which the details are lost. In our camera attachments we use constant slit widths between 0·4 and 0·6 mm and as a rule vary the transportation speed of the film or the diaphragm. Thus, through the regulation of the lamp voltage or the use of a neutral density filter, adaptation to the light requirements of a particular film sensitivity is possible.

The time during which the film or diaphragm transport is carried out is defined as the duration of registration. This time, which also depends on the speed of the film, determines the length of film used. The duration of registration is limited when a multiple slit diaphragm is used for step-MKG and screen-MKG/MG and can be calculated from the following relationship:

$$\text{Duration of registration (sec)} = \frac{\text{distance between slits (mm)}}{\text{film speed (mm/sec)}}$$

When using the SMG technique, the distortion of the picture, in the sense of an elongation or compression of the object (Fig. 4) can be avoided if the speed of the stage and that of the film are exactly synchronized with each other, so that the movement of the image and that of the film are identical in direction and speed as already discussed. Since the apparent speed of an object viewed through the microscope depends on the magnification, the following relationships arise:

$$\text{Stage speed (mm/sec)} = \frac{\text{film speed (mm/sec)}}{\text{total optical magnification}}$$

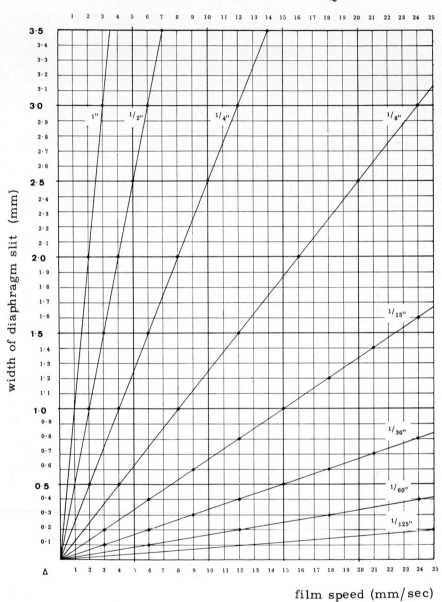

FIG. 7. Nomogram for rapid determination of exposure time in MKG and SMG. The standard exposure time values commonly used in photography are represented by individual straight lines.

The total optical magnification is the product of the magnifications of the objective, eyepiece and tube length factor.

Since in most cases the objective–eyepiece combination is chosen in order to display or reproduce the special features of the object, it is generally necessary to adapt the film and stage speeds to the optical magnification. If the speed of stage movement is fixed, then only the speed of the film transport can be varied. Figure 8 shows graphs relating optical magnification (up to × 250) to film transport speed for three different values of stage speed, namely 12·5, 50 and 200 μm/sec which are available with the stage motor device (E. Leitz) we use.

The SMG can produce a record in the form of a long narrow strip as in Fig. 12(1) or individual records can be fitted together in the form of a raster to make up a photomontage showing the whole of a two-dimensional extended object as in Fig. 12(2). See also Section VI.

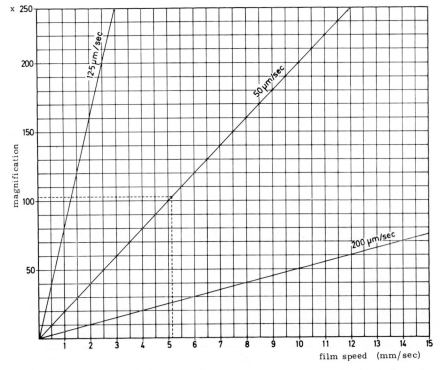

FIG. 8. Nomogram relating optical magnification, film speed and stage speed in SMG. The three lines correspond to the three speeds of stage movement (12·5, 50 and 200 μm/sec) obtainable with the stage drive mechanism used.

In methods such as step MKG or stripe MKG which employ a moving film with a stationary diaphragm, if one wishes to record a particular section of the specimen, it is necessary to know the exact position of the diaphragm window at the moment of recording. This is made possible by placing index marks at suitable positions in the observation field of the seeker eyepiece or on the focusing screen of the attachment camera of the microscope.

VI. Picture Content and Quantitative Evaluation

As already emphasized, the special techniques of MKG and SMG make it possible to display the object in a wide variety of different ways. With SMG or area MKG static objects appear in their true form; if the object moves, deviations are superimposed on the record. On the other hand, in the stripe or step-MKG techniques only narrow sections of the object are recorded in the form of abstract line or band patterns or as rough contours (Fig. 3). Movement and other dynamic processes are best recognized and analysed by the latter procedures.

In contrast, area and screen MKG and SMG are less suited for the quantitative analysis of functions observed through the microscope. They are much more useful for studying the relationship between structure and function. Their special value lies in the ability to locate certain movements or colour phenomena in the preparation. Thus moving elements of the preparation can easily be distinguished from non-moving ones. In addition SMG is able to record an unusually large area of the object during one registration (Fig. 12(1)). Thus the advantages of this procedure lie, among other things, in the possibility of making a composite picture on long strips of film. Thus a picture covering a very large area can be built up without the need for further photographic enlargement. Contrary to other photomontage techniques the high initial optical resolution is maintained.

In general the picture quality of a microkymograph or of a stripe photo-micrograph is determined by several factors. The speed of the film and diaphragm transport as well as the width of the slit have already been mentioned. Other important factors contributing to the sharpness and detail of the record include the quality of the microscope image, the properties of the film material, the light source, and the elimination of all external vibrations transmitted to the apparatus. In order to reproduce and quantitatively evaluate the details of rapid movement one must operate with high transport speeds and a narrow diaphragm in order to ensure good temporal resolution in the kymograph curve. The quality of the recording with MKG and SMG is occasionally spoilt by the appearance of an artificial line or band pattern. In such cases the individual lines of the pattern always run perpendicular to the direction of the film or diaphragm transport. Various reasons should be considered: irregularity in the transport, fluctuations in light intensity, and the choice of an unsuitable film emulsion with a steep gradation.

The question is often raised whether one should use the original negative or an enlargement for the quantitative evaluation of a kymographic record. If the record is high in contrast then much of the work can be carried out on the negative. If, however, the contrast is poor, then an enlargement may help. Individual details often become clearer, without of course improving the optical resolution.

A. Stripe Pattern, Motion Curves and Colour Phenomena

By means of the pattern of the curves in the microkymograph, the direction and type of movement, for example a regular or irregular rhythmic movement, can be recognized immediately. For rhythmic motions the periodicity is easily estimated by studying the wave-like record (Fig. 9(1)). In the same way the amplitude of the motion can be measured if the direction of movement of the object corresponds to that of the slit window during the registration. If this is not the case, then the amplitude of the record appears either too large or too small. Further details on the interpretation of the kymograph curves can be found in Stumpf et al. (1936).

For microscopical preparations containing free cells, the speed of movement of individual cells can be determined from the angle of inclination of the line produced by each cell to the axis of the film. Examples are shown in Fig. 9(2). It is easy to distinguish between moving and non-moving cells under these conditions with the help of SMG. In this case, it is also possible to measure the number of cells which cross the slit window per unit of time (Fig. 9(3)). Dynamic processes which are manifested through changes in colour rather than in movement are displayed in the microkymograph

---

FIG. 9. Diagrams showing possibilities of quantitative evaluation in stripe MKG. M = bar indicating optical magnification, TM = time mark.
(1) Rhythmic motion curve of a single cell (spermatozoon). The beat frequency can be calculated from the wavelength (W). The transverse deflection of the sperm tail at any moment can be derived from the amplitude (A). (2) Determination of the corpuscular velocity (flow rate) of single cells (e.g. blood cells) from the relationship between the parameters a and b, which determine the angle of inclination (α) of an individual cell. (3) Registration of moving and non-moving cells (spermatozoa) by means of SMG (left part of the record). Determination of the number of actively moving spermatozoa with the help of stripe MKG (right part). (4) Representation and temporal determination of two colour changes in the time periods a and b (for example: the passage of vital dyes through individual vessels).

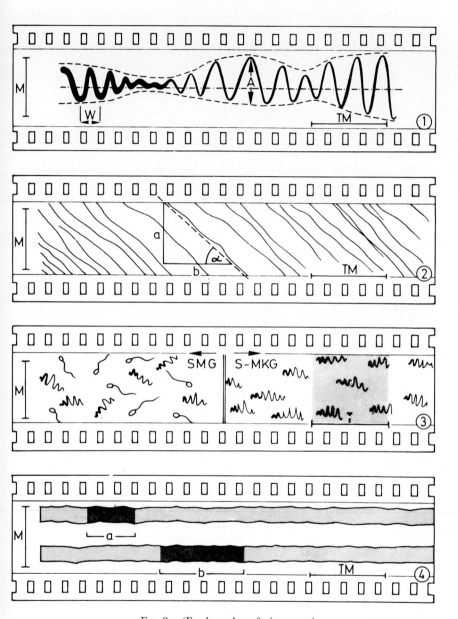

FⁱG. 9.   (For legend see facing page.)

in the form of changing intensity or colour phenomena. Such kymographs can be quantitatively analysed in a way similar to those involving movement (Fig. 9(4)). In this way, for example, the filling and emptying phases of organs which are supplied with blood can be recorded objectively and the exact timing can be determined (Figs 9(4), 14(2)). For this purpose one would normally use colour film, though in some situations black and white film could prove satisfactory.

B. *Special Methods for Quantitative Analysis and Projection*

The analysis of movement and colour phenomena in the kymographic record requires, as a rule, no special devices other than a ruler, a pair of dividers and, if need be, a magnifying glass with a millimetre scale. Knowledge of the time scale (dependent on the speed of transport) and the total optical magnification is essential for quantitative work. Each record should include a time or frequency pattern and a scale showing the chosen magnification.

Apart from these simple methods of picture evaluation, special techniques and apparatus have been developed for particular purposes. Procedures which have been used for certain problems, especially in X-ray kymography will be mentioned briefly here.

Changes in the density and movement curves of a microkymograph can be evaluated photoelectrically in such a way that the colour changes and movements of an object are depicted as a purely abstract curve. The course of a functional process can be made especially clear in this manner. The relationship to the structural picture of the object is, however, lost. The equipment for this type of photoelectric "densograph" (Stumpf *et al.*, 1936) consists of a light source and photocell between which the negative is moved. Variations in light transmission on the kymograph are transformed into variations of current or voltage which can be plotted on a suitable recorder.

Another approach to the quantitative analysis of movement arises from the combination of microkymography with cinematographic or television techniques. Here microkymography serves purely as a means of analysing records primarily obtained by another technique. In the procedure of "indirect microkymography" employed by Wolf and Krause (1971), the processes of movement are first recorded cinematographically as a time-lapse film, and this can be re-recorded as a kymograph during projection. In this way the slit window can be applied to any required part of the object and a kymographic recording can be made at any time and as often as one wishes. Another advantage is that one can always compare the kymograph with the original movement seen in the motion picture.

Asano *et al.* (1973) recorded moving microscopical objects by means of a TV video recording system. The monitor picture was projected onto the film plane of a microkymographic camera (Fig. 10). In this way, kymographs are obtained which have advantages similar to those of the technique just

Fig. 10. Photograph showing a kymography recording system (right) in combination with a TV monitor and video recorder.

described. In addition the television system as an intermediary medium makes the adjustment of brightness and an increase in contrast possible. By the same principles, kymographic registration can be carried out from the image on the screen of an infrared image converter system. This procedure allows a kymographic analysis of invisible, infrared illuminated objects to be made with ordinary film emulsions. An example of the application of this technique in the diagnosis of pupillary malfunction is given below.

There are various possibilities for the subjective viewing of dynamic phenomena by microkymography. Any movement in a recorded object can be clearly distinguished by reversing the conditions of recording. This is accomplished by moving the recording, illuminated from behind, in front of a stationary diaphragm, or by moving the diaphragm in front of the stationary recording. In X-ray diagnosis similar equipment is known by the term "kymoscope". The projection of kymographs on a screen is also possible under these conditions (for further details see Stumpf *et al.*, 1936). Such kymoscopic procedures are useful for the subjective viewing of the recorded process rather than for its analytical evaluation. On the other hand, special advantages are offered by the projection of stripe photomicrographs by a method described by Castenholz (1974a). Stripe microphotographs in a slide projector can be shown to a large group by means of a simple device which allows continuous transport of the film during projection (Fig. 11). Thus large areas of the object can be displayed con-

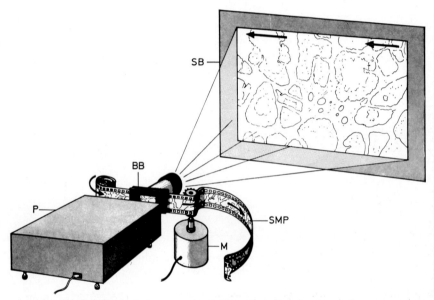

Fig. 11. Diagram illustrating the special method of projecting stripe-photomicrographical pictures.

P, slide projector; BB, film stage through which the record (SMP) is moved at constant speed by the motor unit (M); SB, screen on which the picture moves continuously from one side to the other (see arrows).

tinuously without changing the picture. This process could be particularly useful for teaching purposes and could complement the ordinary slide projector.

VII. Applications

The various techniques of microkymography are basically suitable for all cytological or histological objects that can be studied with the common light microscope. This principle, combined with a one-step magnification

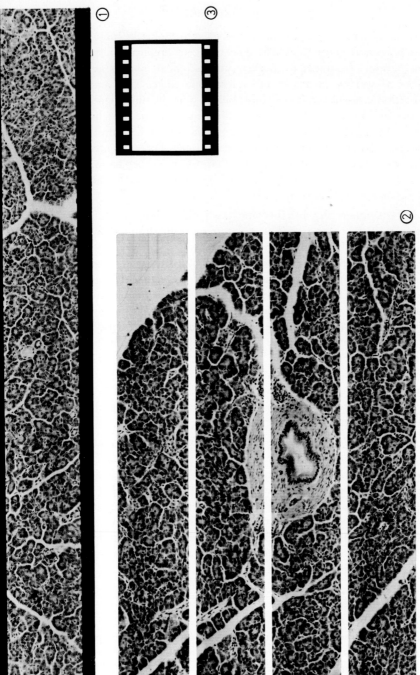

FIG. 12. Stripe-photomicrographic (SMG) reproductions of a histological section of the pancreas. (1) A continuous record through a cross-sectional zone of the object. (×128.) (2) Representation of a larger two-dimensional area of the object made by joining together four single recordings. (×128.) (3) Picture format (negative, slide) normally used in photomicrography compared with those of SMG shown in (1) and (2).

system, can also be used for larger (macro-) objects such as organs and organ systems (Fig. 13(1, 2)). The range of application for stripe photomicrography is limited to smaller (microscopical) objects as the object has to be moved by means of the microscope stage. The versatility of both procedures opens up many possibilities for the investigation of various functional–morphological relationships in biology. In the choice of a particular modification of registration, the researcher must be guided by the special dynamic conditions of the specimen. For static objects practically any registration procedures can be used. On the other hand, freely moving objects can only be properly recorded by means of stripe photomicrography and stripe microkymography.

Microkymography has become particularly important in the form of stripe microkymography. This technique, originally used by Basler (1917) for studies on blood flow and for the determination of the speed of red blood cells, is still being used in the field of microcirculatory studies for the determination of different haemodynamic parameters in experiments with living animals (Hugues, 1953; Castenholz, 1969; Böttcher and Steinhausen, 1976). Recently the latter authors successfully measured the velocity of blood cells in the medulla of the rat kidney. Urbaschek and his group (1976) carried out a similar analysis on the cheek pouch vessels of the hamster under the influence of endotoxin. Asano et al. (1973) determined for the first time various haemodynamic parameters of the human terminal vascular bed in a transparent chamber system. The results of microkymography were compared with those obtained on the same object by microplethysmography.

A further field of application is the study of the pupil and its movement. Such experiments were already carried out during the last century by Bellarminoff (1885) and Garten (1897). These are probably the earliest recorded kymographs and were achieved by means of a simple optical system. All modern methods of kymography as well as stripe microkymography can be employed for the examination of the pupil. This is the result of modern technical developments, above all the possibility of using an infrared image converter system. Thus area and screen kymographs can be taken, even of the human eye (Castenholz, 1973b) (Fig. 13(3,4)).

Wolf and Krause (1971) were able, by means of indirect stripe kymography, to record and analyse the movement of the ooplasm of Hymenoptera. The initial contractions of the embryonic heart of the chicken and a comparison between the circulatory systems of a parabiotic pair of tadpoles were the subjects of other microkymographical investigations (Castenholz and Flórez-Cossio, 1972; Castenholz and von Kraft, 1974). Recently the technique has entered the field of functional seminal analysis for studying

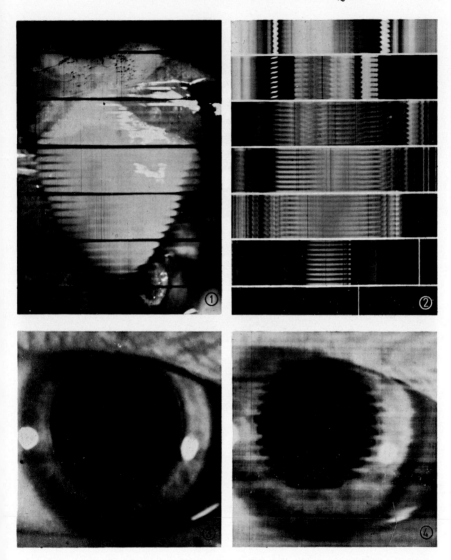

Fig. 13. (1) Screen MKG of a beating frog heart. Note the continuous course of the organ's serrated contours from one section of the picture to the next. (Approx. × 8.) (2) Step MKG of the same object. The contours of the organ are aligned parallel to edge of the picture and are separated stepwise. (3) Photograph of a human pupil illuminated with infrared light. This picture was recorded from the screen of an i.r. image converter system. (× 6.) (4) Area MKG of the human eye illuminated with infrared light. The eye was stimulated by short rhythmic light impulses during exposure.

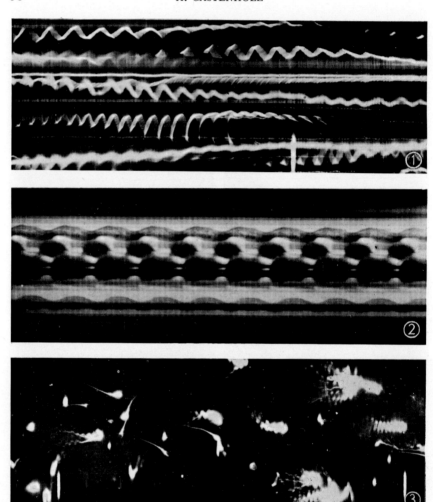

Fig. 14. (1) Stripe MKG of a transparent chamber preparation with living hamster spermatozoa. Wavy and serrated lines are seen indicating the tail beat action of the individual cells. (Dark field illumination, × 74.) (2) Stripe MKG of the living embryonic heart of a parabiotic newt larva. The wave-like stripe patterns are caused by the contraction activity of different sections of the heart tube. The oval black zones show the rhythmic changes of blood content in the atrial and ventricular chambers. (× 14.) (3) Stripe photomicrograph of a chamber preparation containing living guinea-pig sperm. In this picture the spermatozoa are represented as "motion figures" as well as in their true form according to whether they are moving or stationary at the moment of exposure. (Dark field, × 150.)

the movement of human and animal sperm cells (Castenholz, 1974b; Hermanns, 1977).

Only a few fields of application of microkymography have been mentioned here. Clearly the method has many possibilities for the study of moving objects at the microscopical level.

With regard to the newer method of stripe photomicrography, it is naturally difficult to predict how useful or popular it may turn out to be in any special field of research. Nevertheless it does appear to have certain advantages as a display method for fixed histological and motile biological material.

REFERENCES

Asano, M., Brånemark, P.-I. and Castenholz, A. (1973). *Adv. Microcirculation* **5**, 1–31.

Basler, A. (1917). *Pflügers Arch. ges. Physiol.* **171**, 134–145.

Bellarminoff, L. (1885). *Pflügers Arch. ges. Physiol.* **37**, 107–122.

Böttcher, W. and Steinhausen, M. (1976). *Kidney Int.* **10**, 74–80.

Castenholz, A. (1967). *Z. wiss. Mikrosk.* **69**, 193–207.

Castenholz, A. (1968a). *Zeiss-Inform.* **70**, 124–128.

Castenholz, A. (1968b). *Graefes Arch. Ophthal.* **175**, 100–110.

Castenholz, A. (1969). *Adv. Microcirculation* **2**, 24–36.

Castenholz, A. (1973a). *Microscopica Acta* **74**, 89–109.

Castenholz, A. (1973b). *In* "Symposium über die normale und gestörte Pupillen-bewegung, Bad Nauheim" (E. Dodt and K. E. Schrader, eds). J. F. Bergmann Verlag, Munich.

Castenholz, A. (1974a). *Microscopica Acta* **75**, 309–320.

Castenholz, A. (1974b). *Andrologia* **6**, 155–168.

Castenholz, A. and Flórez-Cossio, T. J. (1972). *Altern und Entwicklung* **4**, 41–61.

Castenholz, A. and van Kraft, A. (1974). *Z. Morph. Tiere* **77**, 51–75.

Garten, S. (1897). *Pflügers Arch. ges. Physiol.* **68**, 68–94.

Gött, T. and Rosenthal, J. (1912). *Münch. Med. Wschr.* **38**, 2033–3035.

Hermanns, H. J. (1977). *Inaugural dissertation.* Marburg/Lahn.

Hugues, J. (1953). *Arch. int. Physiol* **16**, 565–711.

Sonne, F. (1940). US Patent 2307649.

Stumpf, P., Weber, H. H. and Weltz, G. A. (1936). "Röntgenkymographische Bewegungslehre innerer Organe". Georg Thieme, Leipzig.

Urbaschek, B. and Urbaschek, R. (1976). Proc. ASM Conference on Endotoxin, Bacterial Antigen and Host Response. Austin, Texas.

Wolf, R. and Krause, G. (1971). *Roux Archiv* **167**, 266–287.

Coherence in Electron Optics

P. W. HAWKES

Laboratoire d'Optique électronique du CNRS,
29, rue Jeanne Marvig, 31055 Toulouse Cedex, France

I. INTRODUCTION

A GLANCE at the history of electron optics shows that the theoreticians have been periodically spurred to explore new or neglected aspects of their subject by the successful endeavours of microscope designers to produce instruments of ever higher resolution. The performance of electron microscopes was for many years limited by the energy spread of the beam incident on the specimen, with the spherical aberration only a secondary obstacle. As stabilizing circuitry was improved, the adverse effects of chromatic and spherical aberration became comparable and the efforts that were made during the late 1950s and 1960s to design correction systems yielded many theoretical and practical results of wider interest than the particular system for which they had originally been derived. By the mid 1960s, the best commercial microscopes could be relied upon to give resolutions within a few ångström units of the classical limit for suitable specimens and it became clear that a detailed study of image formation in the electron microscope close to the limit of resolution was urgently needed. This produced the body of theory associated with transfer functions and spatial frequency analysis of the image-forming process. In the past few years, the scanning transmission electron microscope (STEM) has changed from a poorly understood experimental machine (the first descriptions of which were coolly received) to a highly perfected instrument, available commercially from at least three firms, and a host of papers have been devoted to the theory of STEM image formation.

The coexistence of the conventional electron microscope, in which a reasonably large area of the specimen is normally illuminated coherently, and the scanning transmission instrument, in which the question of coherence requires discussion of the detector geometry, furnishes one of the reasons for current interest in coherence in electron optics. Moreover, transfer function theory is being used increasingly widely by practising microscopists who need to know how the generalizations about resolution and image fidelity derived with the aid of this theory are affected by such instrumental parameters as source size and beam energy spread; these are precisely the factors that oblige us to replace the idealization of perfectly coherent illumination at the specimen by the mathematically less tractable reality of partially coherent conditions. Also in connection with the theory of transfer functions, attempts are being made in several laboratories to treat sampled electron images by computer and the relation between the source coherence in the electron microscope and the signal-to-noise ratio in the image is of extreme importance.

Electron optical coherence has not of course been completely neglected in the past and there have been sporadic discussions of its effects in the literature, particularly in connection with electron interference experiments. We shall return to this work in Section IV. Before considering the specifically electron optical aspects of partial coherence, however, we recapitulate in Section II the relevant portions of the optical literature, stressing any differences between the optical and electron optical situations. We then discuss image formation with partially coherent illumination in detail, showing that, in certain quite realistic conditions, the familiar coherent phase and amplitude transfer functions can be modified in a simple way to represent partially coherent conditions. In Section IV, we consider image formation in the different types of electron microscope, and attempt to show when the effects of partial coherence are important. In particular, we examine the illumination system of the conventional transmission electron microscope and the collector system of the STEM. Some unconventional situations are also considered in Section IV, such as electron interference, electron holography and the Schwarz–Hora effect, in which coherence is an important consideration.

The literature of partial coherence in light optics is very large, and in the present review we shall refer wherever possible to recent texts or reviews. Particularly good accounts, with thorough coverage of the literature, are to be found in Born and Wolf (1959), Mandel and Wolf (1965) and Peřina

(1972) and a relatively early text by Beran and Parrent (1964) is also extremely clear; the question of image formation in partially coherent illumination has been examined in detail in a useful review by Thompson (1969).

Comparatively few papers have been devoted specifically to the problem of coherence in electron optics, though it is of course mentioned and to some extent analysed in much of the work dealing with electron image formation and interference. We have attempted to cover the electron optical literature reasonably thoroughly though for some specialized topics, such as small-angle diffraction, we have referred rather to reviews than to all the original papers. This brings us to the problem of notation. The first major treatise to discuss modern coherence theory in detail was Born and Wolf's "Principles of Optics" (1959) and most later authors have adhered, with minor variations, to their notation. We have adopted this in the present review, again with some variations to suit the formalism of electron optical transfer theory. There is unfortunately much less uniformity in the electron optical literature on image formation; the notation used here is very similar to that of Hawkes (1973), except that single vector symbols replace pairs of cartesian coordinates.

We conclude this introduction with a concise account of some important formulae from the transfer theory of systems with coherent illumination, as we shall repeatedly refer to these in later sections. For isoplanatic systems, only spherical aberration (C_s) and defocus measured at the object plane $(\varDelta)$ are important in studying departures from perfect paraxial imaging. (For simplicity, we neglect residual astigmatism here.) The wave function (ψ) at the image plane, in which we use a cartesian coordinate system $(\mathbf{x}_i, z_i)$ is related to that at the object plane (coordinates $\mathbf{x}_o, z_o$) by a convolution, provided that the illumination is perfectly coherent (monochromatic source). We have (Glaser, 1952)

$$\psi(\mathbf{x}_i, z_i)E_i = \frac{1}{M} \int K(\mathbf{x}_i/M - \mathbf{x}_o)\psi(\mathbf{x}_o, z_o)E_o \, d\mathbf{x}_o \qquad (1.1)$$

where E_i and E_o are quadratic factors:

$$\begin{aligned}
E_i &= \exp\left(\frac{i\pi r}{\lambda M}\mathbf{x}_i \cdot \mathbf{x}_i\right) \\
E_o &= \exp\left(\frac{i\pi r'}{\lambda}\mathbf{x}_o \cdot \mathbf{x}_o\right)
\end{aligned} \qquad (1.2)$$

and r, r' are geometrical factors; in practice E_o can often be replaced by unity $(r' \approx 0)$. Here and elsewhere, M denotes the magnification and λ the electron wavelength. The function K is the Fourier transform of the aperture function:

$$K(\mathbf{x}_i/M - \mathbf{x}_o) = \frac{1}{\lambda^2 f^2} \int A(\mathbf{x}_a) \exp \{2\pi i(\mathbf{x}_i/M - \mathbf{x}_o) \cdot \mathbf{x}_a/\lambda f\} \, d\mathbf{x}_a \quad (1.3)$$

in which f is the objective focal length. The function $A(\mathbf{x}_a)$ is equal to zero outside the objective aperture and is given by the phase shift introduced by C_s and Δ within the aperture:

$$A(\mathbf{x}_a) = \bar{a}(\mathbf{x}_a) \exp \{- i\bar{\gamma}(\mathbf{x}_a)\}$$
$$\bar{a}(\mathbf{x}_a) = 0 \text{ outside the aperture} \quad (1.4)$$
$$\bar{a}(\mathbf{x}_a) = 1 \text{ inside the aperture}$$

The phase shift $\bar{\gamma}$ is in turn given by

$$\bar{\gamma}(\mathbf{x}_a) = \frac{2\pi}{\lambda} \left\{ \frac{1}{4} C_s \frac{(\mathbf{x}_a \cdot \mathbf{x}_a)^2}{f^4} - \frac{1}{2} \cdot \Delta \frac{\mathbf{x}_a \cdot \mathbf{x}_a}{f^2} \right\}. \quad (1.5)$$

We frequently write

$$\mathbf{p} = \mathbf{x}_a/\lambda f \quad (1.6)$$

so that Eqn (1.3) becomes

$$K(\mathbf{x}_i/M - \mathbf{x}_o) = \int A(\lambda f \mathbf{p}) \exp \{2\pi i(\mathbf{x}_i/M - \mathbf{x}_o) \cdot \mathbf{p}\} \, d\mathbf{p} \quad (1.7)$$

while Eqn (1.5) becomes

$$\bar{\gamma}(\lambda f \mathbf{p}) = \frac{2\pi}{\lambda} \left\{ \frac{1}{4} C_s \lambda^4 (\mathbf{p} \cdot \mathbf{p})^2 - \frac{1}{2} \Delta \lambda^2 \mathbf{p} \cdot \mathbf{p} \right\}. \quad (1.8)$$

It is usual to write

$$\gamma(\mathbf{p}) = \bar{\gamma}(\lambda f \mathbf{p})$$
$$a(\mathbf{p}) = \bar{a}(\lambda f \mathbf{p}). \quad (1.9)$$

A convenient notation introduced by Hanszen (e.g. 1971) is also in wide use and is indispensable when universal curves are desired. We write

$$\hat{\mathbf{p}} = \left(\frac{C_s}{\lambda}\right)^{1/4} \frac{\mathbf{x}_a}{f} = (C_s \lambda^3)^{1/4} \, \mathbf{p} \quad (1.10)$$

and

$$\hat{\Delta} = \Delta/(C_s \lambda)^{1/2} \quad (1.11)$$

so that

$$\gamma(\mathbf{p}) = 2\pi \left\{ \frac{1}{4} (\hat{\mathbf{p}} \cdot \hat{\mathbf{p}})^2 - \frac{1}{2} \hat{\Delta} \hat{\mathbf{p}} \cdot \hat{\mathbf{p}} \right\}. \quad (1.12)$$

Generalized object and image coordinates are defined by

$$\hat{\mathbf{x}}_o = \frac{\mathbf{x}_o}{(C_s \lambda^3)^{1/4}} \qquad \hat{\mathbf{x}}_i = \frac{\mathbf{x}_i}{(C_s \lambda^3)^{1/4}}. \quad (1.13)$$

For objects that only scatter the incident beam weakly, we may write

$$\psi(\mathbf{x}_o, z_o) = \{1 - s(\mathbf{x}_o)\} \exp i\phi(\mathbf{x}_o)$$

$$\approx 1 - s(\mathbf{x}_o) + i\phi(\mathbf{x}_o) \qquad (1.14)$$

and we can show that the image current density, j, is then given by

$$j(M\mathbf{x}_i) = M^2 \psi_i \psi_i^* \propto 1 - 2 \int a\tilde{s} \cos \gamma \exp 2\pi i(\mathbf{p} \cdot \mathbf{x}) \, d\mathbf{p}$$

$$+ 2 \int a\tilde{\phi} \sin \gamma \exp 2\pi i(\mathbf{p} \cdot \mathbf{x}) \, d\mathbf{p} \qquad (1.15)$$

where $\tilde{s}$ and $\tilde{\phi}$ are the Fourier transforms or spatial frequency spectra of s and ϕ. Hence

$$\tilde{j}(\mathbf{p}) \propto \delta(\mathbf{p}) - 2a\tilde{s} \cos \gamma + 2a\tilde{\phi} \sin \gamma. \qquad (1.16)$$

The functions $-2\cos\gamma$ and $2\sin\gamma$ are the amplitude and phase transfer functions of the microscope for weak objects. We write

$$B_s(\mathbf{p}) = -2 \cos \gamma(\mathbf{p}) \qquad (1.17)$$

$$B_\phi(\mathbf{p}) = 2 \sin \gamma(\mathbf{p}). \qquad (1.18)$$

We have chosen to express the effect of the wave aberration in the exit pupil by a term of the form $\exp(-i\gamma)$, since this is the convention adopted in Born and Wolf (1959) and, implicitly, in Glaser (1952), whereas $\exp(i\gamma)$ was adopted in Hanszen (1971) and Hawkes (1973); both signs are permissible, as pointed out in Hawkes (1976b), but the sign of the phase term in the specimen transparency must be chosen appropriately: positive for $\exp(-i\gamma)$ and negative for $\exp(i\gamma)$, when the optical path length is greater through the specimen than through its surroundings, as is normally the case in electron optics. In reality, however, the choice $\exp(-i\gamma)$ is mandatory for, as H. Rose has pointed out (private communication), the frequency of electron waves, which is involved here, is always positive ($E = \hbar\omega$). By choosing $\exp(i\gamma)$, therefore, we are tacitly working with the complex conjugate of the wave function which, though not wrong, is undeniably perverse (Hawkes, 1977b; Maclachlan, 1977).

II. Classical Coherence Theory

A. *Mutual Coherence*

Considerable efforts are made in designing electron microscope guns and their associated circuitry to ensure that the energy spread of the beam is kept as narrow as possible. The original reason for striving towards high stability was of course the immense chromatic aberration of all conventional electron lenses but a consequence is that electron sources are always quasi-monochromatic, if we regard the crossover of the gun as seen from the first condenser lens as the effective source; for an energy spread of 4 eV and an accelerating voltage (V) of 100 kV, we have

$$\left|\frac{\Delta\lambda}{\lambda}\right| = \frac{1}{2}\frac{\Delta V}{V} \approx 2 \times 10^{-5}$$

where λ denotes the electron wavelength. ($\lambda \propto V^{-1/2}$ where V denotes the accelerating voltage, relativistically corrected if necessary.) We shall regard the crossover as the effective electron source throughout this review but it must be realized that the region between the emitting filament and this crossover, in which the electrons are accelerated from energies of a few electron-volts to 100 keV or more in high voltage devices, does not fit easily into the usual framework of classical coherence theory. The electrons initially form a beam that is far from quasi-monochromatic and are emitted into a wide conical zone; they emerge from the gun as a highly mono-chromatic beam directed into a very narrow cone, their angular spread thus being extremely small. Classical coherence theory is sufficiently general to cover this abrupt transition from one extreme situation to the other but the approximations that are usually made, and which we shall make below, are invalid. Fortunately, a recent and extremely interesting result obtained by Wolf and Carter (1975; Carter and Wolf, 1975) permits us to regard the virtual crossover as our effective source for all practical purposes and we shall therefore not consider the accelerating region in detail here (the rapid acquisition of coherence in the gun will be discussed in a separate pub-lication). Carter and Wolf have examined the intimate relation that exists between the angular distribution of radiant intensity from light sources and the coherence properties of these sources; they show that with certain approximations, which are satisfied in electron microscopes, the directional properties of the beam determine the source coherence and we may there-fore treat the virtual crossover as a source, the coherence properties of which are determined by the distribution of electron directions in the beam.

Electron sources are thus quasi-monochromatic and, for a different reason, they are also small in the instruments we are considering. Once the choice has been made between thermal and field emission, and more recently laser-heated Schottky emission must be added to the list (van der Mast *et al.*, 1974; van der Mast, 1975), little can be done to modify the emitting area. Nevertheless, it is inevitably an idealization to regard electron sources as monochromatic point emitters and it is these two physical features of real electron guns—finite energy and hence wavelength spread and finite emitting area—that take us into the domain of partial coherence.

Very recently, Ferwerda and van Heel (1977) have used the results of Carter and Wolf to calculate the mutual coherence over a virtual electron source and conclude that such sources should not strictly be treated as

incoherent. This may, as they point out, modify to some extent the conclusions based on the assumption that virtual sources do radiate incoherently. It has not been possible to pursue this further in the present review
but it seems unlikely that their findings will have any serious repercussions,
except perhaps for unconventional modes of operation such as hollow-cone
illumination.

An ideal monochromatic point source would produce a wave field in
which the amplitude at any point remained constant while the phase varied
linearly. As soon as some wavelength spread is allowed and the source size
is made finite, though still small, both phase and amplitude will fluctuate
though it is intuitively reasonable to expect that the fluctuations will be
very similar for points sufficiently close together. This in turn suggests
that we should be able to represent the behaviour of the field in terms of the
cross-correlation between the wave functions at pairs of points in the wave
field. With this approach in mind, we consider the simple situation shown
in Fig. 1 where a source S radiates towards a plane Π containing pinholes

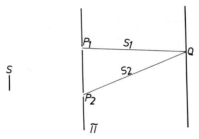

FIG. 1. Propagation from a source S to a screen Π containing small openings at
P_1 and P_2.

at P_1 and P_2 and we examine the disturbance at an arbitrary point Q
beyond Π. Denoting the wave function at P_1 by Ψ_1, at P_2 by Ψ_2 and at
Q by Ψ_Q, we have

$$\Psi_Q(t) = c_1\Psi_1(t - t_1) + c_2\Psi_2(t - t_2) \qquad (2.1)$$

where t_1 and t_2 are the electron times of flight between P_1 and Q and P_2
and Q respectively; since we are regarding the pinholes as secondary
sources, c_1 and c_2 are imaginary. The intensity observed at Q, $I(Q)$ will be
given by the time average of $\Psi_Q\Psi_Q^*$ which, we denote $<\Psi_Q\Psi_Q^*>$:

$$
\begin{aligned}
I(Q) &= <\Psi_Q\Psi_Q^*> \\
&= c_1c_1^* <\Psi_1(t - t_1)\Psi_1^*(t - t_1)> + c_2c_2^* <\Psi_2(t - t_2)\Psi_2^*(t - t_2)> \\
&\quad + c_1c_2^* <\Psi_1(t - t_1)\Psi_2^*(t - t_2)> + c_1^*c_2 <\Psi_1^*(t - t_1)\Psi_2(t - t_2)>
\end{aligned}
$$

$$(2.2)$$

We introduce the assumption that the wave field is wide-sense stationary (Papoulis, 1965) that is, that $< \Psi(t) >$ is independent of time or that $< \Psi_i(t + t_1) \Psi_j^*(t + t_2) > (i, j = 1, 2)$ depends only on $t_1 - t_2$. Writing

$$I_i = < \Psi_i(t) \Psi_i^*(t) > \qquad i = 1, 2 \tag{2.3}$$

Eqn (2.2) becomes

$$I(Q) = c_1 c_1^* I_1 + c_2 c_2^* I_2 + 2|c_1 c_2| \text{ Re} < \Psi_1(t + t_2 - t_1) \Psi_2^*(t) >. \tag{2.4}$$

Putting

$$\tau = t_2 - t_1 = (s_2 - s_1)/v$$

where s_1 and s_2 are the distances between P_1 and Q and P_2 and Q and v is the electron velocity, Eqn (2.4) becomes

$$I(Q) = c_1 c_1^* I_1 + c_2 c_2^* I_2 + 2|c_1 c_2| \text{ Re } \Gamma_{12}(\tau) \tag{2.5}$$

where

$$\Gamma_{12}(\tau) = < \Psi_1(t + \tau) \Psi_2^*(t) >. \tag{2.6}$$

Equation (2.5) shows that a knowledge of $\Gamma_{12}(\tau)$, which is the *cross-correlation function* of the individual wave functions Ψ_1 and Ψ_2, is sufficient to characterize the wave field at any point. In coherence theory, this function is known as the *mutual coherence function*. When the two points P_1 and P_2 coincide, we have

$$\Gamma_{11}(\tau) = < \Psi_1(t + \tau) \Psi_1^*(t) > \tag{2.7}$$

and when $\tau = 0$, $\Gamma_{11}(\tau)$ reduces to the ordinary intensity I_1:

$$\Gamma_{11}(0) = I_1. \tag{2.8}$$

The function $\Gamma_{11}(\tau)$, the *autocorrelation function* of Ψ_1, is known as the *self-coherence* at P_1.

In practice, a normalized form of the mutual coherence function $\Gamma_{12}(\tau)$ is more convenient. This is defined as follows:

$$\gamma_{12}(\tau) = \frac{\Gamma_{12}(\tau)}{\{\Gamma_{11}(0)\Gamma_{22}(0)\}^{1/2}} = \frac{\Gamma_{12}(\tau)}{(I_1 I_2)^{1/2}}. \tag{2.9}$$

The effect of this normalization is to ensure that $|\gamma_{12}|$ lies between zero and unity. Proofs of this are to be found in Born and Wolf (1959) and Peřina (1972) and we merely mention here that the difficult step in the proof is the justification of the use of the Schwarz inequality; once this has been achieved, we have only to write

$$\left| \int_{-\infty}^{\infty} \Psi_1(t+\tau) \Psi_2^*(t) \, dt \right|^2 \leqslant \int_{-\infty}^{\infty} \Psi_1(t+\tau) \Psi_1^*(t+\tau) \, dt \times \int_{-\infty}^{\infty} \Psi_2(t) \Psi_2^*(t) \, dt$$

from which it follows after averaging over time that

$$|\Gamma_{12}(\tau)|^2 \leqslant \Gamma_{11}(0)\Gamma_{22}(0) \tag{2.10}$$

or

$$|\gamma_{12}| \leqslant 1. \tag{2.11}$$

The function $\gamma_{12}(\tau)$ is known as the *complex degree of coherence*.

Returning to Eqn (2.5) and introducing the intensities at Q when P_1 alone or P_2 alone is contributing,

$$I^{(1)}(Q) = c_1 c_1^* I_1 \qquad I^{(2)}(Q) = c_2 c_2^* I_2 \qquad (2.12)$$

we have

$$I(Q) = I^{(1)}(Q) + I^{(2)}(Q) + 2\{I^{(1)}(Q)I^{(2)}(Q)\}^{1/2} \operatorname{Re} \gamma_{12}(\tau). \qquad (2.13)$$

We can now see the significance of the extreme values of $|\gamma_{12}|$. If $\gamma_{12} = 0$, the intensity at Q is equal to the sum of the intensities generated by P_1 and P_2 separately; there are no interference effects and the disturbances at Q add *incoherently*. If, at the other extreme, $|\gamma_{12}(\tau)| = 1$, then

$$I(Q) = I^{(1)}(Q) + I^{(2)}(Q) + 2\{I^{(1)}(Q)I^{(2)}(Q)\}^{1/2} \cos \{\arg \gamma_{12}(\tau)\} \qquad (2.14)$$

or

$$I(Q) = (\Phi_1 + \Phi_2)(\Phi_1^* + \Phi_2^*) \qquad (2.15)$$

where

$$\Phi_1 \Phi_1^* = I^{(1)}(Q) \qquad \Phi_2 \Phi_2^* = I^{(2)}(Q) \qquad (2.16a)$$

and

$$\arg (\Phi_2 - \Phi_1) = \arg \gamma_{12}(\tau) \qquad (2.16b)$$

so that the intensity at Q is now the same as that we should obtain with monochromatic sources at P_1 and P_2 radiating with a fixed phase difference. The disturbances at Q are now said to be *coherent*.

Although our original aim was to construct a theory in which the effects of finite energy spread and finite source size were included and to show how this theory could be applied in practice, it is far from obvious how the functions that occur in the foregoing set of definitions are related to these practical quantities. The mutual coherence function $\Gamma_{12}(\tau)$ is, however, well adapted to the treatment of both spatial coherence (finite source size) and temporal coherence (finite wavelength spread); moreover, subject to certain not unduly restrictive conditions, spatial and temporal effects can be separated and treated independently. Temporal coherence is always associated with the self-coherence function, $\Gamma_{11}(\tau)$, or the equivalent normalized function $\gamma_{11}(\tau)$ and spatial coherence with the mutual intensity $\Gamma_{12}(0)$ or $\gamma_{12}(0)$, as we now show. Consider first a beam divided at some point into two beams, which are subsequently recombined; if a path difference has been introduced between them, the resulting intensity distribution will be given by $< \Psi(t + \tau)\Psi^*(t) >$ which is of course the self-coherence function, $\Gamma(\tau)$ (dropping the subscript 11). The narrower the wavelength spread, the greater the path difference and the corresponding time-lag τ can be without loss of visibility of any interference effects and it is therefore natural to define the coherence time and effective spectral width in terms of

$\Gamma(\tau)$ or $\gamma(\tau)$. The various definitions are further discussed in Peřina (1972) and a clear account is also given by Mandel (1963).

The reason for associating source size with $\Gamma_{12}(0)$ or $\gamma_{12}(0)$ will be obvious when we have considered the van Cittert–Zernike theorem but can be understood qualitatively by again considering the fringes produced at a point by two pinholes illuminated by a finite source. Fringes will always be visible around the central point if the pinholes are sufficiently close together and the fringe visibility in the vicinity of the central point is clearly given by $\Gamma_{12}(0)$ since the paths are approximately equal.

Although we can associate $\Gamma(\tau)$ or $\gamma(\tau)$ with temporal coherence and $\Gamma_{12}(0)$ or $\gamma_{12}(0)$ with spatial coherence, we can separate these two effects only if $\Gamma_{12}(\tau)$ or $\gamma_{12}(\tau)$ can be written as a product of a spatial part and a temporal part; when this is possible, we have

$$\Gamma_{12}(\tau) = \Gamma_{12}(0)\Gamma(\tau) \qquad (2.17a)$$

or

$$\gamma_{12}(\tau) = \gamma_{12}(0)\gamma(\tau). \qquad (2.17b)$$

The field is then said to be *cross-spectrally pure* (Mandel and Wolf, 1976).

In many cases in both light and electron optics, the variation of $\Gamma_{12}(\tau)$ and hence of $\gamma_{12}(\tau)$ with τ is small and we can then replace these functions by their values at $\tau = 0$ together with an exponential factor. In order to explore the validity of such an approximation, we write

$$\gamma_{12}(\tau) = |\gamma_{12}(\tau)| \exp i\{a_{12}(\tau) + 2\pi\bar{\nu}\tau\} \qquad (2.18)$$

where

$$a_{12}(\tau) = \arg \gamma_{12}(\tau) - 2\pi\bar{\nu}\tau \qquad (2.19)$$

and $\bar{\nu}$ is the mean frequency. Introducing the Fourier transform‡ of $\Gamma_{12}(\tau)$ with respect to τ,

$$\Gamma_{12}(\tau) = \int_{-\infty}^{\infty} \tilde{\Gamma}_{12}(\nu) \exp(2\pi i\nu\tau) \, d\nu \qquad (2.20)$$

we have

$$|\Gamma_{12}(\tau)| \exp ia_{12}(\tau) = \Gamma_{12}(\tau) \exp(-2\pi i\bar{\nu}\tau)$$

$$= \int_{-\infty}^{\infty} \tilde{\Gamma}_{12}(\nu) \exp\{2\pi i\tau(\nu - \bar{\nu})\} \, d\nu. \qquad (2.21)$$

If, therefore, the condition

$$|(\nu - \bar{\nu})\tau| \ll 1 \qquad (2.22)$$

‡ In electron optics, the sign convention most widely used for the Fourier transform is that of Eqn (2.20) while Born and Wolf (1959) and Peřina (1972) prefer the alternative form (with $\exp(-2\pi i\nu\tau)$). The results are of course the same but both conventions are in use.

is satisfied, the integral on the right-hand side of Eqn (2.21) can be replaced by $\int_{-\infty}^{\infty} \tilde{\Gamma}_{12}(\nu) \, d\nu$ which is the same as $|\Gamma_{12}(0)| \exp ia_{12}(0)$. Summing up, the following approximations can be used if and only if condition (2.22) is satisfied:

$$\Gamma_{12}(\tau) \approx \Gamma_{12}(0) \exp (2\pi i \bar{\nu} \tau) \qquad (2.23a)$$

$$\gamma_{12}(\tau) \approx \gamma_{12}(0) \exp (2\pi i \bar{\nu} \tau). \qquad (2.23b)$$

We recall that

$$\Gamma_{12}(0) = |\Gamma_{12}(0)| \exp ia_{12}(0) \qquad (2.24a)$$

$$\gamma_{12}(0) = |\gamma_{12}(0)| \exp ia_{12}(0). \qquad (2.24b)$$

Owing to the considerable practical importance of cases for which condition (2.22) is satisfied, Born and Wolf (1959) introduce new symbols for the values of $\Gamma_{12}(\tau)$ and $\gamma_{12}(\tau)$ at $\tau = 0$:

$$\begin{aligned} J_{12} &= \Gamma_{12}(0) \\ \mu_{12} &= \gamma_{12}(0). \end{aligned} \qquad (2.25)$$

This notation is not adopted here; instead we write Γ_{12} and γ_{12} with their arguments whenever the latter are not equal to zero. We refer to $\Gamma_{12}(0)$ as the *mutual intensity*; $\gamma_{12}(0)$ is again called the *complex degree of coherence* or, for reasons which we have seen to be appropriate, the *degree of spatial coherence*.

A practical case will give us some idea of the physical restriction imposed by condition (2.22). We have

$$\begin{aligned} |\tau \Delta \nu| &= \left(\frac{\lambda \Delta \Phi}{2\pi v} \right) \left(\frac{v \Delta \lambda}{\lambda^2} \right) \\ &= \frac{\Delta \phi \Delta \lambda}{2\pi \lambda} = \frac{\Delta \phi}{4\pi} \frac{\Delta V}{V} \end{aligned} \qquad (2.26)$$

where $\Delta \phi$ denotes the phase difference corresponding to the time lag τ so that if $\Delta V/V = 10^{-5}$, the condition $|\tau \Delta \nu| \ll 1$ implies

$$\Delta \phi \ll 10^6 \text{ rad.} \qquad (2.27)$$

The condition will therefore be satisfied in many situations in which partial coherence needs to be taken into account.

The mutual coherence function and the mutual intensity are not the only functions that can be used for analysing partially coherent illumination. During the past few years, the merits of using the cross-spectral density—the Fourier transform of $\Gamma_{12}(\tau)$ with respect to time—have gradually been emerging. The basic analysis is to be found in a series of papers from the Rochester group (Marchand and Wolf, 1972a, b, 1974; Carter and Wolf,

1977, *q.v.* for other references) and extensions of this are given in Marathay (1976), Baltes (1977), Bastiaans (1977a, b) and especially in the *Proceedings of the Fourth Rochester Conference on Coherence and Quantum Optics* (to be published 1977/8). The cross-spectral density has been introduced into electron optics, where it is particularly well-suited whenever electron energy is of importance; this is easily understood from the fact that the cross-spectral density has frequency as one of its arguments, instead of time, and electron frequency is, apart from a change of scale and dimensions, a direct measure of electron energy. Some preliminary exploration of the role of cross-spectral density in electron optics is described in Hawkes (1977a, c, d).

Our next task is to study the propagation of the various coherence functions through an optical system and to show how they can be used to predict the effect of finite source size and energy spread on image contrast. Before embarking on this, we draw attention to an extremely important difference between light and electron optical coherence theory, which emerges even at this early stage and has repercussions throughout the subsequent discussion. For electromagnetic waves, scalar coherence theory is concerned with *real* functions, one component of one of the field vectors, for example; from this real function, a complex function known as the analytic signal is generated, the real part of which is the original real function while the imaginary part is the Hilbert transform of the real part. The Fourier transform of an analytic signal can easily be shown to be one-sided and this property is repeatedly invoked in the theory of partial coherence. For electrons, however, we cannot and need not introduce an analytic signal since the electron wave function is essentially complex. In the analysis presented here, the complex electron wave function replaces the analytic signal used in texts on optical coherence and no assumptions about its Fourier spectrum have been made; in practice, of course, the complex wave function will have a one-sided transform (with respect to time).

B. *The Propagation of Mutual Intensity*

So far, we have given little more than a list of definitions and terminology. We justify introducing all these quantities by showing that they propagate along the electron microscope in a simple way and that we can use them to derive the image of an extended object in partially coherent illumination. In the present section, we first calculate the mutual intensity $\Gamma_{12}(0)$ and the complex degree of coherence $\gamma_{12}(0)$ in an arbitrary plane between the electron gun and the first condenser lens; this yields the van Cittert–Zernike theorem. We then generalize this result to include propagation through lenses and introduce a formula due to Hopkins which is particularly well-adapted to instrumental coherence problems. It is these laws of propagation that we shall use in Section III to derive microscope transfer functions for partially coherent conditions.

Consider an extended source S, which we take to be the asymptotic image of the filament, that is, the crossover as seen from the field-free region beyond the gun. The electrons are then travelling with a small velocity spread about the mean velocity corresponding to the accelerating voltage. We shall need to discuss the form of the velocity distribution, and in particular the difference between symmetric and asymmetric distributions, when we examine the envelope representation of temporal partial coherence in Section III, Part B but we need not dwell upon it at this stage.

It can be shown (e.g. Born and Wolf, 1959, Section 10.4.2) that the mutual intensity $\Gamma_{12}(0)$ between two points P_1 and P_2 in an arbitrary plane Π downstream from the source (Fig. 2) is given by

$$\Gamma_{12} = \int_S I(S) \, \frac{\exp\{i\bar{k}(R_1 - R_2)\}}{R_1 R_2} \, \mathrm{d}S \tag{2.28}$$

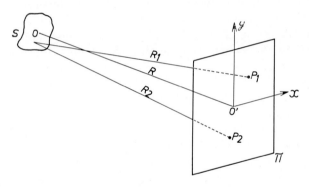

FIG. 2. Geometrical arrangement introducing the concept of mutual intensity and its propagation.

where R_1 and R_2 are the distances from an arbitrary source point to P_1 and P_2, $\bar{k} = 2\pi/\lambda$ and λ is the mean wavelength. The complex degree of coherence is then given by

$$\gamma_{12} = \frac{\Gamma_{12}}{(I_1 I_2)^{1/2}}. \tag{2.29}$$

In these expressions, we have dropped the argument from $\Gamma_{12}(0)$ and $\gamma_{12}(0)$ and we have introduced the intensity per unit area of the source, $I(S)$. As usual (Eqn 2.8),

$$I_1 = \Gamma_{11}, \; I_2 = \Gamma_{22} \tag{2.30}$$

and from Eqn (2.28) we see that

$$I_1 = \Gamma_{11} = \int_S \frac{I(S)}{R_1^2} \, dS \qquad (2.31)$$

with a similar expression for I_2. This relation justifies our earlier comment that $\Gamma_{11}(0)$ or $\gamma_{11}(0)$ is a measure of the amount of partial coherence introduced by finite source size.

Equations (2.28) and (2.29) are the mathematical expression of the van Cittert–Zernike theorem (van Cittert, 1934; Zernike, 1938), which we state in the form given by Born and Wolf (1959): "...The complex degree of coherence, which describes the correlation of vibrations at a fixed point P_2 and a variable point P_1 in a plane illuminated by an extended quasi-monochromatic primary source, is equal to the normalized complex amplitude at the corresponding point P_1 in a certain diffraction pattern, centred on P_2. This pattern would be obtained on replacing the source by a diffracting aperture of the same size and shape as the source, and on filling it with a spherical wave converging to P_2, the amplitude distribution over the wave-front in the aperture being proportional to the intensity distribution across the source." If $I(S)$ is taken to be uniform, the diffraction pattern reduces to that of a uniform spherical wave by an aperture equal in size (and shape) to the source. A generalization of the van Cittert–Zernike theorem to include sources of any state of coherence has recently been obtained by Wolf and Carter (1976). This differs from the form given here only in that the mean intensity of the source is replaced by the generalized radiance, introduced by Walther (1968) and Marchand and Wolf (1974). This is extremely important for electron optics since it permits us to relate the concepts of brightness and coherence in a precise way (Hawkes, 1977a).

For our present purposes, an approximate form of the general expression (2.28) is adequate. For sources that are small and points that are close together compared with the distances R_1 and R_2, which is generally the case, a calculation familiar from diffraction theory tells us that

$$\gamma_{12} = \frac{\exp i\psi \int_S I(\xi, \eta) \, \exp \{-i\bar{k}(p\xi + q\eta)\} \, d\xi \, d\eta}{\int_S I(\xi, \eta) \, d\xi \, d\eta} \qquad (2.32)$$

where

$$p = \frac{x_1 - x_2}{R}, \; q = \frac{y_1 - y_2}{R}, \; R \approx R_1 \approx R_2.$$

In these conditions, therefore, the modulus of γ_{12} is given by the modulus of the Fourier transform of the source intensity, normalized with respect to the total intensity. The angle ψ is equal to the phase difference between waves arriving at P_1 and P_2 from the centre point of the source and the exponential factor can thus be neglected only if the corresponding path difference is much smaller than the mean wavelength. Since the latter is of the order of picometres, this is a stringent condition.

In the idealized case of a uniform circular source, we have

$$\gamma_{12} = \frac{2J_1(\theta)}{\theta} \, e^{i\psi} \tag{2.33}$$

where J_1 is a first-order Bessel function and its argument θ is given by

$$\theta = \frac{2\pi}{\lambda} \frac{a}{R} \, |\mathbf{x}_1 - \mathbf{x}_2| \tag{2.34}$$

where a is the radius of the source, $R \approx R_1 \approx R_2$ and $\mathbf{x}_j = (x_j, y_j), j = 1,2$, are the coordinates of the P_j. From the behaviour of the function $2J_1(\theta)/\theta$, we can deduce that $|\gamma_{12}|$ decreases from unity at $\theta = 0$, where P_1 and P_2 coincide, to 0·88 at $\theta = 1$, where P_1 and P_2 are separated by a distance 0·16 $R\lambda/a$, falling to zero when $\theta = 3·83$ corresponding to a separation of 0·61 $R\lambda/a$. It is usual to regard the intermediate value ($\theta = 1$) as an "acceptable" departure from perfect coherence; the quantity

$$d = 0·16 \, \lambda/\alpha \tag{2.35}$$

therefore gives a good idea of the diameter of the area that is, to a good approximation, coherently illuminated by a quasi-monochromatic uniform source of angular semi-aperture $\alpha(=a/R)$. (This result may equally well be "derived" from the uncertainty principle.) For an electron wavelength of 4 pm therefore (we recall that 3·7 pm corresponds to 100 kV), we find that $d = 100$ nm if $\alpha \approx 6$ μrad. The uniform intensity model of the source is of course crude but the order of magnitude of the result is not much altered if we choose a Gaussian distribution of comparable width.

Important though these results are, we are more likely to wish to calculate the mutual intensity or complex degree of coherence after the electrons have propagated through a lens system—at the specimen beyond the condensers and any objective pre-field, for example. For this we must introduce the point-spread (or impulse-response) of the lens system. If we denote the wave function at a point P due to a source point on S by $\bar{K}(S, P, \nu)$, where ν is as usual the frequency, Eqn (2.28) must be replaced by

$$\Gamma_{12} = \lambda^2 \int_S I(S) \bar{K}(S, P_1, \bar{\nu}) \bar{K}^*(S, P_2, \bar{\nu}) \, \mathrm{d}S \tag{2.36}$$

and Eqn (2.29) by

$$\gamma_{12} = \frac{\lambda^2}{(I_1 I_2)^{1/2}} \int_S I(S) \bar{K}(S, P_1, \bar{\nu}) \bar{K}^*(S, P_2, \bar{\nu}) \, \mathrm{d}S. \tag{2.37}$$

An interesting form of Eqn (2.37) was proposed by Hopkins (1951) which is particularly convenient in studying the propagation of γ_{12} through particular instruments. We introduce the notation

$$U_j^* = i\lambda \bar{K}(S, P_j, \bar{v})\{I(S)\}^{1/2}, j = 1, 2. \tag{2.38}$$

The quantity U_j is the same as the disturbance that a monochromatic point source at S of strength $\{I(S)\}^{1/2}$ would produce at P_j. If, however, we substitute from Eqn (2.38) into Eqns (2.36) and (2.37), we obtain

$$\Gamma_{12} = \int_S U_1 U_2^* \, dS \tag{2.39a}$$

$$\gamma_{12} = \frac{1}{(I_1 I_2)^{1/2}} \int_S U_1 U_2^* \, dS \tag{2.39b}$$

which give Γ_{12} and γ_{12} in terms of the disturbances produced by each point of an "associated" monochromatic source.

It now only remains to derive an expression for the relation between the mutual intensity distribution in the plane Π and that in some other plane Π' downstream from Π. With the notation of Fig. 2, we can use Eqns (2.36) and (2.37) to show that

$$\Gamma(P_1', P_2') = \iint_\Pi \Gamma(P_1, P_2)\bar{K}(P_1, P_1')\bar{K}^*(P_2, P_2') \, dP_1 \, dP_2 \tag{2.40}$$

in which the frequency $\bar{v}$ has been dropped from $\bar{K}$ and the integration is taken over all pairs of points, P_1, P_2, in the plane Π.

This very important formula is a generalization of the expressions for the propagation of the wave function and of the intensity in the cases of fully coherent and completely incoherent illumination respectively. Our calculation of the effect of partial coherence on image formation in the electron microscope will be based on this formula.

We mentioned in Section II, Part A that the cross-spectral density is often more useful than the mutual coherence function and hence, the mutual intensity. The propagation of this function through general systems is examined in Hawkes (1977a) and through isoplanatic systems in Hawkes (1977c, d).

III. PARTIAL COHERENCE AND ELECTRON IMAGE FORMATION

In the preceding section, we saw that the mutual coherence function and the complex degree of coherence provide a convenient representation of the effects of partial coherence and we gave formulae from which the variation of the mutual intensity through an optical system could be deduced. We now use these formulae, and in particular Eqn (2.40), to derive the relation between the electron wave functions in conjugate planes. We then introduce a function representing the effect of a specimen in the object plane and derive an expression for the image spectrum in terms of the object spectrum; this expression is considerably more complicated than the relations obtained in the extreme cases of perfect coherence and complete incoherence.

Simpler expressions can, however, be deduced if the specimen is a weak scatterer. In Part B of this section, we show that imaging with partially coherent illumination can then be represented by simple transfer functions, just as in the coherent case, which are obtained by multiplying the corresponding coherent transfer functions by envelope functions. The section ends with a brief discussion of the reduction of the information-carrying capacity of image-forming electrons in partially coherent conditions.

A. Transfer Functions: the General Case

Throughout this part, we shall consider a composite system consisting of an illuminating system, a specimen and an image-forming system. Position coordinates in the object plane are denoted by $\mathbf{x}_o = (x_o, y_o)$ and $\bar{\mathbf{x}}_o$ (since we repeatedly need to consider pairs of points) and those in the image plane by $\mathbf{x}_i$ and $\bar{\mathbf{x}}_i$.

1. Transfer of mutual intensity

From Eqn (2.40), we know that the mutual intensity at the image $\Gamma(\mathbf{x}_i, \bar{\mathbf{x}}_i)$ is given in terms of that at the object by the formula

$$\Gamma(\mathbf{x}_i, \bar{\mathbf{x}}_i) = \iint \Gamma(\mathbf{x}_o, \bar{\mathbf{x}}_o) \bar{K}(\mathbf{x}_o, \mathbf{x}_i) \bar{K}^*(\bar{\mathbf{x}}_o, \bar{\mathbf{x}}_i) \, \mathrm{d}\mathbf{x}_o \, \mathrm{d}\bar{\mathbf{x}}_o. \quad (3.1)$$

The function $\bar{K}(\mathbf{x}_o, \mathbf{x}_i)$ is the point-spread or impulse-response function relating the wave function $\psi(\mathbf{x}_i)$ in the image plane to that at the object plane, $\psi(\mathbf{x}_o)$. We have already given the formula connecting these wave functions in Eqn (1.1); the function $\bar{K}$ that appears in Eqn (3.1) is related to K by the simple formula

$$\bar{K}(\mathbf{x}_o, \mathbf{x}_i) = \frac{E(\mathbf{x}_o)}{M E(\mathbf{x}_i)} K\left(\frac{\mathbf{x}_i}{M} - \mathbf{x}_o\right) \quad (3.2)$$

and so Eqn (3.1) may be written in terms of known functions as follows:

$$\Gamma(\mathbf{x}_i, \bar{\mathbf{x}}_i) = \frac{1}{M^2 E(\mathbf{x}_i) E^*(\bar{\mathbf{x}}_i)} \iint \Gamma(\mathbf{x}_o, \bar{\mathbf{x}}_o)$$

$$\times K\left(\frac{\mathbf{x}_i}{M} - \mathbf{x}_o\right) K^*\left(\frac{\bar{\mathbf{x}}_i}{M} - \bar{\mathbf{x}}_o\right) E(\mathbf{x}_o) E^*(\bar{\mathbf{x}}_o) \, \mathrm{d}\mathbf{x}_o \, \mathrm{d}\bar{\mathbf{x}}_o \quad (3.3)$$

or writing the quadratic phase factors more compactly,

$$\Gamma(\mathbf{x}_i, \bar{\mathbf{x}}_i) = \frac{E(\bar{\mathbf{x}}_i, \mathbf{x}_i)}{M^2} \iint \Gamma(\mathbf{x}_o, \bar{\mathbf{x}}_o)$$

$$K\left(\frac{\mathbf{x}_i}{M} - \mathbf{x}_o\right) K^*\left(\frac{\bar{\mathbf{x}}_i}{M} - \bar{\mathbf{x}}_o\right) E(\mathbf{x}_o, \bar{\mathbf{x}}_o) \, d\mathbf{x}_o \, d\bar{\mathbf{x}}_o \quad (3.4)$$

where

$$E(\bar{\mathbf{x}}_i, \mathbf{x}_i) = \exp\left\{\frac{i\pi r}{\lambda M} (\bar{\mathbf{x}}_i \cdot \bar{\mathbf{x}}_i - \mathbf{x}_i \cdot \mathbf{x}_i)\right\} \quad (3.5)$$

$$E(\bar{\mathbf{x}}_o, \mathbf{x}_o) = \exp\left\{\frac{i\pi r'}{\lambda} (\bar{\mathbf{x}}_o \cdot \bar{\mathbf{x}}_o - \mathbf{x}_o \cdot \mathbf{x}_o)\right\}. \quad (3.6)$$

Equation (3.4) has the form of an elaborate convolution and we therefore introduce the Fourier transforms of the component groups of functions in order to use the convolution theorem. Writing

$$\tilde{\Gamma}_o(\mathbf{p}, \bar{\mathbf{p}}) = \iint E(\mathbf{x}_o, \bar{\mathbf{x}}_o) \Gamma(\mathbf{x}_o, \bar{\mathbf{x}}_o) \exp\left\{-2\pi i(\mathbf{x}_o \cdot \mathbf{p} + \bar{\mathbf{x}}_o \cdot \bar{\mathbf{p}})\right\} d\mathbf{x}_o \, d\bar{\mathbf{x}}_o \quad (3.7)$$

and

$$\tilde{\Gamma}_i(\mathbf{p}, \bar{\mathbf{p}}) = \iint E(\mathbf{x}_i, \bar{\mathbf{x}}_i) \Gamma(\mathbf{x}_i, \bar{\mathbf{x}}_i) \exp\left\{-2\pi i(\mathbf{x}_i \cdot \mathbf{p} + \bar{\mathbf{x}}_i \cdot \bar{\mathbf{p}})\right\} d\mathbf{x}_i \, d\bar{\mathbf{x}}_i \quad (3.8)$$

we find

$$\tilde{\Gamma}_i(\mathbf{p}, \bar{\mathbf{p}}) = \frac{1}{M^2} \tilde{L}(\mathbf{p}, \bar{\mathbf{p}}) \tilde{\Gamma}_o(\mathbf{p}, \bar{\mathbf{p}}) \quad (3.9)$$

with

$$\tilde{L}(\mathbf{p}, \bar{\mathbf{p}}) = \iint K(\mathbf{u}) K^*(\bar{\mathbf{u}}) \exp\left\{-2\pi i(\mathbf{u} \cdot \mathbf{p} + \bar{\mathbf{u}} \cdot \bar{\mathbf{p}})\right\} d\mathbf{u} \, d\bar{\mathbf{u}}. \quad (3.10)$$

Equation (3.9) tells us that the mutual intensity is transformed *linearly* between object and image in an electron microscope, the latter acting as a linear scalar filter—*linear* in the sense that each component of the frequency spectrum of the mutual intensity in the object plane is multiplied by a factor, the resulting modulated spectrum being the frequency spectrum of the mutual intensity in the image plane; *scalar* in the sense that each frequency component in the image is given by a single component at the object. We again speak of spatial frequencies in this context, though the physical picture of this concept is not so obvious for mutual intensity as it is when we discuss the spatial frequency spectra of an object or its image.

It is clear from Eqn (3.9) that if we could obtain a set of sample values of $\Gamma(\mathbf{x}_i, \bar{\mathbf{x}}_i)$ and hence an array $\{G_{ijkl}^{(i)}\}$ corresponding to $\tilde{\Gamma}_i(\mathbf{p}, \bar{\mathbf{p}})$ we could reconstruct sample values $\{G_{ijkl}^{(o)}\}$ of $\tilde{\Gamma}_o$ and hence of $\Gamma(\mathbf{x}_o, \bar{\mathbf{x}}_o)$ since (absorbing M into the sampling raster)

$$G_{ijkl}^{(o)} = G_{ijkl}^{(i)} / L_{ijkl} \quad (3.11)$$

where $\{L_{ijkl}\}$ is the array of sample values of $\tilde{L}(\mathbf{p}, \bar{\mathbf{p}})$.

We note in passing that a technique for reconstructing images of partially coherently illuminated objects using samples of the mutual intensity has been proposed by Dutta and Goodman (1977); see also Ueha *et al.* (1976). In electron optics, however, the mutual intensity is not readily accessible.

Inverting Eqn (1.7), we have

$$A(\lambda f \mathbf{p}) = \int K(\mathbf{u}) \exp\left(-2\pi i \, \mathbf{u} \cdot \mathbf{p}\right) d\mathbf{u} \tag{3.12}$$

and combining this with Eqn (3.10), we see that

$$\tilde{L}(\mathbf{p}, \bar{\mathbf{p}}) = A(\lambda f \mathbf{p})A^*(-\lambda f \bar{\mathbf{p}}). \tag{3.13}$$

The filter thus truncates the mutual intensity spectrum wherever $\mathbf{p} \cdot \mathbf{p}$ or $\bar{\mathbf{p}} \cdot \bar{\mathbf{p}}$ exceeds $a^2/\lambda^2 f^2$, where a is the radius of the objective aperture. Wherever $\tilde{L}(\mathbf{p},\bar{\mathbf{p}})$ is non-zero, it takes the form

$$\tilde{L}(\mathbf{p}, \bar{\mathbf{p}}) = \exp\left\{-i\gamma(\mathbf{p}, \bar{\mathbf{p}})\right\} \tag{3.14}$$

with

$$\gamma(\mathbf{p}, \bar{\mathbf{p}}) = \frac{2\pi}{\lambda}\left[\frac{1}{4}C_s\lambda^4\{(\mathbf{p}\cdot\mathbf{p})^2 - (\bar{\mathbf{p}}\cdot\bar{\mathbf{p}})^2\} - \frac{1}{2}\Delta\lambda^2\{(\mathbf{p}\cdot\mathbf{p}) - (\bar{\mathbf{p}}\cdot\bar{\mathbf{p}})\}\right] \tag{3.15}$$

where C_s is as usual the spherical aberration coefficient and Δ is the defocus, referred back to the object plane. We note in passing that the array $\{L_{ijkl}\}$ can be constructed from two matrices $\{L_{ij}\}$

$$L_{ijkl} = L_{ij}L_{kl}^\dagger \tag{3.16}$$

with the aid of Eqn (3.13), where L_{ij} is an array derived from $A(\lambda f \mathbf{p})$ and $L_{kl}^\dagger$, from $A^*(-\lambda f \bar{\mathbf{p}})$.

2. *Introduction of the specimen*

We assume that the wave function describing electrons emerging from the specimen is related to that describing the incident beam by a complex two-dimensional specimen transmission function, $\sigma(\mathbf{x}_o)$. Denoting the incident wave produced by a source point S by $\psi_S(S; \mathbf{x}_o)$ and the emergent wave by $\psi_o(S; \mathbf{x}_o)$, we thus write

$$\psi_o(S; \mathbf{x}_o) = \sigma(\mathbf{x}_o)\psi_S(S; \mathbf{x}_o). \tag{3.17}$$

The incident and emergent mutual intensities are therefore related by the expression

$$\Gamma_o(\mathbf{x}_o, \bar{\mathbf{x}}_o) = \sigma(\mathbf{x}_o)\sigma^*(\bar{\mathbf{x}}_o)\Gamma_S(\mathbf{x}_o, \bar{\mathbf{x}}_o). \tag{3.18}$$

For most cases of practical interest, the mutual intensity of the incident beam is a function of the separation between its arguments but not of their individual values, so that

$$\Gamma_S(\mathbf{x}_o, \bar{\mathbf{x}}_o) = \Gamma_S(\mathbf{x}_o - \bar{\mathbf{x}}_o). \tag{3.19}$$

The image intensity, $\Gamma(\mathbf{x}_i, \mathbf{x}_i)$, is given by Eqn (3.4); we obtain

$$j(\mathbf{x}_i) = \Gamma(\mathbf{x}_i, \mathbf{x}_i)$$

$$= \frac{1}{M^2} \int \int \sigma(\mathbf{x}_o)\sigma^*(\bar{\mathbf{x}}_o)\Gamma_S(\mathbf{x}_o - \bar{\mathbf{x}}_o)K(\mathbf{x}_i/M - \mathbf{x}_o)K^*(\mathbf{x}_i/M - \bar{\mathbf{x}}_o) \times$$

$$\times\ E(\mathbf{x}_o, \bar{\mathbf{x}}_o)\ \mathrm{d}\mathbf{x}_o\ \mathrm{d}\bar{\mathbf{x}}_o. \tag{3.20}$$

Introducing the Fourier transform or spatial frequency spectrum of $\sigma(\mathbf{x}_o)$, in which we include $E(\mathbf{x}_o, \bar{\mathbf{x}}_o)$ for convenience, thus:

$$\tilde{\sigma}(\mathbf{p}) = \int E(\mathbf{x}_o)\sigma(\mathbf{x}_o) \exp(-2\pi i\, \mathbf{p}.\mathbf{x}_o)\ \mathrm{d}\mathbf{x}_o \tag{3.21}$$

the image intensity becomes

$$j(\mathbf{x}_i) = \frac{1}{M^2} \int \int \tilde{\sigma}(\mathbf{p})\tilde{\sigma}^*(\bar{\mathbf{p}})\tilde{T}(\mathbf{p}, \bar{\mathbf{p}}) \exp\{2\pi i(\mathbf{p} - \bar{\mathbf{p}}).\mathbf{x}_i/M\}\ \mathrm{d}\mathbf{p}\ \mathrm{d}\bar{\mathbf{p}} \tag{3.22}$$

where

$$\tilde{T}(\mathbf{p}, \bar{\mathbf{p}}) = \int \int \Gamma_S(\bar{\mathbf{u}} - \mathbf{u})K(\mathbf{u})K^*(\bar{\mathbf{u}}) \exp\{2\pi i(\bar{\mathbf{p}}.\bar{\mathbf{u}} - \mathbf{p}.\mathbf{u})\ \mathrm{d}\mathbf{u}\ \mathrm{d}\bar{\mathbf{u}} \tag{3.23}$$

and

$$\mathbf{u} = \mathbf{x}_i/M - \mathbf{x}_o,\ \bar{\mathbf{u}} = \mathbf{x}_i/M - \bar{\mathbf{x}}_o. \tag{3.24}$$

The nature of the transfer function $\tilde{T}$ is more easily understood if we introduce the Fourier transforms of Γ_S and K under the integral in Eqn (3.23). We obtain

$$\tilde{T}(\mathbf{p}, \bar{\mathbf{p}}) = \int \tilde{\Gamma}_S(\mathbf{v})\tilde{K}(\mathbf{p} + \mathbf{v})\tilde{K}^*(\bar{\mathbf{p}} + \mathbf{v})\ \mathrm{d}\mathbf{v}. \tag{3.25}$$

Equation (3.22) is not yet in the form we should like, that of a spectral filter. We can convert it into a form resembling such a filter by taking the Fourier transform of the image intensity, $j(\mathbf{x}_i)$. The resulting spatial frequency spectrum is then of the form

$$\tilde{j}(\mathbf{p}') = \int \tilde{\sigma}(\bar{\mathbf{p}} + \mathbf{p}'M)\tilde{\sigma}^*(\bar{\mathbf{p}})\tilde{T}(\bar{\mathbf{p}} + \mathbf{p}'M, \bar{\mathbf{p}})\ \mathrm{d}\bar{\mathbf{p}}. \tag{3.26}$$

The right-hand side of Eqn (3.26) consists of a function determined by the specimen, $\tilde{\sigma}(\bar{\mathbf{p}} + \mathbf{p}'M)\tilde{\sigma}^*(\bar{\mathbf{p}})$, multiplied by a function determined jointly by the illuminating system and the image-forming lenses, $\tilde{T}(\bar{\mathbf{p}} + \mathbf{p}'M, \bar{\mathbf{p}})$, integrated over the variable $\bar{\mathbf{p}}$. Each component ($\mathbf{p}'$) of the spatial frequency spectrum of the image therefore contains contributions from the whole range of spatial frequency components ($\bar{\mathbf{p}}$) at the object. The filter function $\tilde{T}$, which determines the weight accorded to each component in the image, is therefore a *vector* filter. It is known as the *transmission cross-coefficient* (Born and Wolf, 1959). The transition from a scalar filter to a vector filter results in a considerable increase in practical complexity and new strategies will be needed in any attempt to reconstruct the specimen function σ, or even its weighted autocorrelation function, from the image intensity. (A simpler though related problem is discussed by Saleh, 1974.) This can be understood most easily by considering the (simplest) discrete form of Eqn (3.26). Suppose that the measured intensities at a set of image points are organized as an image array $\{j_{ij}\}$ and that the sampled values of σ are likewise written as a matrix, $\{\sigma_{ij}\}$. Then (with proper attention to the scaling) we have

$$\tilde{j}_{ij} = \sum_{u,v} \tilde{\sigma}_{u+i,\,v+j}\, \tilde{\sigma}^*_{uv}\, \tilde{T}_{u+i,\,v+j;\,u,\,v} \qquad (3.27)$$

where $\tilde{T}$ is a four-tensor which has some useful symmetry properties but is not strikingly sparse. The complexity of Eqns (3.26) and (3.27) adds additional importance to the weak phase-amplitude specimen, considered in Part B of this section.

We have scarcely considered the limits of integration of the numerous integrals that occur in the foregoing analysis. These have been examined in detail by Hanszen and Ade (1975) and Ade (1975), who observe that for sufficiently low spatial frequencies—that is, for coarse spacings in the specimen—the integral of Eqn (3.26) can be written as the product of two integrals, the autocorrelation function of the specimen function, $\tilde{\sigma}$, and a similar integral over $\tilde{T}$. For this case, which excludes high resolution, the object and image intensities are related linearly by a scalar filter. This conclusion follows directly from the remark on limits that follows Eqn (3.13).

We now show that the foregoing expressions for transfer functions collapse to the familiar forms in the extreme cases of coherent and incoherent illumination. If the illumination is perfectly coherent, we have $\Gamma_S(\mathbf{x}_o, \bar{\mathbf{x}}_o) = \psi_S(\mathbf{x}_o)\psi_S(\bar{\mathbf{x}}_o)$ so that Eqn (3.20) may be written

$$j(\mathbf{x}_i) = \frac{1}{M^2} \int \sigma(\mathbf{x}_o)\psi_S(\mathbf{x}_o)K(\mathbf{x}_i/M - \mathbf{x}_o)E(\mathbf{x}_o)\mathrm{d}\mathbf{x}_o$$

$$\times \int \sigma^*(\bar{\mathbf{x}}_o)\psi_S(\bar{\mathbf{x}}_o)K^*(\mathbf{x}_i/M - \bar{\mathbf{x}}_o)E^*(\bar{\mathbf{x}}_o)\,\mathrm{d}\bar{\mathbf{x}}_o$$

$$= \left| \frac{1}{M} \int \sigma(\mathbf{x}_o)\psi_S(\mathbf{x}_o)K(\mathbf{x}_i/M - \mathbf{x}_o)E(\mathbf{x}_o)\,\mathrm{d}\mathbf{x}_o \right|^2$$

as expected. If, at the other extreme, the illumination is incoherent, $\Gamma_S(\mathbf{x}_o - \bar{\mathbf{x}}_o) \propto \delta(\mathbf{x}_o - \bar{\mathbf{x}}_o)$ so that Eqn (3.20) now becomes

$$j(\mathbf{x}_i) \propto \frac{1}{M^2} \int \sigma(\mathbf{x}_o)\sigma^*(\mathbf{x}_o)K(\mathbf{x}_i/M - \mathbf{x}_o)K^*(\mathbf{x}_i/M - \mathbf{x}_o)\,\mathrm{d}\mathbf{x}_o$$

$$= \frac{1}{M^2} \int |\sigma(\mathbf{x}_o)|^2 |K(\mathbf{x}_i/M - \mathbf{x}_o)|^2\,\mathrm{d}\mathbf{x}_o$$

again as expected. Equation (3.26) may be analysed in a similar way, though the reasoning is a little more tortuous. Representing the mutual intensity by a delta-function is obviously physically meaningless, since the intensity would have to be infinite. With care, however, use of this representation of $\Gamma_S(\mathbf{x}_o - \bar{\mathbf{x}}_o)$ can be justified: we refer to Beran and Parrent (1963) and Section 4.4 of Beran and Parrent (1964) for more discussion of this point.

Systems with finite energy spread and finite source size have been considered in some detail by Misell (1971a, b; 1973a), who also considers the question, very important in electron microscopy, of loss of coherence in the specimen as a result of inelastic scattering. Gabor (1956) had already shown that the temporal coherence of the electron beams commonly used in electron microscopy is sufficient to ensure that elastically scattered and unscattered electrons can be regarded as coherent, in the sense that we must add wave functions, not intensities, when calculating any interference effects produced by them (see also Burge, 1973). Conversely, inelastically scattered electrons will be incoherent relative to the elastically scattered and unscattered beam though, for a relatively narrow energy window, inelastically scattered electrons may be expected to interfere together coherently. Misell (1971a, b) therefore introduces the finite angular spread of the incident beam and, separately, the finite energy spread and evaluates the image current density for a variety of situations. In particular, Misell (1971a) derives the form of Eqn (3.20) corresponding to finite source size and gives the expression for this equation in polar coordinates, which is convenient for rotationally symmetric sources. He then derives expressions for the image current density, j_i, when the source size is negligible but the electrons are not perfectly monochromatic. Two sets of results are obtained, one set corresponding to the case in which the individual contributions to the image from electrons of different energy are added incoherently, the other set to the case in which coherence is assumed over a (narrow) energy range. Finally, an expression is given for the composite effect of finite source size and energy spread. In a companion paper, Misell (1971b) investigates very thoroughly the effects of spatial and temporal coherence on the image formed by inelastically scattered electrons. In a series of later papers (Misell, 1973b, c; Misell and Atkins, 1973), Misell uses this theoretical framework to calculate the resolution and contrast to be expected in electron microscopy for various conditions of coherence and for both the elastically and the inelastically scattered components of the electron beam. We return to this work briefly in Part B of this section. A detailed account of Misell's contributions in this domain are to be found in Misell (1973a).

B. *Transfer Functions for Weakly Scattering Specimens*

A good idea of the behaviour of electron microscopes close to the limit of resolution and with coherent illumination can be obtained by considering specimens that only scatter the incident beam by small amounts although great care must be taken when interpreting real images on the basis of this approximation (Misell, 1976). We may therefore expect to obtain useful insight into the effect of partial coherence in a real microscope by considering such specimens, for which we write

$$\sigma(\mathbf{x}_o) = \{1 - s(\mathbf{x}_o)\} \exp \{i\phi(\mathbf{x}_o)\}$$
$$\approx 1 - s(\mathbf{x}_o) + i\phi(\mathbf{x}_o) \tag{3.28}$$

and neglect quadratic and higher order terms in $\phi(\mathbf{x}_o)$. This case was studied in the early days of modern light-optical coherence theory by Menzel (1958, 1960), Slansky (1959, 1960, 1962; Slansky and Maréchal, 1960) and Hauser (1962); for a recent account, see Menzel $et\ al.$ (1973, Section 6.2–d). Its relevance for electron microscopy was realized by Hanszen and Trepte (1971a, b) and, in the context of optical image deblurring techniques, by Stroke and Halioua (1972). Finally, Frank (1973) showed that it yields results of more general application than those obtained by Hanszen and Trepte (1971b), as we see in detail below. We shall demonstrate that, for such types of specimen, it is possible to recover a linear $scalar$ transfer theory relating image spatial frequency spectrum and the spatial frequency spectra of the amplitude and phase functions, $s(\mathbf{x}_o)$ and $\phi(\mathbf{x}_o)$. Moreover, the appropriate contrast transfer functions can be written as products of the coherent transfer functions and envelope functions; the latter modulate the coherent functions, eventually attenuating them to such an extent that the information about the specimen that reaches the image cannot be distinguished from noise.

Transfer functions for extended sources were first calculated by Erickson and Klug (1970a, b, 1971, see Erickson, 1973) and by Hanszen and Trepte (1971b) but the possibility of writing these as a product of the coherent transfer functions and an envelope function did not emerge from their calculations. Shortly before, the latter authors (Hanszen and Trepte, 1970, 1971a) had studied the effects of current and voltage variations and of the finite energy spread of the electron beam on the coherent transfer functions and in this case, they showed that under reasonable conditions, the effect of temporal partial coherence could be expressed as a product of the coherent function and an envelope function. A similar result is mentioned by Misell (1971a). Erickson and Klug (1970a, b, 1971) also included temporal effects in their calculations but did not arrive at the envelope representation. Subsequently, Frank (1973) observed that the zeros of the curves of Hanszen and Trepte (1971b) corresponding to finite source size, like those published later by Hirt and Hoppe (1972), remained approximately stationary for a wide range of source diameters and that it should therefore be possible to write the transfer functions for $spatial$ partial coherence as a product of the coherent functions and envelope functions. We now consider these two cases in detail. We note in passing that the envelope representation has been used to predict the appearance of single-atom images by Hahn and Seredynski (1974). Extensive calculations of the effects of both spatial and temporal coherence on the transfer functions are to be found in Hahn (1973).

1. *Finite source size*

We set out from Eqn (3.26), in the form

$$\tilde{\jmath}(\mathbf{p}/M) = \int \tilde{\sigma}(\bar{\mathbf{p}} + \mathbf{p})\tilde{\sigma}^*(\bar{\mathbf{p}})\, \tilde{T}(\bar{\mathbf{p}} + \mathbf{p}, \bar{\mathbf{p}})\, \mathrm{d}\bar{\mathbf{p}} \qquad (3.29)$$

into which we substitute the Fourier transform of Eqn (3.28):

$$\tilde{\sigma}(\mathbf{p}) = \delta(\mathbf{p}) - \tilde{s}(\mathbf{p}) + i\tilde{\phi}(\mathbf{p}). \qquad (3.30)$$

This yields

$$\tilde{\jmath}(\mathbf{p}/M) = \int \delta(\bar{\mathbf{p}}+\mathbf{p})\delta(\bar{\mathbf{p}})\, \tilde{T}(\bar{\mathbf{p}}+\mathbf{p}, \bar{\mathbf{p}})\, \mathrm{d}\bar{\mathbf{p}} - \int \delta(\bar{\mathbf{p}}+\mathbf{p})\tilde{s}^*(\bar{\mathbf{p}})\, \tilde{T}(\bar{\mathbf{p}}+\mathbf{p}, \bar{\mathbf{p}})\, \mathrm{d}\bar{\mathbf{p}}$$

$$-i\int \delta(\bar{\mathbf{p}}+\mathbf{p})\tilde{\phi}^*(\bar{\mathbf{p}})\, \tilde{T}(\bar{\mathbf{p}}+\mathbf{p}, \bar{\mathbf{p}})\, \mathrm{d}\bar{\mathbf{p}} - \int \tilde{s}(\bar{\mathbf{p}}+\mathbf{p})\delta(\bar{\mathbf{p}})\, \tilde{T}(\bar{\mathbf{p}}+\mathbf{p}, \bar{\mathbf{p}})\, \mathrm{d}\bar{\mathbf{p}}$$

$$+i\int \tilde{\phi}(\bar{\mathbf{p}}+\mathbf{p})\delta(\bar{\mathbf{p}})\, \tilde{T}(\bar{\mathbf{p}}+\mathbf{p}, \bar{\mathbf{p}})\, \mathrm{d}\bar{\mathbf{p}}$$

$$+\text{quadratic terms in } s \text{ and } \phi \text{ not containing } \delta \text{ functions.} \qquad (3.31)$$

Simplifying, we find

$$\tilde{\jmath}(\mathbf{p}/M) = \tilde{T}(\mathbf{p}, 0)\delta(\mathbf{p}) - \{\tilde{s}^*(-\mathbf{p})\, \tilde{T}(0, -\mathbf{p}) + \tilde{s}(\mathbf{p})\, \tilde{T}(\mathbf{p}, 0)\}$$
$$+i\{-\tilde{\phi}^*(-\mathbf{p})\, \tilde{T}(0, -\mathbf{p}) + \tilde{\phi}(\mathbf{p})\, \tilde{T}(\mathbf{p}, 0)\}$$
$$+\text{higher order terms.} \qquad (3.32)$$

Since $s(\mathbf{x}_o)$ and $\phi(\mathbf{x}_o)$ are real, we know that

$$\tilde{s}(\mathbf{p}) = \tilde{s}^*(-\mathbf{p})$$
$$\tilde{\phi}(\mathbf{p}) = \tilde{\phi}^*(-\mathbf{p}). \qquad (3.33)$$

Hence

$$\tilde{\jmath}(\mathbf{p}/M) = \tilde{T}(\mathbf{p}, 0)\delta(\mathbf{p}) - \tilde{s}(\mathbf{p})\{\tilde{T}(\mathbf{p}, 0) + \tilde{T}(0, -\mathbf{p})\}$$
$$+ i\tilde{\phi}(\mathbf{p})\{\tilde{T}(\mathbf{p}, 0) - \tilde{T}(0, -\mathbf{p})\} + \text{higher order terms.} \qquad (3.34)$$

From Eqn (3.25), we note in passing that

$$\tilde{T}(0, -\mathbf{p}) = \int \tilde{\Gamma}_s(\mathbf{v})\tilde{K}(\mathbf{v})\tilde{K}^*(-\mathbf{p} + \mathbf{v})\, \mathrm{d}\mathbf{v}$$
$$= \tilde{T}^*(-\mathbf{p}, 0) \qquad (3.35)$$

Equation (3.34) may thus be written

$$\tilde{\jmath}(\mathbf{p}/M) = \text{unscattered beam} + \tilde{s}(\mathbf{p})\, T_s(\mathbf{p}) + \tilde{\phi}(\mathbf{p})\, T_\phi(\mathbf{p})$$
$$+ \text{higher order terms} \qquad (3.36)$$

where

$$T_s(\mathbf{p}) = -\{\tilde{T}(\mathbf{p}, 0) + \tilde{T}(0, -\mathbf{p})\}$$
$$T_\phi(\mathbf{p}) = i\{\tilde{T}(\mathbf{p}, 0) - \tilde{T}(0, -\mathbf{p})\}. \qquad (3.37)$$

This is exactly analogous to the relation between the image and specimen functions in the case of coherent illumination, where

$$T_s(\mathbf{p}) \to B_s(\mathbf{p}) = -2 \cos \gamma(\mathbf{p})$$
$$T_\phi(\mathbf{p}) \to B_\phi(\mathbf{p}) = 2 \sin \gamma(\mathbf{p})$$

(3.38)

and we recall that $\gamma(\mathbf{p})$ is given by

$$\gamma(\mathbf{p}) = \frac{2\pi}{\lambda} \left\{ \frac{1}{4} C_s(\mathbf{p} \cdot \mathbf{p})^2 \lambda^4 - \frac{1}{2} \varDelta \mathbf{p} \cdot \mathbf{p} \lambda^2 \right\}$$

(3.39)

(cf. Eqns 1.8 and 1.9). As usual, C_s denotes the spherical aberration coefficient and $\varDelta$ the defocus.

The result expressed by Eqn (3.36) is in itself extremely interesting, since it allows us to use the various filters that have been proposed for the extraction of information from focal series without serious modification (Schiske, 1968, 1973; Hawkes, 1974a, b). Nevertheless, as we mentioned earlier, it can be shown that the functions T_ϕ and T_s can be written as products of $B_s(\mathbf{p})$ and $B_\phi(\mathbf{p})$ (Eqns 1.17 and 1.18 or 3.38) and appropriate envelope functions. The following account follows Frank (1973) closely.

From Eqns (3.37) and (3.25), we have

$$T_s(\mathbf{p}) = - \int \tilde{\varGamma}_s(\mathbf{v}) \{ \tilde{K}(\mathbf{p} + \mathbf{v}) \tilde{K}^*(\mathbf{v}) + \tilde{K}(\mathbf{v}) \tilde{K}^*(-\mathbf{p} + \mathbf{v}) \} \, d\mathbf{v}$$
$$T_\phi(\mathbf{p}) = i \int \tilde{\varGamma}_s(\mathbf{v}) \{ \tilde{K}(\mathbf{p} + \mathbf{v}) \tilde{K}^*(\mathbf{v}) - \tilde{K}(\mathbf{v}) \tilde{K}^*(-\mathbf{p} + \mathbf{v}) \} \, d\mathbf{v}$$

(3.40)

and, for symmetric apertures,

$$\tilde{K}(\mathbf{p}) = A(\lambda f \mathbf{p})$$

(3.41)

(Eqn 1.7) with $A(\lambda f \mathbf{p}) = a(\mathbf{p}) \exp \{-i\gamma(\mathbf{p})\}$, $\gamma(\mathbf{p})$ and $a(\mathbf{p})$ being defined by Eqn (1.9). Equations (3.40) can therefore be written

$$T_s(\mathbf{p}) = -2 \int \tilde{\varGamma}_s(\mathbf{v}) a(\mathbf{p} + \mathbf{v}) a(\mathbf{v}) \cos \{\gamma(\mathbf{p} + \mathbf{v}) - \gamma(\mathbf{v})\} \, d\mathbf{v}$$
$$T_d(\mathbf{p}) = 2 \int \tilde{\varGamma}_s(\mathbf{v}) a(\mathbf{p} + \mathbf{v}) a(\mathbf{v}) \sin \{\gamma(\mathbf{p} + \mathbf{v}) - \gamma(\mathbf{v})\} \, d\mathbf{v}$$

(3.42)

for a symmetric source. In practice, the terms in a can frequently be neglected (see Frank, 1973) and Eqns (3.42) may be written

$$T_s(\mathbf{p}) = -2 \int \tilde{\varGamma}_s(\mathbf{v}) \cos \{\gamma(\mathbf{p} + \mathbf{v}) - \gamma(\mathbf{v})\} \, d\mathbf{v}$$
$$T_\phi(\mathbf{p}) = 2 \int \tilde{\varGamma}_s(\mathbf{v}) \sin \{\gamma(\mathbf{p} + \mathbf{v}) - \gamma(\mathbf{v})\} \, d\mathbf{v}.$$

(3.43)

or values of $|\mathbf{p}|$ much larger than the source aperture, we may expand $\gamma(\mathbf{p} + \mathbf{v})$ to give

$$\gamma(\mathbf{p} + \mathbf{v}) \approx \gamma(\mathbf{p}) + \mathbf{v} \cdot \text{grad} \, \gamma(\mathbf{p}).$$

(3.44)

Since the lowest order terms in $\gamma(\mathbf{v})$ are quadratic in $\mathbf{v}$, we may neglect them in comparison with those of Eqn (3.44); Eqns (3.43) then become

$$T_s(\mathbf{p}) = -2\{\cos\gamma(\mathbf{p})E(\mathbf{p}) - \sin\gamma(\mathbf{p})\hat{E}(\mathbf{p})\}$$
$$T_\phi(\mathbf{p}) = \ \ 2\{\sin\gamma(\mathbf{p})E(\mathbf{p}) + \cos\gamma(\mathbf{p})\hat{E}(\mathbf{p})\}$$

(3.45a)

or

$$T_s(\mathbf{p}) = B_s(\mathbf{p})E(\mathbf{p}) + B_\phi(\mathbf{p})\hat{E}(\mathbf{p})$$
$$T_\phi(\mathbf{p}) = B_\phi(\mathbf{p})E(\mathbf{p}) - B_s(\mathbf{p})\hat{E}(\mathbf{p})$$

(3.45b)

where

$$E(\mathbf{p}) = \int \tilde{\Gamma}_s(\mathbf{v}) \cos\{\mathbf{v}.\mathrm{grad}\,\gamma(\mathbf{p})\}\,d\mathbf{v}$$
$$\hat{E}(\mathbf{p}) = \int \tilde{\Gamma}_s(\mathbf{v}) \sin\{\mathbf{v}.\mathrm{grad}\,\gamma(\mathbf{p})\}\,d\mathbf{v}.$$

(3.46)

Since we have assumed that the source is symmetric, we have

$$\hat{E}(\mathbf{p}) = 0.$$

(3.47)

Equations (3.45) therefore give the desired envelope representation of the effect of finite source size on the perfectly coherent transfer functions. The envelope function, $E(\mathbf{p})$ is moreover related formally to the mutual intensity:

$$E(\mathbf{p}) = \Gamma_s\left\{\frac{1}{2\pi}\,\mathrm{grad}\,\gamma(\mathbf{p})\right\}.$$

(3.48)

In regions where $\gamma(\mathbf{p})$ is constant or only slowly varying with $\mathbf{p}$, the envelope will alter the coherent transfer function very little. For perfectly coherent, uniform illumination, $\Gamma_s(\mathbf{x}_o, \bar{\mathbf{x}}_o)$ and hence $E(\mathbf{p})$ is equal to unity so that T_s and T_ϕ degenerate to the familiar coherent transfer functions, as they should.

The form of the envelope function has been derived by Frank (1973) for a uniform disc-shaped source and for a source with a Gaussian intensity distribution. Numerical calculations showed that the first order approximation begins to break down beyond spatial frequencies of the order of $2(C_s\lambda^3)^{-1/4}$ for sources smaller than $0.07\ (C_s\lambda^3)^{-1/4}$ in semi-angular extent and of the order of $1.5\ (C_s\lambda^3)^{-1/4}$ for sources less than $0.14\ (C_s\lambda^3)^{-1/4}$. These source sizes correspond to 1 and 2 mrad for $C_s = 1.35$ mm and $\lambda = 3.7$ pm: $(C_s\lambda^3)^{1/4} \approx 0.5$ nm, so that $2(C_s\lambda^3)^{-1/4}$ corresponds to approximately 15 mrad.‡ This is illustrated in Figs 3 and 4. We note that for a disc-shaped source, for which

$$s(\mathbf{v}) = \tilde{\Gamma}_s(\mathbf{v}) = \left.\begin{array}{l} \dfrac{1}{\pi v_o^2} \quad |\mathbf{v}| \leqslant v_o \\[4mm] 0 \quad \text{elsewhere} \end{array}\right\}$$

‡ If α is the semi-angular spread of the incident beam, the reduced value $\hat{\alpha}$ is given by $\hat{\alpha} = (C_s\lambda^3)^{1/4}\,\alpha/\lambda$. In the above examples, $\hat{\alpha} = 0.07$ corresponds to $2\alpha = 1$ mrad and $\hat{\alpha} = 0.14$ to $2\alpha = 2$ mrad.

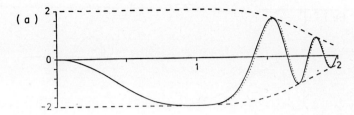

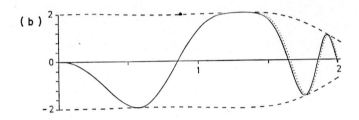

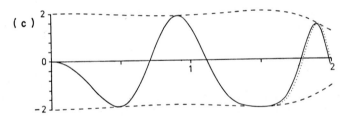

Fig. 3. Phase contrast transfer function for a Gaussian source distribution as a function of the reduced or generalized spatial frequency $\hat{p}$ ($\hat{p} = |\hat{\mathbf{p}}| = (C_s\lambda^3)^{1/4}\,|\mathbf{p}|$). The source half-width is $0{\cdot}07\;(C_s\lambda^3)^{-1/4}$. (a) $\hat{\varDelta} = 1$. (b) $\hat{\varDelta} = \sqrt{3}$. (c) $\hat{\varDelta} = \sqrt{5}$. (After Frank, 1973.)

we have

$$E(\mathbf{p}) = 2\,\frac{J_1\{v_o|\operatorname{grad}\gamma(\mathbf{p})|\}}{v_o|\operatorname{grad}\gamma(\mathbf{p})|}$$
$$= 2\,\operatorname{besinc}\{v_o\,\operatorname{grad}|\gamma(\mathbf{p})|\}.$$

For a Gaussian source, for which

$$s(\mathbf{v}) = \frac{1}{\pi v_o^2}\exp\left(-\frac{v^2}{v_o^2}\right)$$

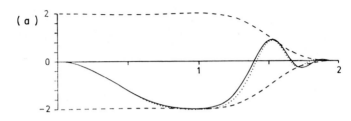

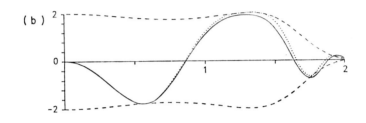

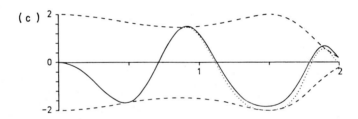

Fig. 4. Phase contrast transfer function for a Gaussian source distribution as a function of the reduced or generalized spatial frequency $\hat{p}$. The source half-width is $0\cdot14\,(C_s\lambda^3)^{-1/4}$. (a) $\hat{A} = 1$. (b) $\hat{A} = \sqrt{3}$. (c) $\hat{A} = \sqrt{5}$. (After Frank, 1973.)

we have

$$E(\mathbf{p}) = \exp\left\{-\frac{1}{4}\,v_o^2|\mathrm{grad}\,\gamma(\mathbf{p})|^2\right\}.$$

The approximation can be improved by retaining second order terms in the expansion of γ (Eqn 3.44); details of the derivation are to be found in Frank (1973), here we simply give the result. Both terms on the right-hand sides of Eqns (3.45) must be retained since the function which now plays the role of $\hat{E}(\mathbf{p})$ does not vanish even for symmetric sources. Instead, we now have

$$\hat{E}(\mathbf{p}) = \int \gamma_2(\mathbf{p},\mathbf{v})\,\tilde{\Gamma}_s(\mathbf{v})\cos\{\mathbf{v}.\mathrm{grad}\,\gamma(\mathbf{p})\}\,d\mathbf{v} \qquad (3.49)$$

where γ_2 is a function involving the second derivatives of $\gamma(\mathbf{p})$. In the absence of axial astigmatism,

$$\gamma_2(\mathbf{p}, \mathbf{v}) = \pi C_s \lambda^3 \{(\mathbf{p}\cdot\mathbf{p})(\mathbf{v}\cdot\mathbf{v}) + 2(\mathbf{p}\cdot\mathbf{v})^2\}. \tag{3.50}$$

For a Gaussian source, $\hat{E}(\mathbf{p})$ can be evaluated in closed form. When $e(\mathbf{p}) = \hat{E}(\mathbf{p})/E(\mathbf{p})$ is small, we can write Eqns (3.45) in the form

$$\begin{aligned} T_s(\mathbf{p}) &= -2E(\mathbf{p})\{\cos\gamma - e(\mathbf{p})\sin\gamma\} \\ &\approx -2E(\mathbf{p})\cos(\gamma + \epsilon) \\ T_\phi(\mathbf{p}) &= 2E(\mathbf{p})\{\sin\gamma + e(\mathbf{p})\cos\gamma\} \\ &\approx 2E(\mathbf{p})\sin(\gamma + \epsilon) \end{aligned} \tag{3.51}$$

with

$$\epsilon(\mathbf{p}) = \text{arc sin } e(\mathbf{p}). \tag{3.52}$$

We have thus obtained an envelope representation of the effect of finite source size that includes the small shifts of the zeros as well as the reduction of the amplitude. Frank (1973) points out that all these effects can be encompassed in a single modification to the coherent transfer theory, namely, replacement of $\gamma(\mathbf{p})$ as given by Eqn (1.9) by an effective wave aberration $\hat{\gamma}(\mathbf{p})$:

$$\hat{\gamma}(\mathbf{p}) = \gamma(\mathbf{p}) + \text{arc sin } e(\mathbf{p}) + i \ln \Gamma_S \left\{ \frac{1}{2\pi} |\text{grad } \gamma(\mathbf{p})| \right\}. \tag{3.53}$$

Some useful curves based on this analysis have been published by Bonhomme *et al.* (1973). These authors have computed $E(\mathbf{p})$ for a range of values of the semi-angular aperture of the illuminating beam and for two values of Δ, $\Delta = 50$ nm and $\Delta = 300$ nm. Their curves are reproduced in Fig. 5; Fig. 5(a) corresponds to a Hitachi HU IIC (Bonhomme and Laberrigue, 1969), Fig. 5(b) to the same microscope with saturated objective polepieces (Riecke, 1972), Fig. 5(c) to the Reims 400 kV superconducting microscope (Séverin *et al.*, 1971) and Fig. 5(d) to the Toulouse 3 MV microscope (Dupouy and Perrier, 1970). Figure 5(e) represents the value of spacing (d) in the specimen (defined by $d = \lambda/p$) for which the image contrast falls to $1/e$ as a function of defocusing. Some complementary experimental work is described in Beorchia and Bonhomme (1974).

2. *Finite energy spread*

The effect of finite energy spread and of voltage and current fluctuations has been fully analysed by Hanszen and Trepte (1970, 1971a), whose work we now describe. These authors show, by analysing the orders of magnitude of the various terms involved, that the variation of the wave aberration (γ)

with current and voltage fluctuations is adequately represented by the following expression:

$$\gamma = \frac{2\pi}{\lambda}\left\{\frac{1}{4}C_s\lambda^4(\mathbf{p}\cdot\mathbf{p})^2 - \frac{1}{2}\varDelta\lambda^2\mathbf{p}\cdot\mathbf{p}\right\} \tag{3.54a}$$

$$\delta\gamma = \pi C_c\lambda(\mathbf{p}\cdot\mathbf{p})\left\{2\frac{\delta J}{J} - \frac{\delta(V_o - V_a)}{V_o - V_a}\right\} \tag{3.54b}$$

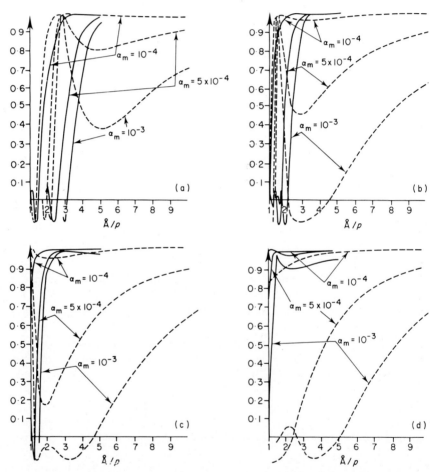

FIG. 5(a)–(d). The envelope of the phase contrast transfer function due to a finite source size for $\varDelta = 50$ nm (full line) and $\varDelta = 300$ nm (broken line) for various values of the semi-angle of the incident beam. (a) Hitachi HU IIC, $C_s = 1\cdot8$ nm at 100 kV. (b) Hitachi HU IIC with saturated objective, $C_s = 0\cdot5$ mm at 100 kV. (c) Reims superconducting microscope, $C_s = 1\cdot4$ mm at 400 kV. (d) Toulouse high-voltage microscope, $C_s = 6$ mm at 3 MV.

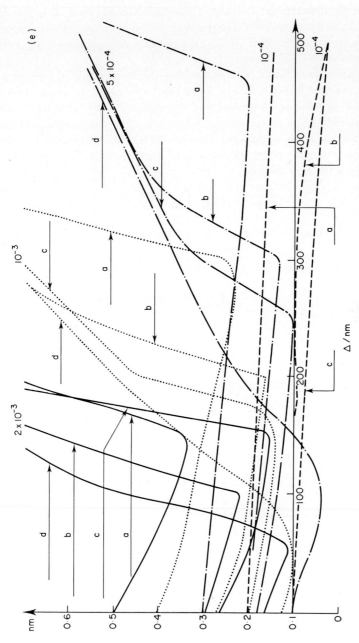

FIG. 5(e). These curves show the spacings that are transmitted by the microscope with an attenuation of 1/e as a function of defocus for the microscopes of (a)–(d). (After Bonhomme *et al*, 1973.)

in which C_c denotes the chromatic aberration coefficient, J is the lens current, V_o is the potential corresponding to the electron emission velocity and V_a is the anode voltage. (If V_c is the cathode voltage, then $|e(V_o - V_c)|$ is the electron emission energy.)

There are various ways of incorporating the fluctuations in current and voltage into the transfer theory formalism; probably the most straight-forward is to associate a probability distribution $H(v)$ with the current density at each point in the image, where v is some convenient parameter such as the variation in defocus. This probability distribution can include the effects of initial energy spread and of fluctuations in lens current and accelerating voltage. Writing

$$\frac{dj}{j} = H(v)\,dv, \quad \int H(v)\,dv = 1 \tag{3.55}$$

where j is the current density at the image, and recalling that for perfect coherence,

$$j(\mathbf{x}) \propto 1 - 2\int a\,\tilde{s}\cos\gamma\,\exp 2\pi i\,\mathbf{p}.\mathbf{x}\,d\mathbf{p}$$
$$+ 2\int a\,\tilde{\phi}\sin\gamma\,\exp 2\pi i\,\mathbf{p}.\mathbf{x}\,d\mathbf{p} \tag{3.56}$$

(Eqn 1.15), we have

$$dj/dv \propto H(v) - 2\int a\,\tilde{s}\cos\gamma(v)H(v)\,\exp 2\pi i\,\mathbf{p}.\mathbf{x}\,d\mathbf{p}$$
$$+ 2\int a\,\tilde{\phi}\sin\gamma(v)H(v)\,\exp 2\pi i\,\mathbf{p}.\mathbf{x}\,d\mathbf{p}. \tag{3.57}$$

Integrating over v and rearranging, we have

$$j \propto 1 - 2\int a\,\tilde{s}\,\{\int \cos\gamma(v)H(v)\,dv\}\exp 2\pi i\,\mathbf{p}.\mathbf{x}\,d\mathbf{p}$$
$$+ 2\int a\,\tilde{\phi}\,\{\int \sin\gamma(v)H(v)\,dv\}\exp 2\pi i\,\mathbf{p}.\mathbf{x}\,d\mathbf{p} \tag{3.58}$$

and we consider the form of

$$T_s(\mathbf{p}) = -2\int \cos\gamma(\mathbf{p}, v)H(v)\,dv$$
$$T_\phi(\mathbf{p}) = 2\int \sin\gamma(\mathbf{p}, v)H(v)\,dv \tag{3.59}$$

when v is the variation in defocus. Writing $\varDelta = \varDelta_o + \delta$ in Eqn (3.54a), we have

$$T_s(\mathbf{p}) = -2\cos\gamma(\mathbf{p})\int H(\delta)\cos(\pi\lambda\delta p^2)\,d\delta$$
$$-2\sin\gamma(\mathbf{p})\int H(\delta)\sin(\pi\lambda\delta p^2)\,d\delta \tag{3.60}$$

$$T_\phi(\mathbf{p}) = 2\sin\gamma(\mathbf{p})\int H(\delta)\cos(\pi\lambda\delta p^2)\,d\delta$$
$$-2\cos\gamma(\mathbf{p})\int H(\delta)\sin(\pi\lambda\delta p^2)\,d\delta \tag{3.61}$$

where $\gamma(p)$ denotes the value of γ at $\varDelta_o$. If $H(\delta)$ is even, the two integrals in $H(\delta) \sin (\pi\delta\lambda p^2)$ vanish so that the functions T_s and T_ϕ simplify to

$$T_s(\mathbf{p}) = -2 \cos \gamma(\mathbf{p}) \int H(\delta) \cos (\pi\delta\lambda p^2)\, d\delta$$
$$T_\phi(\mathbf{p}) = 2 \sin \gamma(\mathbf{p}) \int H(\delta) \cos (\pi\delta\lambda p^2)\, d\delta. \tag{3.62}$$

Denoting the integrals over δ as follows:

$$H_c(\lambda p^2) = \int H(\delta) \cos (\pi\delta\lambda p^2)\, d\delta \tag{3.63}$$

we see that the familiar phase and amplitude transfer functions, B_s and B_ϕ (Eqns 1.17 and 1.18) are modulated by the function $H_c(\lambda p^2)$:

$$T_s(\mathbf{p}) = H_c(\lambda p^2) B_s(\mathbf{p}) \tag{3.64}$$
$$T_\phi(\mathbf{p}) = H_c(\lambda p^2) B_\phi(\mathbf{p}). \tag{3.65}$$

The form of H_c can easily be calculated for typical forms of $H(\delta)$. The following expressions are modified forms of those given by Hanszen and Trepte (1971a).

For

$$H(\delta) = \begin{cases} 1/2 & \delta = \pm\delta_o \\ 0 & \delta \neq \pm\delta_o \end{cases}$$
$$H_c(\lambda p^2) = \cos (\pi\delta_o\lambda p^2). \tag{3.66}$$

This corresponds to an abrupt change in $\varDelta$ for a limited time.

For

$$H(\delta) = \begin{cases} \dfrac{1}{\pi\delta_o(1 - \delta^2/\delta_o^2)^{1/2}} & |\delta| < \delta_o \\ 0 & |\delta| \geqslant \delta_o \end{cases}$$
$$H_c(\lambda p^2) = J_o(\pi\delta_o\lambda p^2). \tag{3.67}$$

This corresponds to a sinusoidal variation of $\varDelta$ with time.

For

$$H(\delta) = \begin{cases} 1/(2\delta_o) & |\delta| \leqslant \delta_o \\ 0 & |\delta| > \delta_o \end{cases}$$
$$H_c(\lambda p^2) = \frac{\sin (\pi\lambda\delta_o p^2)}{\pi\lambda\delta_o p^2} = \text{sinc} (\pi\lambda\delta_o p^2). \tag{3.68}$$

This corresponds to a linear variation of $\varDelta$ with time.

For

$$H(\delta) = \frac{1}{2\pi^{1/2}\delta_o} \exp \left(-\frac{\delta^2}{4\delta_o^2}\right)$$
$$H_c(\lambda p^2) = \exp \{-(\pi\delta_o\lambda p^2)^2\}. \tag{3.69}$$

The effect of this last case, in which $H(\delta)$ is a Gaussian function of δ, is illustrated in Fig. 6.

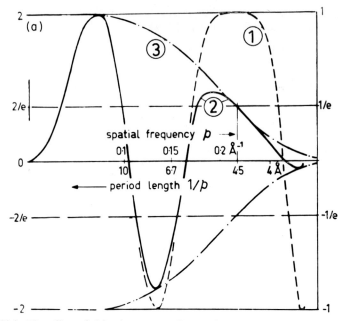

FIG. 6(a). The effect of objective current fluctuations on the phase contrast transfer function. The current fluctuations have a Gaussian distribution with half-width $2\delta I/I = 2\cdot9 \times 10^{-5}$. $\Delta = 272$ nm, $C_s = 4$ mm and $C_c = 2\cdot1$ mm at 100 kV. Curve 3 modulates 1 to give 2.

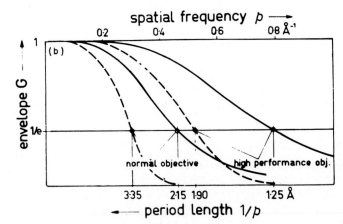

FIG. 6(b). The envelope as a function of spatial frequency for a normal objective ($C_c = 2\cdot1$ mm) and a high-performance objective ($C_c = 0\cdot7$ mm). The consequences of the Boersch effect (half-width $1\cdot5$ eV: broken curve) and of the Maxwellian source distribution ($0\cdot61$ eV: full curve) are illustrated.

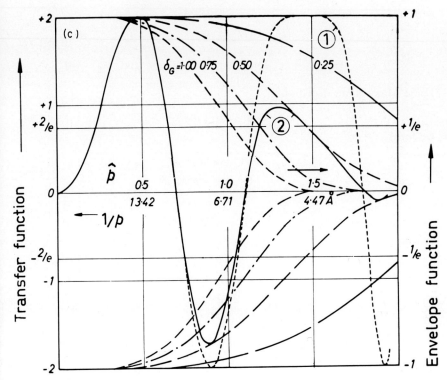

FIG. 6(c). The ideal phase contrast transfer function (dotted curve) and the attenuated form due to a Gaussian distribution, in reduced and normal notation. $\hat{\Delta} = \sqrt{5}$. Envelope functions corresponding to various half-widths are shown.

((a) and (b) After Hanszen and Trepte, 1970; (c) after Hanszen and Trepte, 1971a.)

If the distribution $H(\delta)$ is not symmetric, which is the case if we consider a Maxwellian distribution of electron velocities, we must retain both terms of Eqns (3.60) and (3.61); writing

$$H_s(\lambda p^2) = \int H(\delta) \sin (\pi\lambda\delta p^2) \, \mathrm{d}\delta \tag{3.70}$$

we now have

$$\begin{aligned} T_s(\mathbf{p}) &= H_c(\lambda p^2)B_s(\mathbf{p}) - H_s(\lambda p^2)B_\phi(\mathbf{p}) \\ T_\phi(\mathbf{p}) &= H_c(\lambda p^2)B_\phi(\mathbf{p}) + H_s(\lambda p^2)B_s(\mathbf{p}) \end{aligned} \tag{3.71}$$

or

$$\begin{aligned} T_s(\mathbf{p}) &= -2 H_t \cos (\gamma - \theta) \\ T_\phi(\mathbf{p}) &= 2 H_t \sin (\gamma - \theta) \end{aligned} \tag{3.72}$$

with

$$H_t = (H_c^2 + H_s^2)^{1/2} \qquad \text{(a)}$$

$$\tan \theta = \frac{H_s}{H_c}. \qquad \text{(b)}$$

(3.73)

For a Maxwellian distribution,

$$H(\delta) = a^2 \delta \exp(-a\delta) \qquad (3.74)$$

we find

$$H_c = \frac{1 - \pi^2 \lambda^2 p^4 / a^2}{(1 + \pi^2 \lambda^2 p^4 / a^2)^2} \qquad (3.75)$$

$$H_s = \frac{2\pi \lambda p^2 / a}{(1 + \pi^2 \lambda^2 p^4 / a^2)^2} \qquad (3.76)$$

so that

$$H_t = \frac{1}{1 + \pi^2 \lambda^2 p^4 / a^2} \qquad \text{(a)}$$

$$\tan \theta = \frac{2\pi \lambda p^2 a}{a^2 - \pi^2 \lambda^2 p^4}. \qquad \text{(b)}$$

(3.77)

In addition to the attenuation associated with the envelope function, there is now a small phase shift; the zeros of the coherent transfer functions are slightly displaced.

Some experimental studies of the effects of temporal partial coherence of various kinds are described in Beorchia and Bonhomme (1974).

A series of useful curves illustrating the effect of both spatial incoherence and temporal partial coherence on the image of a weakly scattering specimen has been computed by Misell (1973c); these are to be compared with those of Misell (1973b) for coherent illumination and elastic scattering and with those of Misell and Atkins (1973) for coherent illumination and inelastic scattering. These curves show the form of the image contrast and image intensity distributions corresponding to a particular object structure for spatially incoherent illumination and also for finite beam energy spread; they thus provide a convenient picture in real space of the effect of these illumination conditions on the image. The corresponding transfer functions are also plotted and the results for temporal partial coherence agree in all essentials with the earlier findings of Hanszen and Trepte (1970, 1971a); Misell's curves usefully complement the latter, their emphasis being on contrast variations at the image.

The combined effect of energy spread and the atomic scattering are examined by Vorob'ev and Zhukov (1974).

3. The envelope representation and imaging efficiency

The possibility of representing the effect of partially coherent illumination by means of envelope functions, which modulate the familiar coherent transfer functions, has produced a practical proposal for estimating the source size and the energy spread in the electron microscope. This will be described in detail in Section IVB. Here, after drawing attention to a problem that has only very recently been studied, we describe a very convenient representation of the effects of partial coherence; based on a suggestion of Linfoot, this approach has been developed in detail by Frank.

The problem concerns the legitimacy of multiplying the envelope functions corresponding to spatial and temporal partial coherence to obtain the combined effect of both; doubts about this product representation were first mentioned by Frank (1976a), who states that the problem was drawn to his attention by S. C. McFarlane. The product representation for finite source size depends upon Eqn (3.44); if we wish to consider both finite source size and energy spread simultaneously, we write

$$T_\phi(\mathbf{p}) = 2 \iint \tilde{\varGamma}_S(\mathbf{v}) \sin \{\gamma(\mathbf{p} + \mathbf{v}, \varDelta_o + \delta)$$
$$- \gamma(\mathbf{v}, \varDelta_o + \delta)\} \, d\mathbf{v} \, H(\delta) \, d\delta \qquad (3.78)$$

in which $H(\delta)$ defines the defocus variation as in the previous section (Eqn 3.55). Writing

$$\gamma(\mathbf{p} + \mathbf{v}, \varDelta_o + \delta) = \gamma(\mathbf{p}, \varDelta_o) + \mathbf{v}.\mathrm{grad}\,\gamma + \delta \frac{\partial \gamma}{\partial \delta}$$
$$+ \frac{1}{2} v^2 \left(\frac{\partial^2 \gamma}{\partial p^2} + \cdots \right) + \mathbf{v}.\left(\frac{\partial^2 \gamma}{\partial p \partial \delta}, \frac{\partial^2 \gamma}{\partial q \partial \delta} \right) \delta \qquad (3.79)$$

and neglecting the small term in v^2, the expression for $T_\phi(\mathbf{p})$ becomes

$$T_\phi(\mathbf{p}) = 2 \sin \gamma(\mathbf{p}, \varDelta_o) \iint \cos \left(\delta \frac{\partial \gamma}{\partial \delta} \right) \cos \left\{ \mathbf{v}.\left(\mathrm{grad}\,\gamma + \delta \frac{\partial^2 \gamma}{\partial \mathbf{p} \partial \delta} \right) \right\}$$
$$\times \tilde{\varGamma}_S(\mathbf{v}) \, d\mathbf{v} \, H(\delta) \, d\delta$$
$$+ 2 \cos \gamma (\mathbf{p}, \varDelta_o) \iint \sin \left(\delta \frac{\partial \gamma}{\partial \delta} \right) \cos \left\{ \mathbf{v}.\left(\mathrm{grad}\,\gamma + \delta \frac{\partial^2 \gamma}{\partial \mathbf{p} \partial \delta} \right) \right\}$$
$$\times \tilde{\varGamma}_S(\mathbf{v}) \, d\mathbf{v} \, H(\delta) \, d\delta$$

or

$$T_\phi(\mathbf{p}) = B_\phi(\mathbf{p})E_1(\mathbf{p}) - B_s(\mathbf{p})E_2(\mathbf{p})$$
$$E_2^1(\mathbf{p}) = \iint \tilde{\varGamma}_S(\mathbf{v}) \, {\cos \atop \sin} \left(\delta \frac{\partial \gamma}{\partial \delta} \right) \cos \left\{ \mathbf{v}.\left(\mathrm{grad}\,\gamma + \delta \frac{\partial^2 \gamma}{\partial \mathbf{p} \partial \delta} \right) \right\} H(\delta) \, d\mathbf{v} \, d\delta.$$
$$(3.80)$$

There can thus be a phase shift, even in the first approximation, but the magnitude of this effect has only recently been investigated.

A careful analysis of the magnitude of the cross-term, that is, the departure from a simple envelope representation, has now been made by Wade and Frank (1977). For the case of axial illumination, considered above, they find that the effect of the cross-term is normally negligible but that for tilted illumination it could be important. A very detailed exploration of the possible effect of this cross-term has also been made by McFarlane (1977/8) who comes to very similar conclusions. The legitimacy of using an envelope representation has been investigated experimentally by Saxton (1977) and Anstis et al. (1977/8). Saxton shows that if an envelope representation is adopted, a very close match indeed can be found between the measured intensity distribution in the spatial frequency spectrum of a thin amorphous specimen and that predicted by theory. Anstis et al. have investigated the combined effect of spatial and temporal coherence; their preliminary conclusion is that, although there are ranges of values of the various para-meters for which the effect of the cross-term could become important, it can usually be disregarded. Nevertheless, since their results show that in the case in question (thin crystals of a niobium oxide, $Nb_{12}O_{29}$), crystal thick-ness has a perceptible effect even for specimens a few nanometres thick, their findings may rather corroborate the remarks of Fertig and Rose (1977a) concerning the effects to be expected if different scatterers in the specimen lie in different defocus planes.

The product representation permits us to regard a partially coherent system as a pair of cascaded systems, the first coherent, the second intro-ducing some blurring as a result of partial coherence. Since the resolution and contrast are poorer in partially coherent conditions, we might regard some of the information-carrying electrons as wasted. This is explained very clearly by Frank (1975a): "We may say that in order to achieve the same signal-to-noise ratio (defined as the respective variances) in the partially coherent as in the coherent image, one has to use a higher electron exposure. The information-carrying capacity per scattered electron is thus reduced." Frank perceived (Frank, 1975a; Beer et al., 1975) that a convenient set of measures of this reduction are Linfoot's image quality criteria (Linfoot, 1956, 1957, 1960, 1964; O'Neill, 1963; Franke, 1966; Frieden, 1966; Röhler, 1967; Frank et al., 1970). One of these is the "dissimilarity", K, between input and output, which for a noise-like specimen becomes

$$K = \frac{\int |1 - E(\mathbf{p})|^2 \, d\mathbf{p}}{\int d\mathbf{p}} \tag{3.81}$$

where $E(\mathbf{p})$ is the envelope function of Eqn (3.48) and the integrals are taken over the aperture. A second criterion is the "structural resolving power", Ξ, which is useful in that it gives a measure of the signal-to-noise ratio in the image for given object and receiver and given noise variance. With the definition

$$\Xi = \frac{\int |E(\mathbf{p})|^2 \, d\mathbf{p}}{\int d\mathbf{p}} \qquad (3.82)$$

we can show that the signal-to-noise ratio will remain constant as the source size is increased if the condition

$$n^2 \, \Xi = 1 \qquad (3.83)$$

is satisfied, where n is the corresponding increase in exposure to compensate for the "wasted" electrons. If the signal-to-noise ratio is limited not by the photographic emulsion but by the electron statistics—at high magnification and in minimum exposure conditions, for example—the condition becomes

$$n^3 \, \Xi = 1. \qquad (3.84)$$

We note in passing that Ξ had been studied earlier by Schade (1952), who used the term "equivalent pass band", and by Fellgett (1953).

Frank (1975a) has computed the dissimilarity K and the structural resolving power Ξ as a function of source size for various values of defocus, together with the "fidelity" $\Phi = 1 - K$ and the "correlation quality" $\Psi = -(\Phi + \Xi)/2$; the latter is identical with the Strehl intensity. Figures 7(a)–(c) show these quantities as a function of the generalized source size $\hat{v}_o$ for a Gaussian source

$$\tilde{\Gamma}_s(\mathbf{v}) = \frac{1}{\pi v_o^2} \exp\left(-\frac{v^2}{v_o^2}\right) \qquad (3.85)$$

with

$$\hat{v}_o = (C_s\lambda^3)^{1/4} v_o. \qquad (3.86)$$

The aperture extends to $p_o = 2/(C_s\lambda^3)^{1/4}$ and the generalized defocus values $\hat{\Delta} = 1, \sqrt{3}, \sqrt{5}$ and $\sqrt{7}$ are studied, where $\hat{\Delta} = \Delta/(C_s\lambda)^{1/2}$ as in Eqn (1.11).

As we should expect, there is a range of small source sizes in which the effect of finite source size is scarcely discernible. By fixing the objective aperture size, we have introduced a bias in favour of high defocus values; if the optimum aperture for the Scherzer focus ($\hat{\Delta} = 1$) had been used, this value would have been favoured, as we can see from Figs 7(d) and (e), in which Ξ is plotted as a function of the generalized aperture, $\hat{p}_o = p(C_s\lambda^3)^{1/4}$ for two values of source size.

These curves can be used in practice to establish the coherence necessary to obtain a given resolution in the electron microscope by adopting some convention as to the acceptable loss of fidelity in the image. A practical application is described in Frank et al. (1974).

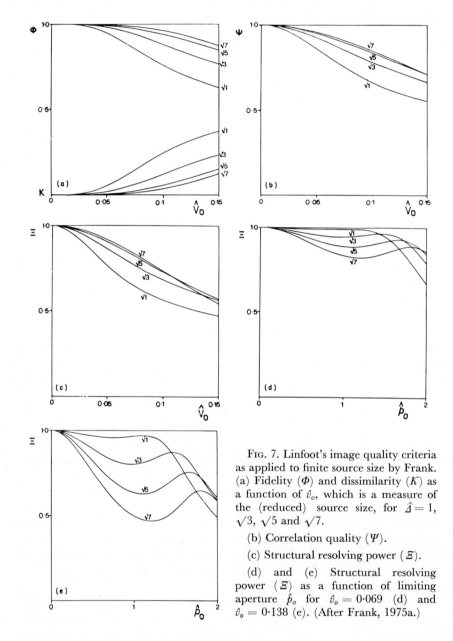

Fig. 7. Linfoot's image quality criteria as applied to finite source size by Frank.
(a) Fidelity (Φ) and dissimilarity (K) as a function of $\hat{v}_o$, which is a measure of the (reduced) source size, for $\hat{\Delta} = 1$, $\sqrt{3}$, $\sqrt{5}$ and $\sqrt{7}$.

(b) Correlation quality (Ψ).

(c) Structural resolving power (Ξ).

(d) and (e) Structural resolving power (Ξ) as a function of limiting aperture $\hat{p}_o$ for $\hat{v}_o = 0.069$ (d) and $\hat{v}_o = 0.138$ (e). (After Frank, 1975a.)

IV. Instrumental Aspects of Coherence

We have attempted to relieve the austerity of the foregoing theoretical framework with practical examples wherever possible; in the present section, we concentrate on the practical implications of the theory, first discussing the illumination system and collector geometry in conventional (fixed-beam) and scanning transmission electron microscopes, then describing various methods of measuring source coherence. We also draw attention to a recent method of measuring coherence for thermal light, which may be applicable to electron sources.

A. Coherence and Illumination

1. Conventional illumination systems

In light optics, two modes of illumination are commonly used in microscopy and the relation between the condenser aperture and the coherence at the specimen has been thoroughly studied for both situations. We are thus in a position to answer the most important question associated with illumination systems: Over what area of the specimen can we regard the illumination as coherent, to a good approximation?

The modes that have been examined in detail for light microscopy are known as Köhler and critical illumination; the essential difference is that in critical illumination, the effective source is conjugate to the specimen plane while in Köhler's method, the source is conjugate to the image focal plane of the (final) condenser lens so that rays from each source point fall on the specimen as a parallel beam. The illumination conditions in commercial electron microscopes are not always easy to ascertain and in some cases probably fall between these two modes; in principle, however, the condenser lenses are excited to give essentially critical illumination so that the illuminated area is determined by the source size and the coherence is determined by the angular spread of rays from each source point and hence by that of the rays arriving at each point on the specimen. Since the degree of coherence is the same for the two illumination modes, calculations based on critical conditions should be a very adequate approximation.

For a uniform disc source, we saw in Section II that points up to about $\lambda/2\pi \sin \alpha$ apart will be illuminated coherently to a good approximation, where 2α is the spread of angles at the object plane; for 100 kV electrons ($\lambda = 3\cdot7$ pm), this distance reaches 100 nm for $\alpha \approx 0\cdot06$ mrad or 60 nm for 10 μrad. The coherence at the specimen is often expressed not in terms of this coherently illuminated area, however, but as the *coherence ratio* or *coherence parameter*, m. This quantity is the ratio of the angular spread of the illuminating beam, a, to that emerging from the specimen at the objective, a_0:

$$m = a/a_0. \tag{4.1}$$

This parameter is relevant because the coherently illuminated patch at the object must be at least as large as the Airy disc, referred of course to the object plane, for coherent image formation:

$$\frac{\lambda}{2\pi \sin a} \gtrsim \frac{0\cdot 6 \, \lambda}{a_0} \tag{4.2}$$

or

$$m = a/a_0 \lesssim 0\cdot 26. \tag{4.3}$$

Thus for values of m much less than $0\cdot 26$, an area many times the Airy disc will be illuminated coherently while if $m \gtrsim 1$, the specimen will be illuminated incoherently.

It is important to consider both the size of the coherently illuminated area and the coherence parameter m not only because there is no point in striving for a higher degree of coherence in the incident beam than is necessary but also because both must be borne in mind when discussing the high resolution scanning transmission electron microscope (STEM). In the latter, a demagnified image of a very bright source is formed in the specimen plane; by scanning this source across the specimen, an image is built up sequentially in the detector plane. Reciprocity arguments permit us to treat the *optical* elements of the STEM as the inverse of those of a conventional electron microscope (Crewe, 1970; Crewe and Wall, 1970; Zeitler and Thomson, 1970a, b; Thomson and Zeitler, 1970; Thomson, 1973, 1975; Engel, 1974; Crewe *et al.*, 1975; Zeitler, 1976; see also Cowley, 1969, 1975c; Barnett, 1973), though great care must be taken to ensure that systems being analysed by such arguments are strictly reciprocal (see Howie, 1972, for example).

We have seen that in the conventional (fixed-beam) instrument, with critical illumination, the area that can be regarded as coherently illuminated in the specimen plane is determined by the angular spread of the illuminating beam and that the ratio of this angle to the objective aperture is a useful parameter, in that it relates this area to the classical limit of resolution. In the STEM, therefore, we expect the geometry and size of the collector to be important, since the latter is the analogue of the electron source in conventional instruments, and we may expect the ratio of the angular apertures of the collector and probe-forming lens to be useful likewise.

The area irradiated by the electron probe will be coherently illuminated if the product of the probe radius (r) and semi-angular aperture of the incident beam (a) is less than $\lambda/2\pi$; for 100 kV electrons, therefore, the condition is $ar \lesssim 0.6$ pm which can only be satisfied with a reasonable probe current for sources of very high brightness (β), since the probe current is given by $\pi^2\beta(ar)^2$. The maximum current that can be concentrated into a coherent probe is therefore given by $\beta\lambda^2/4$ (Barnett, 1974b). For $\lambda = 4$ pm, the current reaches 40 pA for $\beta = 10^9$ A cm^{-2} sr^{-1}, which is a reasonable brightness for a field emission or laser-heated (van der Mast, 1975) source; if we take $\beta = 10^5$ A cm^{-2} sr^{-1}, however, which is a typical value for a thermionic cathode, the current is only 4×10^{-4} pA (0.4 fA). Some effects to be expected if the probe is not coherent are described by Zeitler and Thomson (1970b); an interesting comment on the probe current distribution has been made by Hardy (1974). A detailed study of the effect of imperfect probe coherence on the transfer function has been made by Burge and Dainty (1976), who suspected that, in some operating conditions, their STEM (a prototype VG HB5) was a borderline case.

In order to study the formation of the STEM image and to decide whether the image formation is coherent, incoherent or partially coherent, we must consider the detector geometry. If the probe is centred on the point ξ in the object plane at some moment during the scan, the wave emerging from the specimen will be of the form

$$\psi(\mathbf{x}_o; \xi) = c\sigma(\mathbf{x}_o)K(\xi - \mathbf{x}_o) \tag{4.4}$$

where σ denotes the specimen transparency and K is the point-spread function of the probe-forming lens (Zeitler and Thomson, 1970a; Lenz, 1973). The factor c represents both a constant and a quadratic phase term. Neglecting scaling factors, in order to emphasize the essential steps in the reasoning, the wave function at the detector plane distant R from the specimen will be given by the Fourier transform of $\psi(\mathbf{x}_o; \xi)$ with respect to $\mathbf{x}_o$:

$$\psi_d(\mathbf{x}_d; \xi) \propto \int \sigma(\mathbf{x}_o)K(\xi - \mathbf{x}_o) \exp(-2\pi i\, \mathbf{x}_d.\mathbf{x}_o/\lambda R)\, d\mathbf{x}_o. \tag{4.5}$$

Suppose now that the detector collects electrons over a zone defined by a function $D(\mathbf{x}_d)$. The current density per picture element will therefore be given by

$$j(\xi) \propto \int |\psi_d(\mathbf{x}_d; \xi)|^2 D(\mathbf{x}_d)\, d\mathbf{x}_d \tag{4.6}$$

or

$$j(\xi) \propto \int \sigma(\mathbf{x}_o)\sigma^*(\bar{\mathbf{x}}_o)K(\xi - \mathbf{x}_o)K^*(\xi - \bar{\mathbf{x}}_o)$$
$$\exp\{-2\pi i\, \mathbf{x}_d.(\mathbf{x}_o - \bar{\mathbf{x}}_o)/\lambda R\}D(\mathbf{x}_d)\, d\mathbf{x}_o\, d\bar{\mathbf{x}}_o\, d\mathbf{x}_d. \tag{4.7a}$$

Writing

$$\tilde{D}\left(\frac{\mathbf{x}_o - \bar{\mathbf{x}}_o}{\lambda R}\right) = \int D(\mathbf{x}_d) \exp\left(-2\pi i \mathbf{x}_d.\frac{\mathbf{x}_o - \bar{\mathbf{x}}_o}{\lambda R}\right) d\mathbf{x}_d \tag{4.8}$$

Eqn (4.7a) becomes

$$j(\xi) \propto \int \sigma(\mathbf{x}_o)\sigma^*(\bar{\mathbf{x}}_o)K(\xi - \mathbf{x}_o)K^*(\xi - \bar{\mathbf{x}}_o)\tilde{D}\left(\frac{\mathbf{x}_o - \bar{\mathbf{x}}_o}{\lambda R}\right) d\bar{\mathbf{x}}_o \, d\mathbf{x}_o. \qquad (4.7b)$$

In the extreme case, uncommon in practice, of a small detector on the axis, $D(\mathbf{x}_d)$ may be regarded as a delta function, so that

$$j(\xi) \propto |\int \sigma(\mathbf{x}_o)K(\xi - \mathbf{x}_o) \, d\mathbf{x}_o|^2. \qquad (4.9a)$$

This corresponds to coherent illumination in the fixed-beam transmission microscope, as we should expect since a very small collector is the STEM analogue of a very small source. If, at the other extreme, we consider a large detector, we may write $D(\mathbf{x}_d) = 1$ for all $\mathbf{x}_d$ and so

$$j(\xi) \propto \int |\sigma(\mathbf{x}_o)|^2|K(\xi - \mathbf{x}_o)|^2 \, d\mathbf{x}_o. \qquad (4.9b)$$

This corresponds to the rare case of incoherent illumination in the conventional instrument; the coherence parameter m is then large.

In practice, however, annular detectors are used, with a central opening through which the unscattered beam and most of the inelastically scattered electrons pass. We can analyse this case by writing

$$\sigma(\mathbf{x}_o) = 1 + \sigma_s(\mathbf{x}_o) \qquad (4.10)$$

so that

$$j(\xi) \propto \int K(\xi - \mathbf{x}_o)K^*(\xi - \bar{\mathbf{x}}_o)\exp\{-2\pi i\,\mathbf{x}_d\cdot(\mathbf{x}_o - \bar{\mathbf{x}}_o)/\lambda R\}D(\mathbf{x}_d)\,d\mathbf{x}_d\,d\mathbf{x}_o\,d\bar{\mathbf{x}}_o$$
$$+\int\{\sigma_s(\mathbf{x}_o)+\sigma_s^*(\bar{\mathbf{x}}_o)\}K(\xi - \mathbf{x}_o)K^*(\xi - \bar{\mathbf{x}}_o)\exp\{-2\pi i\,\mathbf{x}_d\cdot(\mathbf{x}_o - \bar{\mathbf{x}}_o)/\lambda R\}$$
$$\times D(\mathbf{x}_d)\,d\mathbf{x}_d\,d\mathbf{x}_o\,d\bar{\mathbf{x}}_o$$
$$+\int \sigma_s(\mathbf{x}_o)\sigma_s^*(\bar{\mathbf{x}}_o)K(\xi - \mathbf{x}_o)K^*(\xi - \bar{\mathbf{x}}_o)\exp\{-2\pi i\,\mathbf{x}_d\cdot(\mathbf{x}_o - \bar{\mathbf{x}}_o)/\lambda R\}$$
$$\times D(\mathbf{x}_d)\,d\mathbf{x}_d\,d\mathbf{x}_o\,d\bar{\mathbf{x}}_o. \qquad (4.11)$$

The first term vanishes, since it represents the unscattered beam which falls on a region where $D(\mathbf{x}_d) = 0$. The second and third terms are linear and quadratic respectively in σ_s. Writing $D(\mathbf{x}_d) = 1$ everywhere in these two terms, we have

$$j(\xi) \propto \int\{\sigma_s(\mathbf{x}_o)+\sigma_s^*(\mathbf{x}_o)\}|K(\xi - \mathbf{x}_o)|^2 \, d\mathbf{x}_o + \int |\sigma_s(\mathbf{x}_o)|^2|K(\xi - \mathbf{x}_o)|^2 \, d\mathbf{x}_o \qquad (4.12)$$

or

$$j(\xi) \propto \int |K(\xi - \mathbf{x}_o)|^2\{2\,\mathrm{Re}\,\sigma_s(\mathbf{x}_o)+|\sigma_s(\mathbf{x}_o)|^2\} \, d\mathbf{x}_o. \qquad (4.13)$$

The quadratic term is identical with that derived by Misell et al. (1974); the importance of the linear term has been underlined by Cowley (1975a, 1976b).

If the specimen is a weak phase object, then Re $\sigma_s = 0$; the image represents $(\text{Im } \sigma_s)^2$ directly, modulated of course by $|K|^2$. This is the justification for Stroke's optical filtering of STEM images (Stroke *et al.*, 1971a, b, 1977; Stroke and Halioua, 1972). For more general types of specimen, the relation between the image and the phase and amplitude parts of σ_s is considerably less direct. This simple treatment is adequate to show that STEM image formation can be the counterpart of coherent or incoherent illumination in the conventional microscope, or of course of any intermediate situation (cf. Barnett, 1974a). Much more thorough analyses of STEM image formation, with particular attention to the specimen and to the exact detector geometry, have been published by Rose (1974a, b, 1975, 1977; Rose and Fertig, 1976). A simple modification of the detector that permits us to separate the phase and amplitude components of the complex transparency of a weakly scattering specimen is described by Dekkers and de Lang (1974, 1977; Dekkers *et al.*, 1976). See also Beck (1977). For criticism of the explanation of the STEM image filtering of Stroke's group given by the authors (e.g. Stroke *et al.*, 1977), see Ade (1977).

We now turn to the more general situation in which the area covered by the probe at each instant need not be perfectly coherently illuminated (Burge and Dainty, 1976). The mutual coherence of the (incoherent) effective source is of the form

$$\Gamma(\mathbf{x}_s, \bar{\mathbf{x}}_s) = \delta(\mathbf{x}_s - \bar{\mathbf{x}}_s)S(\mathbf{x}_s).$$

Propagating the mutual intensity to the exit pupil (coordinates $\mathbf{x}_a$) of the probe-forming lens and introducing the aperture function of the latter, we find

$$\Gamma(\mathbf{x}_a, \bar{\mathbf{x}}_a) = \Gamma_s(\mathbf{x}_a - \bar{\mathbf{x}}_a)A(\mathbf{x}_a)A^*(\bar{\mathbf{x}}_a)$$

where

$$\Gamma_s(\mathbf{x}_a - \bar{\mathbf{x}}_a) = \int S(\mathbf{x}_s) \exp\left\{-\frac{2\pi i\, \mathbf{x}_s}{\lambda R'} \cdot (\mathbf{x}_a - \bar{\mathbf{x}}_a)\right\} d\mathbf{x}_s$$

and R' is the distance between effective source and probe-forming lens.

At the probe, therefore, we have

$$\Gamma(\mathbf{x}_o, \bar{\mathbf{x}}_o) = \int\int \Gamma_s(\mathbf{x}_a - \bar{\mathbf{x}}_a)A(\mathbf{x}_a)A^*(\bar{\mathbf{x}}_a) \exp\left\{\frac{2\pi i}{\lambda f}(\mathbf{x}_o.\mathbf{x}_a - \bar{\mathbf{x}}_o.\bar{\mathbf{x}}_a)\right\} d\mathbf{x}_a\, d\bar{\mathbf{x}}_a$$

and we note that the intensity $j(\mathbf{x}_o)$ is given by

$$j(\mathbf{x}_o) = \Gamma(\mathbf{x}_o, \mathbf{x}_o)$$

$$= \int\int \Gamma_s(\mathbf{x}_a - \bar{\mathbf{x}}_a)A(\mathbf{x}_a)A^*(\bar{\mathbf{x}}_a) \exp\left\{\frac{2\pi i\, \mathbf{x}_o}{\lambda f} \cdot (\mathbf{x}_a - \bar{\mathbf{x}}_a)\right\} d\mathbf{x}_a\, d\bar{\mathbf{x}}_a$$

$$= \int \left[\int A(\mathbf{x}_a) \exp \left\{ \frac{2\pi i}{\lambda f} \, \mathbf{x}_a \cdot \left(\mathbf{x}_o - \frac{f}{R'} \, \mathbf{x}_s \right) \right\} d\mathbf{x}_a \right]$$

$$\times \left[\int A^*(\bar{\mathbf{x}}_a) \exp \left\{ - \frac{2\pi i}{\lambda f} \, \bar{\mathbf{x}}_a \cdot \left(\mathbf{x}_o - \frac{f}{R'} \, \mathbf{x}_s \right) \right\} d\bar{\mathbf{x}}_a \right] S(\mathbf{x}_s) \, d\mathbf{x}_s.$$

As expected, therefore, the intensity at the probe is equal to that of the source, appropriately scaled, convolved with the incoherent point-spread function of the probe-forming lens.

The mutual intensity beyond the specimen when the probe is centred on the point $\boldsymbol{\xi}$ in the specimen plane is of the form $\Gamma(\boldsymbol{\xi} - \mathbf{x}_o, \boldsymbol{\xi} - \bar{\mathbf{x}}_o) \, \sigma(\mathbf{x}_o) \sigma^*(\bar{\mathbf{x}}_o)$. In the detector plane (suffix d), therefore, which is conjugate to the exit pupil (whereas the specimen is conjugate to the source), Γ is given by

$$\Gamma(\mathbf{x}_d, \bar{\mathbf{x}}_d; \boldsymbol{\xi}) = \int \int \Gamma(\boldsymbol{\xi} - \mathbf{x}_o, \boldsymbol{\xi} - \bar{\mathbf{x}}_o)$$

$$\times \sigma(\mathbf{x}_o)\sigma^*(\bar{\mathbf{x}}_o) \exp \left\{ - \frac{2\pi i}{\lambda R} (\mathbf{x}_o . \mathbf{x}_d - \bar{\mathbf{x}}_o . \bar{\mathbf{x}}_d) \right\} d\mathbf{x}_o \, d\bar{\mathbf{x}}_o$$

(where R is the distance between specimen and detector). Integrating over the detector, $D(\mathbf{x}_d)$, as in Eqn (4.6), we obtain the image intensity, $j(\boldsymbol{\xi})$:

$$j(\boldsymbol{\xi}) = \int \Gamma(\mathbf{x}_d, \mathbf{x}_d; \boldsymbol{\xi}) D(\mathbf{x}_d) \, d\mathbf{x}_d$$

$$= \int \int \int \Gamma(\boldsymbol{\xi} - \mathbf{x}_o, \boldsymbol{\xi} - \bar{\mathbf{x}}_o)\sigma(\mathbf{x}_o)\sigma^*(\bar{\mathbf{x}}_o)$$

$$\times \exp \left\{ - \frac{2\pi i}{\lambda R} \mathbf{x}_d \cdot (\mathbf{x}_o - \bar{\mathbf{x}}_o) \right\} D(\mathbf{x}_d) \, d\mathbf{x}_d \, d\mathbf{x}_o \, d\bar{\mathbf{x}}_o$$

which differs from Eqn (4.7a) only in that Γ replaces KK^*. As before (Eqn 4.8), we may write

$$\tilde{D}\left(\frac{\mathbf{x}_o - \bar{\mathbf{x}}_o}{\lambda R} \right) = \int D(\mathbf{x}_d) \exp \left\{ - \frac{2\pi i}{\lambda R} \mathbf{x}_d \cdot (\mathbf{x}_o - \bar{\mathbf{x}}_o) \right\} d\mathbf{x}_d$$

to give

$$j(\boldsymbol{\xi}) = \int \int \Gamma(\boldsymbol{\xi} - \mathbf{x}_o, \boldsymbol{\xi} - \bar{\mathbf{x}}_o)\sigma(\mathbf{x}_o)\sigma^*(\bar{\mathbf{x}}_o)\tilde{D}\left(\frac{\mathbf{x}_o - \bar{\mathbf{x}}_o}{\lambda R} \right) d\mathbf{x}_o \, d\bar{\mathbf{x}}_o.$$

The spatial frequency spectrum of the image, $\tilde{j}(\mathbf{p})$, may be written in the form

$$\tilde{j}(\mathbf{p}) = \Gamma_s(\lambda f \mathbf{p}) \int \{ \int D(\mathbf{x}_d) A(\lambda f \mathbf{p} + \lambda f \mathbf{w} - f \mathbf{x}_d/R)$$

$$\times A^*(\lambda f \mathbf{w} - f \bar{\mathbf{x}}_d/R) \, d\mathbf{x}_d \} \tilde{\sigma}(\mathbf{p} + \mathbf{w}) \tilde{\sigma}^*(\mathbf{w}) \lambda^2 f^2 \, d\mathbf{w}$$

with

$$\mathbf{w} = \frac{\bar{\mathbf{x}}_a}{\lambda f} + \frac{\mathbf{x}_d}{\lambda R}$$

in which we recognize the transmission cross-coefficient of Eqn (3.25). The image intensity spectrum is thus equal to that given by a STEM with a coherently illuminated probe modulated by $\Gamma_s(\lambda f \mathbf{p})$, the mutual intensity in the exit pupil of the probe-forming lens.

Hanszen and Ade (1976c, 1977) have developed a consistent representation of image formation in the conventional electron microscope and the STEM, with particular reference to the legitimacy of expressing STEM image formation in holographic terms. Their work usefully complements the paper by Burge and Dainty since the viewpoint is somewhat different. Image formation in the STEM when the weak-scattering approximation is not acceptable has been investigated by Cowley (1976). The signal-to-noise ratios in the STEM and fixed-beam electron microscope are analysed in depth in a review by Misell (1977).

2. Tilted and conical illumination

This brief mention of annular detectors in the STEM leads us naturally to the question of image formation in the conventional transmission microscope with hollow conical illumination. The idea of using an annular condenser aperture has been discussed on many occasions (Riecke, 1964; Hanszen et al., 1965; Lenz and Wilska, 1966/67; Dupouy et al., 1969; Hanszen and Trepte, 1971b; Thon and Willasch, 1972; Niehrs, 1973; Willasch, 1973; Hanszen and Ade, 1974a, b, 1975, 1976a). Recent contributions have concentrated on the possibility of describing (bright- and dark-field) image formation with conical illumination by means of a linear theory, since this would permit us to use a transfer function representation and hence linear image interpretation and processing. A full discussion of the complicated relation between object and image in the various dark-field modes would take us too far from the main theme of this review and we refer the reader to the detailed analyses that have been published by Hanszen and Ade (1975, 1976a), Ade (1975) and Burge and Dainty (1976); some comments by Cowley (1975b) are also relevant. (Accounts in English of much of the work of Hanszen and Ade are to be found in Hanszen, 1974a and Hanszen and Ade, 1974a.) Here we merely raise some of the problems and give an idea of the role of partial coherence theory in their solution.

Conical illumination produced by a narrow annular condenser aperture may be regarded as a generalization of tilted illumination, in which the tilt angle is fixed but all azimuths are present; more generally, conical illumination may itself be tilted, in the sense that the axis of the cone is inclined with respect to the microscope axis. If the condenser aperture is annular but the ring is broad enough to produce a wide beam, which may be pictured as a cone with a wall of tapering thickness, the situation is very different; this last mode, which is common in the STEM, has become known as incoherent dark-field illumination when the main conical beam is intercepted by the objective aperture. The extent to which it is incoherent clearly depends on the geometry and in practice, it will normally give partially coherent illumination since the degree of coherence at the specimen is obtained by adding (incoherently) the contributions at the specimen from all points on the ring (Engel, 1974); except for very broad rings, which could not easily be filled with electrons in practice, the resulting illumination will be partially coherent. It is not immediately obvious that the contributions should be added incoherently; this point has been investigated and the assumption justified by Ferwerda (1976a, b).

We first consider tilted coherent bright-field illumination and the effect of partial coherence on the transfer functions when the envelope representation is adequate. We then investigate its natural generalization, conical illumination with a narrow annulus.

For tilted illumination, phase and amplitude transfer functions can again be derived for weakly scattering specimens (Hanszen and Trepte, 1971b; Hawkes, 1973; Downing, 1975; Goldfarb et al., 1975; Hoppe et al., 1975; Krivanek, 1975; McFarlane, 1975; McFarlane and Cochran, 1975). The effect of partial coherence can easily be incorporated provided that the envelope representation is valid (Hoppe et al., 1975; Downing, 1975). If the wave incident on the specimen is of the form $\exp(2\pi i\, \mathbf{m}.\mathbf{x}_o)$, the emergent wave will be $\sigma(\mathbf{x}_o) \exp(2\pi i\, \mathbf{m}.\mathbf{x}_o)$. Writing $\sigma = 1 - s + i\phi$, the spectrum of the image wave function will be given by

$$\tilde{\psi}_i(\mathbf{p}) = \frac{1}{M} A(\lambda f \mathbf{p})\{\delta(\mathbf{p} - \mathbf{m}) - \tilde{s}(\mathbf{p} - \mathbf{m}) + i\tilde{\phi}(\mathbf{p} - \mathbf{m})\} \quad (4.14)$$

where $A = \exp(-i\gamma)$ inside the aperture for perfectly coherent illumination. In the partially coherent situation, we simply replace $A(\lambda f \mathbf{p})$ by $E(\mathbf{p}) \exp\{-i\gamma(\mathbf{p})\}$. We obtain

$$M\psi_i(M\mathbf{x}) = \int [E(\mathbf{p}) \exp\{-i\gamma(\mathbf{p})\}\delta(\mathbf{p}-\mathbf{m}) - E(\mathbf{p})\exp\{-i\gamma(\mathbf{p})\}\{\tilde{s}(\mathbf{p}-\mathbf{m})$$

$$-i\tilde{\phi}(\mathbf{p}-\mathbf{m})] \exp(2\pi i\, \mathbf{p}.\mathbf{x})\, d\mathbf{p}$$

$$= \exp(2\pi i\mathbf{m}.\mathbf{x}) \int [E(\bar{\mathbf{p}} + \mathbf{m}) \exp\{-i\gamma(\bar{\mathbf{p}} + \mathbf{m})\}\delta(\bar{\mathbf{p}})$$

$$- E(\bar{\mathbf{p}} + \mathbf{m}) \exp\{-i\gamma(\bar{\mathbf{p}} + \mathbf{m})\}\{\tilde{s}(\bar{\mathbf{p}})$$

$$- i\tilde{\phi}(\bar{\mathbf{p}})\}] \exp(2\pi i\, \bar{\mathbf{p}}.\mathbf{x})\, d\bar{\mathbf{p}} \quad (4.15)$$

with

$$\bar{\mathbf{p}} = \mathbf{p} - \mathbf{m}. \quad (4.16)$$

After some rearrangement, the image current density is thus given by

$$j(M\mathbf{x}) \propto M^2\psi_i(M\mathbf{x})\psi_i^*(M\mathbf{x})$$

$$= E^2(\mathbf{m}) - E(\mathbf{m}) \int \tilde{s}(\mathbf{p})[E(\mathbf{m} - \bar{\mathbf{p}}) \exp -i\{\gamma(\mathbf{m}) - \gamma(\mathbf{m} - \mathbf{p})\}$$
$$+ E(\mathbf{m} + \bar{\mathbf{p}}) \exp i\{\gamma(\mathbf{m}) - \gamma(\mathbf{m} + \mathbf{p})\}] \exp (2\pi i\, \bar{\mathbf{p}}.\mathbf{x})\, d\bar{\mathbf{p}}$$
$$- iE(\mathbf{m}) \int \tilde{\phi}(\bar{\mathbf{p}})[E(\mathbf{m} - \bar{\mathbf{p}}) \exp -i\{\gamma(\mathbf{m}) - \gamma(\mathbf{m} - \bar{\mathbf{p}})\}$$
$$- E(\mathbf{m} + \bar{\mathbf{p}}) \exp i\{\gamma(\mathbf{m}) - \gamma(\mathbf{m} + \bar{\mathbf{p}})\}] \exp (2\pi i\, \bar{\mathbf{p}}.\mathbf{x})\, d\bar{\mathbf{p}} \quad (4.17)$$

or

$$\tilde{j}(\bar{\mathbf{p}}) = E^2(\mathbf{m})\delta(\bar{\mathbf{p}}) + \tilde{s}(\bar{\mathbf{p}})t_s(\bar{\mathbf{p}}) + \tilde{\phi}(\bar{\mathbf{p}})t_\phi(\bar{\mathbf{p}}) \qquad (4.18)$$

where

$$t_s(\bar{\mathbf{p}}) = - E(\mathbf{m})[E(\mathbf{m} - \bar{\mathbf{p}}) \exp -i\{\gamma(\mathbf{m}) - \gamma(\mathbf{m} - \bar{\mathbf{p}})\}$$
$$+ E(\mathbf{m} + \bar{\mathbf{p}}) \exp i\{\gamma(\mathbf{m}) - \gamma(\mathbf{m} + \bar{\mathbf{p}})\}]$$
$$t_\phi(\bar{\mathbf{p}}) = - iE(\mathbf{m})[E(\mathbf{m} - \bar{\mathbf{p}}) \exp -i\{\gamma(\mathbf{m}) - \gamma(\mathbf{m} - \bar{\mathbf{p}})\}$$
$$- E(\mathbf{m} + \bar{\mathbf{p}}) \exp i\{\gamma(\mathbf{m}) - \gamma(\mathbf{m} + \bar{\mathbf{p}})\}] \qquad (4.19)$$

These expressions for t_s and t_ϕ can be written compactly

$$t_s(\bar{\mathbf{p}}) = - E(\mathbf{m})[E_c(\mathbf{p}) \cos \{\gamma(\mathbf{m}) - \gamma_c(\bar{\mathbf{p}})\}$$
$$+ iE_s(\mathbf{p}) \sin \{\gamma(\mathbf{m}) - \gamma_s(\bar{\mathbf{p}})\}]$$
$$t_\phi(\bar{\mathbf{p}}) = - E(\mathbf{m})[- E_c(\bar{\mathbf{p}}) \sin \{\gamma(\mathbf{m}) - \gamma_c(\bar{\mathbf{p}})\}$$
$$+ iE_s(\bar{\mathbf{p}}) \cos \{\gamma(\mathbf{m}) - \gamma_s(\bar{\mathbf{p}})\}] \qquad (4.20)$$

with

$$E_c^2(\bar{\mathbf{p}}) = \{E(\mathbf{m} - \bar{\mathbf{p}}) \cos \gamma(\mathbf{m} - \bar{\mathbf{p}}) + E(\mathbf{m} + \bar{\mathbf{p}}) \cos \gamma(\mathbf{m} + \bar{\mathbf{p}})\}^2$$
$$+ \{E(\mathbf{m} - \bar{\mathbf{p}}) \sin \gamma(\mathbf{m} - \bar{\mathbf{p}}) + E(\mathbf{m} + \bar{\mathbf{p}}) \sin \gamma(\mathbf{m} + \bar{\mathbf{p}})\}^2$$
$$E_s^2(\bar{\mathbf{p}}) = \{E(\mathbf{m} - \bar{\mathbf{p}}) \cos \gamma(\mathbf{m} - \bar{\mathbf{p}}) - E(\mathbf{m} + \bar{\mathbf{p}}) \cos \gamma(\mathbf{m} + \bar{\mathbf{p}})\}^2$$
$$+ \{E(\mathbf{m} - \bar{\mathbf{p}}) \sin \gamma(\mathbf{m} - \bar{\mathbf{p}}) - E(\mathbf{m} + \bar{\mathbf{p}}) \sin \gamma(\mathbf{m} + \bar{\mathbf{p}})\}^2$$
$$\tan \gamma_c = \frac{E(\mathbf{m} - \bar{\mathbf{p}}) \sin \gamma(\mathbf{m} - \bar{\mathbf{p}}) + E(\mathbf{m} + \bar{\mathbf{p}}) \sin \gamma(\mathbf{m} + \bar{\mathbf{p}})}{E(\mathbf{m} - \bar{\mathbf{p}}) \cos \gamma(\mathbf{m} - \bar{\mathbf{p}}) + E(\mathbf{m} + \bar{\mathbf{p}}) \cos \gamma(\mathbf{m} + \bar{\mathbf{p}})}$$
$$\tan \gamma_s = \frac{E(\mathbf{m} - \bar{\mathbf{p}}) \sin \gamma(\mathbf{m} - \bar{\mathbf{p}}) - E(\mathbf{m} + \bar{\mathbf{p}}) \sin \gamma(\mathbf{m} + \bar{\mathbf{p}})}{E(\mathbf{m} - \bar{\mathbf{p}}) \cos \gamma(\mathbf{m} - \bar{\mathbf{p}}) - E(\mathbf{m} + \bar{\mathbf{p}}) \cos \gamma(\mathbf{m} + \bar{\mathbf{p}})}. \qquad (4.21)$$

If the illumination is not tilted, $\mathbf{m} = 0$ and

$$E_c(\bar{\mathbf{p}}) = E_c(\mathbf{p}) = 2E(\mathbf{p})$$
$$E_s(\bar{\mathbf{p}}) = E_s(\mathbf{p}) = 0$$
$$\tan \gamma_c(\bar{\mathbf{p}}) = \tan \gamma_c(\mathbf{p}) = \tan \gamma(\mathbf{p}) : \gamma_c(\bar{\mathbf{p}}) = \gamma(\mathbf{p}) \qquad (4.22)$$

so that

$$t_s(\bar{\mathbf{p}}) \to - 2E(\mathbf{p}) \cos \gamma(\mathbf{p})$$
$$t_\phi(\bar{\mathbf{p}}) \to 2E(\mathbf{p}) \sin \gamma(\mathbf{p}) \qquad (4.23)$$

as anticipated.

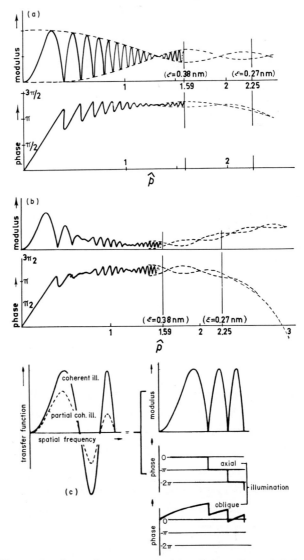

Fig. 8. Hanszen's alternative representation of the effect of finite source size (a) and wavelength spread (b) on the phase contrast transfer function for tilted illumination. Each pair of curves shows the modulus (above) and phase (below) of the transfer function.

(a) Finite source size: angular aperture = $0.02 \times$ tilt angle; reduced tilt angle = $\sqrt{2}$ (defined as the reduced spatial frequency point at which the tilted beam would intercept the aperture plane); $\Delta = 0$. (b) Finite energy spread: $\Delta E/E = 4 \times 10^{-5}$; reduced tilt angle = $\sqrt{2}$; $\Delta = 0$. (c) For comparison, the conventional coherent phase contrast transfer function in modulus and phase representation. (After Hanszen, 1975.)

An interesting form of $t_\phi(\bar{\mathbf{p}})$ has been discussed by Hanszen (1975); instead of dividing t_ϕ into real and imaginary parts, Hanszen splits this function into modulus and argument:

$$t_\phi(\bar{\mathbf{p}}) = |t_\phi(\bar{\mathbf{p}})| \exp i\tau_\phi(\bar{\mathbf{p}}). \qquad (4.24)$$

Using Eqn (4.19), we see that

$$|t_\phi(\bar{\mathbf{p}})| = E(m)[E^2(\mathbf{m} - \bar{\mathbf{p}}) + E^2(\mathbf{m} + \bar{\mathbf{p}})$$
$$- 2E(\mathbf{m} - \bar{\mathbf{p}})E(\mathbf{m} + \bar{\mathbf{p}}) \cos \{2\gamma(\mathbf{m})$$
$$- \gamma(\mathbf{m} - \bar{\mathbf{p}}) - \gamma(\mathbf{m} + \bar{\mathbf{p}})\}]^{1/2} \qquad (4.25a)$$

and

$$\tan \tau_\phi(\bar{\mathbf{p}})$$

$$= -\frac{E(\mathbf{m}+\bar{\mathbf{p}}) \cos \{\gamma(\mathbf{m})-\gamma(\mathbf{m}+\bar{\mathbf{p}})\}-E(\mathbf{m}-\bar{\mathbf{p}}) \cos \{\gamma(\mathbf{m})-\gamma(\mathbf{m}-\bar{\mathbf{p}})\}}{E(\mathbf{m}+\bar{\mathbf{p}}) \sin \{\gamma(\mathbf{m})-\gamma(\mathbf{m}+\bar{\mathbf{p}})\}+E(\mathbf{m}-\bar{\mathbf{p}}) \sin \{\gamma(\mathbf{m})-\gamma(\mathbf{m}-\bar{\mathbf{p}})\}}$$

$$= \frac{E_s(\bar{\mathbf{p}}) \cos \{\gamma(\mathbf{m}) - \gamma_s(\bar{\mathbf{p}})\}}{E_c(\bar{\mathbf{p}}) \sin \{\gamma(\mathbf{m}) - \gamma_c(\bar{\mathbf{p}})\}}. \qquad (4.25b)$$

It is clear from Eqn (4.25a) that the modulus of $t_\phi(\mathbf{p})$ is an oscillatory function, fluctuating about the central value

$$E(\mathbf{m})\{E^2(\mathbf{m} - \bar{\mathbf{p}}) + E^2(\mathbf{m} + \bar{\mathbf{p}})\}^{1/2}.$$

Hanszen (1975) has plotted both $|t_\phi|$ and τ_ϕ for finite source size and finite energy spread (Figs 8a, b). Figure 8(b) draws our attention to another feature of image formation with a tilted beam, the existence of an "achromatic circle" corresponding to the point at which $|t_\phi|$ returns to the value at the first maximum. We encounter this again below. Hanszen discusses tilted illumination further in Hanszen (1976) and Hanszen and Ade (1976b), in which extensive calculations of the effect of partial spatial coherence are set out.

Hoppe *et al.* (1975) have computed the form of the transfer functions for various types of envelope function for the Siemens Elmiskop 101 at 100 kV with $C_s = 1\cdot35$ mm and $C_c = 1\cdot6$ mm. Their curves show the coherent transfer functions modulated by real envelope functions; this is only a first approximation, as we can see from Eqns (4.20), but Hoppe *et al.* remark that the imaginary parts of t_s and t_ϕ can be ignored by suitable choice of the defocus, Δ, and that the real parts can be written as products of B_s and B_ϕ and an envelope to a reasonable approximation. Their curves, which show this envelope for various tilt angles, source sizes and energy spreads (expressed as defocus ranges), are reproduced in Fig. 9. A more detailed examination of a single case is given by Downing (1975), who also shows the optical transform of a micrograph of a thin carbon film supporting gold particles in order to illustrate the effects described. For further comment, see Wade (1976b, c). Subsequently, Typke and Köstler (1976) have critically examined the papers of Downing (1975) and Wade (1976b). They establish the conditions in which Downing's results are valid and comment on the need for a physical aperture with tilted illumination when single-sideband transfer is desired. (Typke and Köstler (1977) have also described a method of obtaining the wave aberration by superposing diffractograms of images obtained with different tilt directions of the illumination.) Further discussion of these questions is to be found in Rose (1977). See also Kiselev and Sherman (1976), who appear to be unaware of the extensive literature that has grown up round this topic, Krakow (1976) and Hoppe and Köstler (1976).

An important feature of image formation with tilted illumination is the existence of an achromatic circle (Hoppe, 1974; Hoppe et al., 1974; see also Willasch, 1976; and Frank, 1976b); this circle corresponds to the points at which the envelopes of the tilted-beam transfer functions pass through a maximum. The curves of Fig. 9 show that if both tilting angle and defocus are chosen suitably, both source size and chromatic effects are compensated around a ring. In a light optical diffractogram of the image of a thin amorphous film, this achromatic circle produces "wings"; attention was drawn

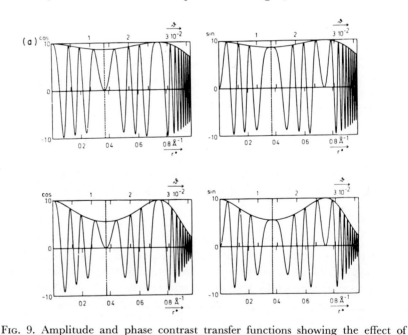

FIG. 9. Amplitude and phase contrast transfer functions showing the effect of finite source size and energy spread with tilted illumination for various values of Δ.
(a) Point source, tilt angle $\theta = 13{\cdot}7$ mrad; $\Delta = 254{\cdot}3$ nm. Above, $\bar{\Delta} = 8$ nm, where $\bar{\Delta}$ denotes the range of Δ due to the energy spread; below, $\bar{\Delta} = 16$ nm.

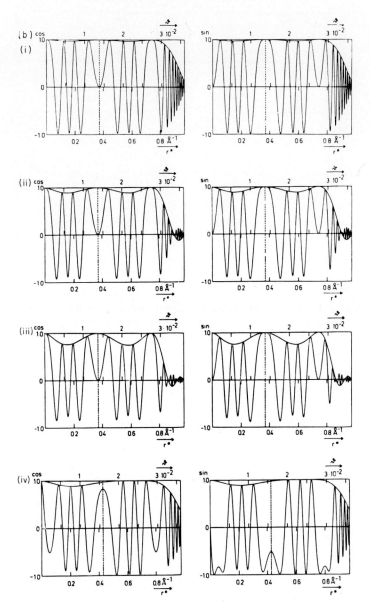

FIG. 9(b). Finite source, no energy spread ($\overline{\Delta} = 0$). (i) $\theta = 13\cdot7$ mrad, $\bar{\theta} = 0\cdot21$ mrad, where $\bar{\theta}$ denotes the angular spread of the tilted illuminating beam. (ii) $\theta = 13\cdot7$ mrad, $\bar{\theta} = 0\cdot43$ mrad. (iii) $\theta = 13\cdot7$ mrad, $\bar{\theta} = 0\cdot64$ mrad. (iv) $\theta = 15\cdot8$ mrad, $\bar{\theta} = 0\cdot21$ mrad.

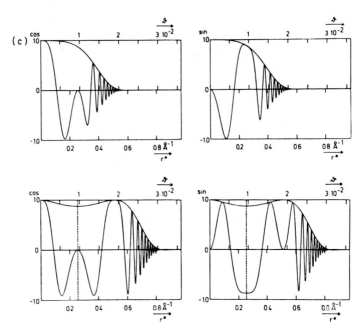

Fig. 9(c). Comparison of the transfer functions with finite source ($\bar{\theta} = 0.21$ mrad) and energy spread ($\bar{\varDelta} = 16$ nm) for $\bar{\varDelta} = 122.4$ nm when the tilt angle is zero (above) and 9·5 mrad (below).

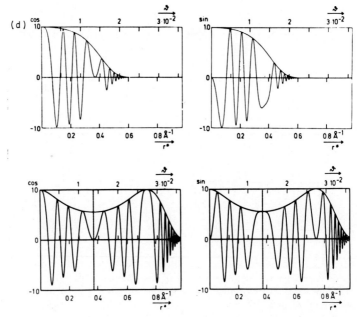

Fig. 9(d). As (c) except that $\varDelta = 254.3$ nm and the tilt angle (below) is 13·7 mrad.

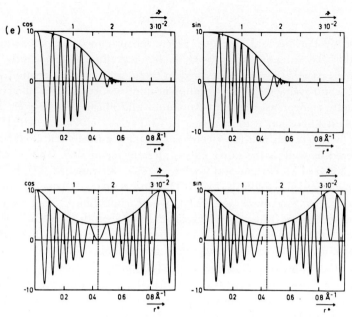

Fig. 9(e). As (c) except that $\varDelta = 353 \cdot 4$ nm and the tilt angle (below) is $16 \cdot 2$ mrad.

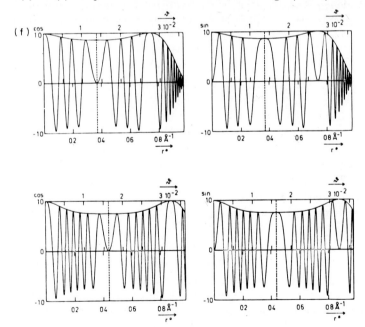

Fig. 9(f). The contrast transfer functions for tilted illumination with finite source size ($\bar{\theta} = 0 \cdot 21$ mrad) and small energy spread ($\bar{\varDelta} = 8$ nm). Above, $\varDelta = 254 \cdot 8$ nm, $\theta = 13 \cdot 7$ mrad; below, $\varDelta = 353 \cdot 4$ nm, $\theta = 16 \cdot 2$ mrad. (After Hoppe *et al.*, 1975.)

to these by Parsons and Hoelke (1974), who proposed an explanation for them that has subsequently proved inadequate (though not wholly false). Numerous papers have been devoted to them, mostly in connection with a related controversy over the genuineness of lattice fringes observed in supposedly amorphous films of germanium and silicon (Howie *et al.*, 1973). The fullest discussion is to be found in McFarlane (1975), in which inter-ference between plasmon-loss electrons and the elastically scattered beam is considered as well as the other effects already mentioned. The problem is also explored in McFarlane and Cochran (1975), Krivanek (1975), Krivanek and Howie (1975), Goldfarb *et al.* (1975) and Krakow (1976a, b), and in a long paper by Krakow *et al.* (1976), whose conclusions are, however, at variance with those drawn by McFarlane (1975). See also Krivanek (1976b), a critical study by Rose (1977), in which the experimental findings and theoretical explanations are examined in great detail, and Oberlin (1977).

If now we suppose not only that the illumination is tilted, with a fixed tilt relative to the microscope axis, but that all azimuths are present, we have the case of illumination with a narrow ring condenser. This mode is a genuine example of partially coherent illumination, the contributions from all the elements of the ring being summed incoherently, and for weakly scattering specimens, amplitude and phase transfer functions can be derived (for the bright-field case) using Eqns (3.37). Typical curves have been published by Hanszen and Trepte (1971b), which display several interesting features; in particular, the resolution for phase or amplitude structures is about double that obtainable with coherent axial illumination but the contrast is at most half as good (Fig. 10). A detailed examination of image formation with this type of illumination has also been made by Niehrs (1973). The types of misleading result that may occur are conveniently summarized in Hanszen (1974a). Conical bright-field illumination has been successfully used by Heinemann and Poppa (1970a, b) for lattice imaging at very high resolution. Two-point resolution with partially coherent illumination has been studied in light optics both for disc-shaped sources and for narrow and wide annular sources. A detailed account is to be found in De and Basuray (1972).

When a wide annular condenser aperture is used, the transmission electron microscope becomes the counterpart of the STEM with a broad annular detector provided that the main beam is excluded by the objective aperture. The bright-field case is an essentially incoherent mode. Considerable attention has been given to the incoherent dark-field case, because of its importance in STEM and conventional microscopy (Hanszen and Ade, 1974a, b, 1975; Ade, 1975; Rose, 1974a, b; Typke *et al.*, 1974; Engel, 1974; Engel *et al.*, 1974). The general conclusion to be drawn from all these investigations, the main theme of which falls outside the scope of this review, is that, in common with all other dark-field modes, the complex amplitude at the object cannot in general be linearly transferred into the image. Nevertheless, there are certain categories of object structure about

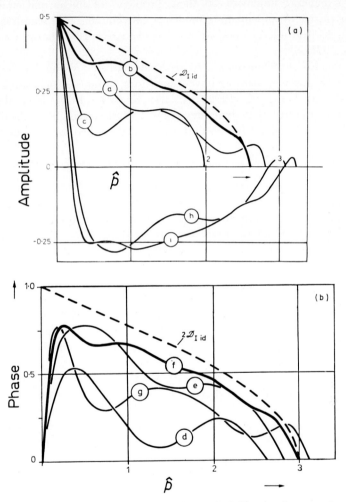

FIG. 10. The contrast transfer functions for conical illumination as a function of reduced spatial frequency. (a) Amplitude contrast transfer functions for the following ring radii (in reduced coordinates): a: 1·00; b: 1·31; c: 1·41; h: 1·55; i: 1·61. The broken curve shows the function corresponding to curve b for an aberration-free lens. (b) Phase contrast transfer functions for the following reduced ring radii: d: 1·31; e: 1·41; f: 1·49; g: 1·55. The broken curve shows the function corresponding to curve f for an aberration-free lens. (After Hanszen and Trepte, 1971b.)

which reliable information can be deduced from the image: for example, reasonably well-separated heavy atoms (Typke *et al.*, 1974). An exhaustive study has been made by Hoch (1976, 1977). (See also Rose and Fertig, 1977 and Fertig and Rose, 1977b.)

For a general statement on these problems of linear and non-linear transfer in the various imaging modes of conventional and scanning transmission electron microscopes, we refer to two surveys by Hanszen and Ade (1976a, 1977).

An obvious problem associated with the use of an annular condenser aperture in practice, with a conventional gun, is the loss of beam current. Krakow and Howland (1976; see also Krakow, 1977) have therefore developed circuitry that generates conical illumination by deflecting the entire beam around a circle so that a cone is described for each deflection.

B. *Measurement of the Degree of Coherence*

Information about the source has traditionally been obtained from electron microscope images by examining Fresnel fringes (see, for example, Heidenreich, 1964, or Reimer, 1967‡). For a systematic study of source properties, the well-known result that the modulus of $\gamma_{12}(0)$ is equal to the visibility of the interference fringes produced by two small sources of equal intensity can be used (e.g. Born and Wolf, 1959, Section 10.4.1, or the review by Françon and Mallick, 1967, of methods of measuring optical coherence). Hibi and Takahashi (1969) have measured the spatial coherence of electron beams from a pointed filament operating in a wide variety of conditions in this way. The interference effects, which were produced with the aid of an electron biprism (see Part C), were used to study the variation of $|\gamma_{12}(0)|$ with gun bias, source size, biprism properties and geometry and cathode temperature. The degree of spatial coherence varied very considerably with these parameters, and the authors show micrographs of test specimens taken with low and comparatively high values of $|\gamma_{12}|$. Comparable micrographs of biological material are to be found in Hibi and Takahashi (1970, 1971) and some general conclusions are drawn in a brief statement by Hibi (1974).

Munch and Zeitler (1974; see also Munch, 1975) have measured the spatial coherence of a field-emission source by observing the fringe pattern from a screen containing numerous randomly spaced holes about 1 μm in diameter. The fringes vanish when the angular spread of the incident beam, $2a$, is equal to λ/D, where D is the separation between holes. This method is relatively insensitive to the microscope performance but very sensitive to source size, exactly as desired.

‡ For recent use of this and a related technique, see Harada *et al.* (1974) and Chiu and Glaeser (1977).

The biprism method has been reconsidered recently by Burge *et al.* (1976a, b), who have measured $|\gamma_{12}|$ for a thermal emitter, a pointed filament and for the field emission source of a commercial STEM (the Vacuum Generators HB5). The phase of γ_{12} is also considered in this work. The problem of determining $\arg(\gamma_{12})$ has been analysed in some detail in the optical case (Wolf, 1962; Kano and Wolf, 1962; Mehta, 1965, 1968; Nussenzveig, 1967; Arsenault and Lowenthal, 1969; and Kohler and Mandel, 1973, in which a fuller list of earlier and related papers is given) and an attempt to solve it iteratively by means of a modified version of the Gerchberg-Saxton algorithm (Gerchberg and Saxton, 1972, 1973) has been made by Saxton (1974, 1978).

An alternative method of measuring source coherence, temporal as well as spatial, by exploiting the envelope representation of these parameters on the coherent transfer functions, has been proposed by Frank (1975b, 1976a). We have seen that the results predicted by the envelope representation are in agreement with the experimental results of Beorchia and Bonhomme (1974) and the earlier results of Thon (1971) are also consistent with the theory. Frank (1975b, 1976a), however, suggested that the envelope representation could be used to deduce quantitative information about the source size and overall energy spread.

Neglecting the problems associated with the envelope representation when both spatial and temporal coherence are considered, we write the (phase) transfer function in the form

$$\hat{B}(\mathbf{p}) = B_\phi(\mathbf{p})E(\mathbf{p})H_c(\lambda p^2) \tag{4.26}$$

where $E(\mathbf{p})$ is given by Eqn (3.48) and $H_c(\lambda p^2)$ by Eqn (3.63). We assume that the variation of the defocus Δ can be represented by a Gaussian (Eqn 3.69) and that the source can likewise be represented by a Gaussian of half-width a. With these assumptions, we have

$$E(\mathbf{p}) = E(|\mathbf{p}|) = \exp\{-\pi^2 q_o^2 (C_s p^3 - \Delta p)^2\}$$
$$H_c(\lambda p^2) = \exp\{-(\pi\delta_o\lambda p^2)^2\} \tag{4.27}$$

in which $q_o = a/2\lambda(\ln 2)^{1/2}$ and $\delta_o = C_c(\Delta V/V)/4\lambda^2 \ln 2$. Writing

$$\hat{E}(\mathbf{p}) = E(\mathbf{p})H_c(\lambda p^2) \tag{4.28}$$

we have

$$\hat{E}(\mathbf{p}) = \exp[-u\{(C_s p^3 - \Delta p)^2 + vp^4\}] \tag{4.29}$$

with

$$u = \frac{\pi^2 a^2}{4\lambda^2 \ln 2} \tag{4.30a}$$

and

$$v = \frac{C_c^2}{4a^2}\left(\frac{\Delta V}{V}\right)^2. \tag{4.30b}$$

Suppose now that the envelope $\hat{E}$ falls to some experimentally determined limit of detection, $\hat{E}(\mathbf{p}) = 1/s$, for $p = p_s$. Then from Eqn (4.29), we have

$$u = \ln s/\{(C_s p_s^3 - \Delta p_s^2)^2 + v p_s^4\} \tag{4.31}$$

or

$$a = \frac{2\lambda}{\pi} (\ln 2)(\ln s)^{1/2}\{(C_s p_s^3 - \Delta p_s^2)^2 + v p_s^4\}^{-1/2} \tag{4.32}$$

in which v is the unknown. The value of a should remain constant for a focal series with fixed illumination so that if we plot a against the defocus, Δ, for a range of values of v, the choice of v for which a varies least should give a good estimate of $\Delta V/V$.

Of the various methods of estimating the bandwidth, s, Frank preferred that in which Young's fringes are produced by superposing two micrographs of an amorphous specimen in a light optical diffractometer (Frank et al., 1970); the extent of the fringe pattern is then regarded as a measure of the range of reproducible information about the specimen. Details of the technique and the necessary precautions are to be found in Frank (1976a). Taking $s = 5$, a source size of $a = 0.54 \pm 0.06$ mrad was obtained with $\Delta V = 1.8 \pm 0.3$ V for a JEM 100B microscope operating with a hairpin filament and the high-resolution polepiece (Fig. 11).

A related method of studying the energy spread of the incident beam has been devised by Krivanek (1975), who considers the effect of this energy spread on the first and second order lattice fringes from a graphite crystal. (First order fringes are produced by interference between the main beam and the Bragg reflections; second order fringes, by interference between the positive and negative Bragg reflected beams.) The second order fringes are (to a good approximation) unaffected by beam energy spread unlike the first order fringes (Komoda, 1972), which are attenuated exponentially (Eqn 4.27). The relative attenuation of these two sets of fringes gives a reproducible measure of the energy spread and permitted Krivanek to show that the anomalous energy spread known as the Boersch effect (Boersch, 1954; see Loeffler, 1969, and Loeffler and Hudgin, 1970, Zimmermann, 1970) may considerably exceed the Maxwellian thermal spread for a spade-edged "semi-pointed hairpin" filament, when the gun design is such that a real crossover is formed (see Franzen and Porter, 1975). Krivanek concludes that due to the energy spread (in his case, of the beam from a high-brightness full-beam mode electron gun based on a design of Johansen, 1973), "The linear contrast transfer function of a present-generation high-resolution conventional instrument ($C_c \lesssim 1.6$ mm, $V \sim 100$ kV) [Siemens 102] equipped with such a gun effectively cuts off for image spacings $\lesssim 0.3$ nm at illumination brightness levels allowing adequate spatial coherence

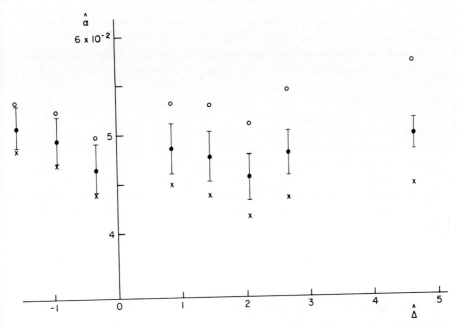

FIG. 11. Values of $\hat{\alpha}$ as a function of generalized defocus $\hat{\Delta}$ for various values of $\hat{v}$ ($\hat{\alpha}$ and $\hat{v}$ are the reduced values of α and v defined in the text) for a JEM 100B microscope. $\bigcirc$: $\hat{v} = 3$; $\bullet$: $\hat{v} = 4$; $\times$: $\hat{v} = 5$. The values lie approximately parallel to the $\hat{\Delta}$-axis for $\hat{v} = 4$. (After Frank, 1976a.)

($a \lesssim 5 \times 10^{-4}$ rad) at high magnification ($\gtrsim 400\,000 \times$) and reasonably short exposure time ($\lesssim 10$ s). The cut-off occurs at much lower spatial frequencies for higher brightness levels. For substantially better results, pointed cathodes operated in the hollow beam condition must be used." (See also Krivanek, 1976a.)

In our discussion of the wave aberration γ, we have not included the effect of (paraxial) astigmatism, since its presence would have rendered the expressions that arise in coherence theory even more cumbersome. It can, however, be incorporated very easily and Burge and Scott (1975) have pointed out that its effect on the optical diffractogram of the electron image of a thin carbon film combines with that of the envelope due to finite source size in a very convenient way. They describe a method that is at once very simple and moderately accurate of estimating source size, provided that the energy spread is narrow enough. Yet another method of measuring spatial coherence has been devised by Troyon (1977).

The images of thin carbon films that are used to establish the phase transfer function of the electron microscope with the aid of an optical diffractometer may be regarded as the electron optical analogues of image speckle patterns, the patterns observed when highly coherent light is used to form the image of a random inhomogeneous medium. This is clearly seen in a note by Nagata *et al.* (1975), who obtained micrographs of a thin carbon film, 5 nm thick, supporting isolated gold particles, with coherent and incoherent illumination in a conventional electron microscope; with "incoherent" illumination (coherence ratio $m = 1$), the noise pattern associated with the carbon film is very much less prominent. We may therefore enquire whether the analysis of such patterns and far-field speckle patterns in partially coherent illumination can be useful in electron optics. The variation of image speckle patterns with the spatial coherence of the incident light has been studied by many authors (see Dainty, 1976a, for a review dealing with speckle statistics and Dainty, 1976b, for a recent collection of surveys and reviews of speckle; of the latter, Parry, 1976, and Dainty, 1976c, are particularly relevant). A technique that may be adaptable to electron microscope conditions is described by Fujii and Asakura (1974, q.v. for references to earlier optical work; cf. Dainty, 1973). These authors showed that if the specimen function, $\sigma(x)$ (in the one-dimensional case), is such that arg σ is a stationary, zero mean, Gaussian random variable, an expression for the average contrast of the image speckle intensity can be derived. This average contrast, V, defined to be the normalized standard deviation of this variation at the image plane, is given by

$$V = \frac{\int \int \int \int G(x_1, x_2, x_3, x_4) \exp \theta(x_1, x_2, x_3, x_4) \, dx_1 \, dx_2 \, dx_3 \, dx_4}{\int \int \Gamma(x_1, x_2) K(x_i - x_1) K^*(x_i - x_2) \hat{s}(x_1) \hat{s}(x_2) \exp \{R(x_1 - x_2)\} \, dx_1 \, dx_2}$$

$$(4.33)$$

in which $\hat{s} = |\sigma|$, R is the autocorrelation function of the specimen phase, G is a complicated function of Γ, K and $\hat{s}$ and θ is a function of R. The results obtained by Fujii and Asakura are not directly relevant to electron microscopy as the model used for K bears little resemblance to the point-spread function of an electron microscope but the general behaviour of their curves is interesting: they show that if V is plotted as a function of the statistical properties of the specimen phase for various values of spatial coherence, a set of well-separated curves is obtained. It is far from clear whether, in the electron case, they would still be well-separated as the range of useful source sizes is relatively limited; furthermore, the properties of thin carbon films may not resemble those of the corresponding optical diffusers sufficiently to be a true analogue. Nevertheless, it would be very interesting to extend this analysis to the electron optical case.

The same authors (Fujii and Asakura, 1973; cf. Asakura *et al.*, 1972) have used far-field speckle patterns—that is, speckle patterns formed in the focal plane of a lens—to measure the spatial coherence of quasi-mono-chromatic thermal light and have confirmed that the effect of temporal partial coherence on such patterns is to produce a pronounced fibrous radial structure. The latter is not relevant in normal electron microscope con-ditions, since the wavelength spreads involved are much larger (of the order of a few per cent) than in electron microscopy. The method of measur-ing Γ could perhaps be useful, however, though more detailed investigation is necessary before its suitability can be assessed. Subject to numerous assumptions, justified in light optics, the mean intensity variation in the Fourier transform (diffraction pattern) of the speckle pattern can be shown to be equal to the product of Γ^2 and a function determined by the lens properties; $|\Gamma|$ can thus be deduced from measurements of the mean intensity across the diffraction pattern of the speckle pattern.

Finally, we draw attention to a review by May (1977), complementing those of Dainty (1976a, b), and to a paper by Jakeman and Welford (1977) on speckle statistics in imaging systems, which is relevant here.

C. Some Important Special Cases

In this section, we draw attention to the importance of coherence in some of the less conventional branches of electron optics. We begin by con-sidering two closely related topics, electron interference and electron holography and we conclude with a brief discussion of the Schwarz-Hora effect.

There are of course other topics that could have been discussed here, such as small angle diffraction which is difficult in the electron microscope because large specimen periodicities correspond to diffraction spots close to the main beam; if the spots are to be sharp, therefore, a large area of the specimen must be illuminated by a beam with a very narrow angular spread, that is, the illumination must have a high spatial coherence. This is achieved in practice by exciting the condenser lenses of the microscope strongly and intercepting the electrons from source points far from the axis at apertures. Electron current is thus traded against coherence. An account of the various modes of operation is given by Ferrier (1969), to which we may add the later suggestion of Drahoš and Delong (1970, 1971). A related case is convergent-beam electron diffraction, where a very small image of the source is required in order to illuminate the specimen with highly coherent spherical waves. The note by Dowell and Goodman (1976) draws attention to this point.

The formation of lattice images in the electron microscope again raises the question of coherence, as we saw in Part B of this section. Lattice images are essentially interference patterns formed by a few small but finite secondary

164   P. W. HAWKES

sources. The lattice images that are currently used as tests of electron microscope performance thus give an indication of the coherence of the illumination falling on the specimen, provided that the conditions are chosen carefully (Sieber and Tonar, 1976). We refer to Zeitler (1968) and to the paper by Krivanek (1975) already mentioned for more detailed analysis and draw attention to the results of Yada and Hibi (1968, 1969, 1970). A short survey by Hutchison (1976) sets out the main features of lattice imagery with more complex specimens. The need for adequate coherence in an intermediate case, a series of crystals with periodic twinning at a spacing of 5–30 nm (alkali feldspars exhibiting albite twinning super-lattices), has been examined by McLaren and MacKenzie (1976) and many other such examples could be cited.

In Lorentz microscopy (Wade, 1973) an interesting situation arises when the scattering angles are so small that the defocusing term in the wave aberration (Eqn 1.8) dominates over the term due to spherical aberration. It can now be shown (Guigay *et al.*, 1971; Wade, 1973) that the effect of spatial coherence can always be represented by an envelope function. This can readily be seen from Eqn (3.42) for, neglecting the terms in a, we have

$$T_s(\mathbf{p}) = -2 \int \tilde{\Gamma}_s(\mathbf{v}) \cos \{\pi \Delta \lambda (p^2 + 2\mathbf{p}.\mathbf{v})\} \, d\mathbf{v}$$
$$= -2 \cos (\pi \Delta \lambda p^2) \int \tilde{\Gamma}_S(\mathbf{v}) \cos (2\pi \Delta \lambda \mathbf{p}.\mathbf{v}) \, d\mathbf{v}$$
$$= -2 \cos (\pi \Delta \lambda p^2) \Gamma_s(\Delta \lambda \mathbf{p})$$
$$T_\phi(\mathbf{p}) = 2 \int \tilde{\Gamma}_S(\mathbf{v}) \sin \{\pi \Delta \lambda (\mathbf{p}^2 + 2\mathbf{p}.\mathbf{v})\} \, d\mathbf{v}$$
$$= 2 \sin (\pi \Delta \lambda p^2) \int \tilde{\Gamma}_S(\mathbf{v}) \cos (2\pi \Delta \lambda \mathbf{p}.\mathbf{v}) \, d\mathbf{v}$$
$$= 2 \sin (\pi \Delta \lambda p^2) \Gamma_S(\Delta \lambda \mathbf{p}). \tag{4.34}$$

1. *Electron interference and electron holography*

The divisions between ordinary bright-field electron image formation, some modes of electron holography and electron interference are blurred. In this section, we draw attention to the principal attempts that have been made to perform electron interferometry and electron holography of various kinds, singling out the role of coherence in the results achieved.

Two types of electron interferometer have been studied, one resembling the Mach-Zehnder interferometer‡ (Marton, 1952; Marton *et al.*, 1953, 1954; Simpson, 1954; see Simpson, 1956), the other the electron analogue of the Fresnel biprism (Düker, 1955; Möllenstedt and Düker, 1955, 1956; Faget and Fert, 1956, 1957; see Fert, 1961, and Komrska, 1971, 1975, for references to subsequent publications and practical applications of electron

‡ In fact, the design is closer to that proposed by Barus (1911, 1912).

interferometry). The theory and coherence requirements of these two types of interferometer were first examined by Simpson (1956) and Gabor (1956) and later by Hibi and Takahashi (1969). Of the two, only the electron biprism has survived; the relation between source coherence and fringe visibility is an exact analogue of the optical counterpart. The experimental implications of this are discussed by Drahoš and Delong (1964), Komrska et al. (1967), Komrska and Lenc (1970), Anaskin and Stoyanova (1968a, c, d; cf. Anaskin et al., 1966, for a description of a Russian UEMV-100 microscope with a biprism incorporated), Hibi and Takahashi (1969) and Sonier (1971) and by Schaal et al. (1966/7), for example; the stringency of the conditions when the separated beams are wide apart (0·12 mm) is vividly illustrated in Fig. 7 of this last paper. An interesting use of the biprism is the electron analogue of the Michelson interferometer (Lichte et al., 1972; Lenz, 1972) in which the temporal coherence length, $\lambda^2/\Delta\lambda$, is the important parameter if large differences in path length are to be measured; at 25 kV, $\lambda^2/\Delta\lambda \simeq 370$ nm if $\Delta V \sim 1V$. The biprism interferometer has also been used to measure the ratio between the coherently and incoherently scattered electrons at the specimen (Stoyanova and Anaskin, 1968). We note that Menu and Evrard (1971) have measured the visibility of biprism fringes when the incident electrons have traversed carbon films of various thicknesses, from 25 to 160 nm; they believed that the absence of variation in this visibility was evidence that individual electrons are uncorrelated—that each electron "interferes with itself". In the light of Glauber's remarks (1970), however, it seems clear that their experiment would not have revealed any such correlations (cf. Section V).

For a general account of electron interferometry, see Hibi and Yada (1976). For completeness, we mention that Ohtsuki and Zeitler (1977) have repeated Young's experiment, using electrons.

Multiple-beam interference has been studied experimentally, using several slits, by Möllenstedt and Jönsson (1959), or several wires instead of one in the "biprism", by Anaskin and Stoyanova (1967, 1968b, e) and Anaskin et al. (1968).

It is a small step from electron interference studies to electron holography, for in practice holography with a tilted reference beam is normally achieved by splitting the electron beam with the aid of an electron biprism (although diffraction in a crystal has also been used by Tonomura, 1969). We recall that the first holographic technique was proposed by Gabor (1948, 1949, 1951) as a means of decreasing the adverse effect of electron lens aberrations by supplementing image formation in the electron microscope with a light optical reconstruction step. Since then, numerous other techniques have been investigated, because of the problems associated with the original proposal, but in recent years interest in electron holography has swung back to Gabor's original idea, with many refinements.

The essence of holography is the formation of an interference pattern, the hologram, between a reference beam and a beam modulated by the specimen. The reference beam may coincide with the image-forming beam in which case we speak of in-line holography; the hologram may then be recorded close to the image plane, that is, any plane conjugate to the specimen, in which case it is known as a Fresnel hologram, or far from the image plane, in which case we speak of a Fraunhofer hologram. The notions of far from and near to the image plane are not absolute; values of the Fresnel number,

$$N = \pi s^2 / \lambda \Delta \qquad (4.35)$$

much greater than unity correspond to the Fresnel region, values of the order of unity or less to Fraunhofer conditions. In Eqn (4.35), s denotes the size of specimen detail of interest and Δ the defocus of the hologram plane relative to the Gaussian image plane, referred back to the object. For fine detail in electron microscopy, therefore—for example $s = 0.4$ nm— we have $N = 40 \, \pi / \Delta$ which, for 100 kV, is only greater than five ($\gg 1$) for $\Delta < 8\pi$ nm. For much coarser detail, $s = 10$ nm say, we find $N = 25\,000 \times \pi / \Delta$ so that $N \geq 5$ for $\Delta \leq 5000 \, \pi$ nm or $\Delta \leq 5 \, \pi \, \mu$m. Except very close to in-focus conditions, then, holographic study of fine detail will always be Fraunhofer holography, whereas larger structures may be recorded in either Fraunhofer or Fresnel conditions. The dominant effect of finite source size is to blur the fine detail in the hologram; if the total angular spread of the beam incident on the specimen is 2α, the smallest detail that can be resolved s_o will be given by

$$s_o \approx 2\alpha\Delta \qquad (4.36)$$

provided that Δ is not too small.

A major disadvantage of in-line Fresnel holography is that the twin-image that is always produced in holographic reconstructions cannot be separated from the main image. In Fraunhofer conditions, the twin image is spread over a very much greater area than the main image and hence has very much lower contrast (Thompson, 1965; DeVelis et al., 1966). By suitable choice of the specimen area used to form the hologram, the effect of the twin image can be reduced to a reasonably featureless background. It can be shown that the field of view, s_m must not exceed $(c\lambda\Delta)^{1/2}$, where c is a constant between 1 and 1·5. For given s_m, therefore, Δ must be at least $s_m^2/c\lambda$; using Eqn (4.36), we see that if a resolution of s_o is desired, we must satisfy the condition

$$\alpha < \frac{cs_o\lambda}{2 s_m^2}. \qquad (4.37)$$

For a resolution of 0·25 nm in an object field 100 nm across at 100 kV, we find $a < 75$ nrad ($c = 1·5$). In view of the absence of any safety factors in the above reasoning, even this estimate will be optimistic: for the same situation, Hanszen estimates $a < 25$ nrad!

The other main technique for avoiding the disturbing presence of the twin image is tilted-beam or sideband holography (Leith and Upatnieks, 1962, 1967), in which the reference beam is inclined to the main image-forming beam. Again, we may form a Fraunhofer or a Fresnel hologram or an image-plane hologram: a Fresnel hologram with effectively no defocus. Image-plane holograms are particularly relevant here because the effect of spatial coherence on resolution is least in this case; the finite source size does of course affect the field of view because the hologram cannot be larger than the area coherently illuminated, referred to the same plane. These and other holographic procedures are fully described in the more recent texts on holography; see in particular Collier *et al.*, 1971, and Menzel *et al.*, 1973. In a short survey, Wade, 1976a, attempts to impose a pattern on this diverse material; for a fuller review, specifically concerned with electron holography, see Wade (1978), and also Section V of the chapter by Misell in the present volume.

We now examine briefly the various theoretical and experimental studies of holography in the electron microscope. Very extensive studies of the influence of partial coherence on the various holographic modes have been made by Menzel, Mirandé and Weingärtner (Mirandé and Weingärtner, 1969; Weingärtner *et al.*, 1969a, b, 1970, 1971; Mirandé *et al.*, 1969, 1970; for a full account, see Menzel *et al.*, 1973). The possibilities of electron holography were surveyed by Boersch as early as 1967.

The first practical attempt to implement Gabor's original idea and the modified version suggested by Haine and Dyson (1950) was made by Haine and Mulvey (1950, 1952). In order to obtain the in-line Fresnel hologram, which was simply an out-of-focus electron image, the electron source coherence was increased at the expense of beam current; in consequence, the exposure time needed to record the hologram was long and the mechanical and electrical instabilities of the instrument (an AE1 EM3) severely blurred the hologram finally obtained (see Gabor, 1968/69). This discouraged further attempts and it was not until 1968 that Tonomura and Watanabe (Tonomura and Watanabe, 1968; Tonomura *et al.*, 1968a, b; Watanabe and Tonomura, 1969) described a successful attempt to reconstruct a Fraunhofer hologram, produced in an electron microscope. With a particle size (s_0) of 10 nm and defocus (Δ) of 1·9 mm, they were operating in the condition $s_0^2/\lambda\Delta \approx 0·012$. The source size is not given. The in-line modes were subsequently studied in very great detail by Hanszen and Ade

(Hanszen, 1970a, b, 1971, 1972a, b, 1973a, b, 1974b; Ade, 1973; Hanszen *et al.*, 1972a, b) who analysed meticulously the electron optical requirements of the hologram step and the conditions necessary for a satisfactory reconstruction. We have already mentioned Hanszen's estimate of the spatial coherence required. In-line Fraunhofer reconstructions were described by Voronin *et al.* (1972). More recently, Munch (1975) has attempted both sideband Fresnel holography and in-line Fraunhofer holography, using a modern microscope (Hitachi HU-12) fitted with a field-emission source. Munch found that with $\Delta = 5$ μm, particles less than 1 nm across could be reconstructed but that for larger values of Δ, the contrast was not sufficient for reconstruction of high resolution detail. The angular spread of the incident beam was about 1 μrad. Hanszen obtained a resolution of the order of 10 nm for an object area of radius 60 nm with $\Delta = 2$ mm and 2 nm for a radius of 10 nm with $\Delta = 0.4$ mm; the illumination angle was 3 μrad.

Sideband holography was first attempted experimentally by Möllenstedt and Wahl (1968), closely followed by Tonomura (1969) and Tomita *et al.* (1970a, b, 1972). A discussion of the theory by Hoppe *et al.* appeared in 1970. Further experiments were performed by Crewe and Saxon (1971) and Saxon (1972a, b) and by Wahl (1973, 1974, 1975); as we have mentioned, Munch (1975) examined both the sideband and in-line modes. With the exception of the work of Tonomura (1969), a biprism is used in all these experiments.

Tomita *et al.* (1970a, b, 1972) obtained a resolution of about 2 nm which agrees with the simple formula (4.36) to within a factor of two for $a = 5$ μrad and $\Delta = 100$ μm. Saxon (1972a, b) used a field emission gun ($a = 0.15$ μrad) and $\Delta = 100$ mm so that $2a\Delta = 30$ nm; he in fact obtained a resolution of the order of 50 nm. Munch (1975) obtained a resolution of the order of 5 nm with $2a \approx 1$ μrad and $\Delta = 25$ μm, so that $2a\Delta \approx 25$ pm.

Wahl (1973, 1974, 1975) has concentrated on image-plane holography, in which the hologram plane is conjugate to the specimen, and which is known to be particularly insensitive to source spatial coherence, although as usual the latter does restrict the field of view (Rosen, 1966; Brandt, 1969). Operating with $a \approx 10$ μrad, Wahl found that the dominant effect limiting the resolution of his reconstructed images was the energy spread of the electron beam; he nevertheless obtained a resolution of the order of 3 nm. A type of image-plane holography is proposed in an ingenious suggestion of Bates and Lewitt (1975), in which the main beam and individual diffracted beams, or groups of such beams, are allowed to interfere in the image plane of the microscope. The method requires special diffraction plane masks but these should not be unduly difficult to fabricate. The source coherence requirements appear to be no more severe than in any other interferometric or holographic technique. A practical problem associated with the scheme of Bates and Lewitt has been raised by Pozzi (1977), namely, that "in actual TEM work, high resolution images of crystal lattices are obtained only with low order diffracted beams and these do not provide the un-modulated reference beam necessary to consider the micrograph as a true image hologram". Pozzi suggests that the method could be used if a biprism were inserted in the back focal plane.

The resolution of the various types of reconstruction has been discussed briefly by Anaskin and Stoyanova (1972).

This does not exhaust the possibilities of holography in the electron microscope: we have merely tried to show what role is played by the electron source coherence in this domain and it is clear that the advent of reliable field-emission sources of very high brightness has rejuvenated many techniques that had been discarded as impractical. The possibility of on-line holography in the STEM has recently been discussed (Veneklasen, 1976) and this preliminary work will no doubt soon generate other experimental and theoretical studies. The holographic aspects of electron microscope image formation, in both the fixed-beam and scanning transmission modes, are analysed briefly in Hanszen and Ade (1976c) and in much greater depth in Hanszen and Ade (1977), with particular reference to the paper by Veneklasen.

2. The Schwarz–Hora effect

In 1969, Schwarz and Hora described an experiment, briefly reported by Schwarz in 1968, in which a 50 kV beam of electrons passing through a crystal appeared to be modulated by a beam of laser light in such a way that it produced the electron diffraction pattern of the crystal at a non-fluorescent target. Considerable efforts were made during the years that followed to elucidate the theory of this effect; a clear account of this work, conveniently divided into categories, is to be found in Favro and Kuo (1973).

Before the phenomenon had been fully analysed, however, abortive attempts to reproduce the effect were made, notably by Hadley et al. (1971); their account of these experiments and the ensuing exchange of notes between Schwarz and various authors focused attention on the need for a very high degree of monochromaticity in the electron beam at least as effectively as the formulae of the theoreticians.

In their attempt to reproduce the Schwarz-Hora effect, Hadley et al. (1971) used a Siemens Elmiskop I at 60 or 80 kV; they estimated the energy spread of the incident beam to be about 0·7 eV (perhaps optimistically). They were unable to detect any effect similar to that described by Schwarz and Hora and, among the reasons for this negative result, they included the possibility that "the effect is much weaker than reported or does not exist at all". In reply, Schwarz (1971b) drew attention to a condition, implicit in his earlier paper (1971a), restricting the permitted voltage spread (ΔV) of the incident beam

$$\frac{\Delta V}{V} < \frac{v\lambda}{cr}$$

where v is the mean electron velocity and r is the distance between the zone of interaction of the laser light with the electron beam and the (non-fluorescent) screen; a similar inequality emerges from the analysis of Favro et al. (1971a). Schwarz stated that, in the original experiment, the limiting value of ΔV was 30 mV and a value of approximately 10 mV was therefore used. In the attempt by Hadley et al. to reproduce the effect, however, the condition was far from satisfied and it was therefore not at all surprising that nothing was seen.

This explanation was challenged by Pfeiffer et al. (1972), who pointed out that the figures given by Schwarz violated Langmuir's law of brightness; Pfeiffer et al. observed—somewhat waspishly—that "it is remarkable that his monochromator exceeds the state of the art by several orders of magnitude". In his rejoinder (Schwarz, 1972a; see also 1972b), after remarking that Pfeiffer et al. seem "to arrive at no other conclusion than that the original experiments were performed under the naive assumption that electron-beam modulation at optical frequencies could be observed at a simple, single electron beam", Schwarz described his experimental arrangement in more detail, making it clear that he had used a beam consisting of many separated filaments; his claims did not therefore conflict with any fundamental principles. The number of filaments is, however, limited (Farago and Sillitto, 1974a, b).

Meanwhile, more light had been shed on the essential conditions that must be respected if the effect is to be seen by Hora (1970) and Favro et al. (1970, 1971a, b, 1973). The latter gave first non-relativistic and later relativistic expressions for the spatial damping of the effect; their curves (Fig. 12) show clearly that the energy spread of the beam is of paramount importance and their formula confirms that Hadley et al. (1971) failed to observe the Schwarz–Hora effect because the energy spread was far too large in their experiment. An explanation of the effect in terms of the electron interference phenomena first described by Ehrenberg and Siday (1949)—the Bohm–Aharanov effect—was attempted by Korobochko et al. (1972).

Finally, the detailed quantum mechanical treatment of the effect by Favro and Kuo (1973) dispelled all doubts as to the reality and origin of the effect. These authors showed that electron-electron phase correlations

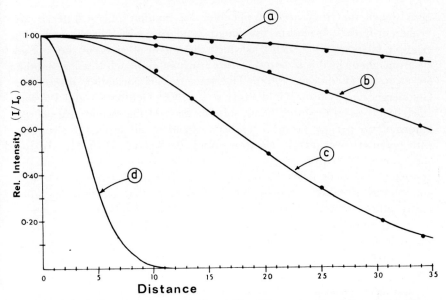

Fig. 12. Visibility of the Schwarz–Hora effect. The curves show the relative fringe intensity for various values of the electron beam energy spread (ΔE) over a short period and of the size ΔS of the exit diaphragm of the velocity-selecting magnet. The abscissa is the distance (in cm) to the plane of observation. The points correspond to Schwarz and Hora's original experiment. a: $\Delta E = 5.5$ meV, $\Delta S = 5$ μm; b: $\Delta E = 11$ meV, $\Delta S = 10$ μm; c: $\Delta E = 22$ meV, $\Delta S = 20$ μm; d: $\Delta E = 110$ meV, $\Delta S = 100$ μm. (After Favro et al., 1971b.)

are produced when the beam first interacts with the electromagnetic radiation: coherence is in effect transferred from the radiation field to the electron beam. The electrons subsequently exhibit collective behaviour in such a way that the coherence properties of the original radiation reappear when radiation is re-emitted by the electron beam.

Very full bibliographies are to be found in Schwarz (1975) and in a paper by Hora (1975), on the possibility that the electrons emitted by a photocathode from which a laser beam is totally reflected exhibit some quantum-mechanical modulation. More recently, Hora (1977) has proposed a formula that predicts a "beating wavelength" in good agreement with the (exceedingly sparse) experimental evidence.

V. CONCLUDING REMARKS

Coherence has received far less attention in electron optics than in classical optics and some approaches that have been found valuable for photons have yet to be explored for electrons, though in some cases it has been shown that they are inapplicable. An example of the latter is the "coherent-states" formalism associated primarily with Glauber (see for example Glauber, 1969, 1970) in which the notion of coherent states of an electromagnetic field is a central feature; such an approach is not so suitable for electrons (Ledinegg, 1967). The wave packet formalism devised by Goldberger and Watson (Goldberger *et al.*, 1963; Goldberger and Watson, 1964, 1965) is, on the other hand, suitable for studying second order corre-lations of any particle beam; it has been extended and applied to electrons, with potential relevance in electron optics, by Bénard (1970a, b). In two very interesting papers, Every (1973, 1975) has attempted to extend this approach to electron fields. He discusses the differences between the electron and photon situations, consequences of the fact that electron operators satisfy anti-commutation rules (cf. Bowring *et al.*, 1971) and proposes a better definition of electron optical coherence than that due to Rocca(1973), which leaned very heavily on its optical counterpart. His papers form a good foundation for further development of quantum electron coherence theory.

Another approach to the study of coherence has yielded the matrix formalism developed independently by Gamo and Gabor, a full account of which is to be found in a review by Gamo (1964). This technique exploits the finite extent of the information-carrying beam from the outset; it should therefore be particularly suitable when computer image processing is envisaged since the arrays of sample values that must then be manipulated are intimately related to the matrices in terms of which the theory is ex-pressed (Hawkes, 1976a).

A branch of coherence theory that has been extensively studied in light optics and exploited in practice in a variety of ways is concerned with speckle patterns (Dainty, 1976a, b). Image speckle patterns have of course been studied in electron optics as we have mentioned in this review but the example of light optics suggests that there is more to be extracted from them than is realized at present; the paper by Frank (1976a) discussed in detail in Part B of Section IV illustrates this clearly.

All studies of electron optical coherence lean heavily on the optical theory but there are differences between photons, which are bosons, and electrons, which are fermions, that prevent the analogy between the two from being perfect. For example, electrons are subject to the exclusion principle, unlike photons. This point is raised by Ferwerda (1976a), who comments that the electron beams used in electron microscopy are so weak that the wave functions do not overlap. (In some of the experiments of Munch, 1975, for example, there was on average only one electron in the microscope at any given time.) Moreover, spin should be taken into account in a fully relativistic treatment of partial coherence but, again, the effects are so small that the adjustments that are usually made in electron optical calculations to incorporate relativistic effects above about 100 kV can be expected to be adequate. The short transition zone between the filament and the region beyond the electron gun needs a careful analysis, since the electron beam is converted from a far from monochromatic state (in the sense that $\Delta\lambda/\lambda$ is large) to a truly quasi-monochromatic condition.

Finally, the extremely short wavelength of electrons may be expected to lead to effects not normally considered in light optics, as Fertig and Rose have pointed out (1977a); the difference arises because the smallest scattering units, individual atoms of the specimen, have effective radii much larger than the electron wavelength and, if efforts to reduce the spherical aberration are successful, larger than the smallest resolvable spacing. When calculating the degree of coherence (and hence the intensity) at the image, it will therefore be necessary to consider the three-dimensional distribution of scatterers in the specimen. This and related points are discussed at some length in the paper by Fertig and Rose.

We conclude on a warning note: a large part of this review has been concerned with the expression of image formation in terms of transfer functions when the illumination is partially coherent. This in turn has led us to lean heavily on the concept of the weakly scattering specimen, the "weak-phase, weak-amplitude object". In the vast majority of real situations, however, such a specimen is no more than a convenient fiction. It permits us to describe the image-forming properties of the microscope in a relatively simple way and gives a good first approximation to the effects observed but no more (Misell, 1976). Not only do we need to consider specimens that scatter more strongly but we should also enquire whether the representation of the specimen by a complex transparency, $\sigma(\mathbf{x}_o)$, is adequate; more generally, we ought certainly to consider the relation between the influence of the specimen and the direction of the beam electrons, thus representing the specimen by a function of both position $(\mathbf{x}_o)$ and direction $(\mathbf{x}_o')$: instead of $\sigma(\mathbf{x}_o)$, we should write $\sigma(\mathbf{x}_o, \mathbf{x}_o')$. This point has been raised by Lenz (1976) but has not yet been pursued in any detail.

REFERENCES‡

Ade, G. (1973). "Der Einfluss der Bildfehler dritter Ordnung auf die elektronen-mikroskopische Abbildung und die Korrektur dieser Fehler durch holographische Rekonstruktion". Dissertation, Braunschweig and PTB-Bericht, APh-3.

Ade, G. (1975). *Optik* **42**, 199–215.

‡ In addition to the papers referred to in the text, a number of introductory or tutorial works are included in this list, in particular Lenz (1965, 1971) and Zeitler (1975, 1976).

Ade. G. (1977). *Optik* **49,** 113–116.

Anaskin, I. F. and Stoyanova, I. G. (1967). *Dokl. Akad. Nauk SSSR* **174,** 56–59. (English transl. in *Sov. Phys. Doklady* **12,** 447–450.)

Anaskin, I. F. and Stoyanova, I. G. (1968a). *Radiotekh. Elektron.* **13,** 913–920. (English transl. in *Radio Eng. Electron. Phys.* **13,** 789–794.)

Anaskin, I. F. and Stoyanova, I. G. (1968b). *Radiotekh. Elektron.* **13,** 1031–1040. (English transl. in *Radio Eng. Electron. Phys.* **13,** 895–902.)

Anaskin, I. F. and Stoyanova, I. G. (1968c). *Radiotekh. Elektron.* **13,** 1273–1280. (English transl. in *Radio Eng. Electron. Phys.* **13,** 1104–1110.)

Anaskin, I. F. and Stoyanova, I. G. (1968d). *Proc. 4th Eur. Reg. Conf. Electron Microscopy, Rome* **1,** 147–148.

Anaskin, I. F. and Stoyanova, I. G. (1968e). *Proc. 4th Eur. Reg. Conf. Electron Microscopy, Rome* **1,** 149–150.

Anaskin, I. F. and Stoyanova, I. G. (1972). *Proc. 5th Eur. Cong. Electron Microscopy, Manchester,* pp. 636–637.

Anaskin, I. F., Stoyanova, I. G. and Chyapas, A. F. (1966). *Izv. Akad. Nauk. SSSR (Ser. Fiz.)* **30,** 766–768. (English transl. in *Bull. Acad. Sci. USSR (Phys. Ser.)* **30,** 793–796.)

Anaskin, I. F., Stoyanova, I. G. and Shpagina, M. D. (1968). *Izv. Akad. Nauk SSSR (Ser. Fiz.)* **32,** 1016–1021. (English transl. in *Bull. Acad. Sci. USSR (Phys. Ser.)* **32,** 941–946.)

Anstis, G. R. and O'Keefe, M. A. (1976). *Proc. 34th Annual Meeting EMSA, Miami Beach,* pp. 480–481.

Anstis, G. R., Iijima, S. and O'Keefe, M. A. (1977/8). *Acta Cryst. A* (to be published).

Arsenault, H. and Lowenthal, S. (1969). *C.r. hebd. Séanc. Acad. Sci., Paris* **B269,** 518–521.

Asakura, T., Fujii, H. and Murata, K. (1972). *Opt. Acta* **19,** 273–290.

Baltes, H. P. (1977). *Appl. Phys.* **12,** 221–244.

Barnett, M. E. (1973). *Optik* **38,** 585–588.

Barnett, M. E. (1974a). *J. Microscopy* **102,** 1–28.

Barnett, M. E. (1974b). *Optik* **39,** 470–474.

Barus, C. (1911 and 1912). *Carnegie Inst. Wash. Publ.* No. 149.

Bastiaans, M. J. (1977a). *Opt. Acta* **24,** 261–274.

Bastiaans, M. J. (1977b). *Opt. Commun.* **21,** 321–323.

Bates, R. H. and Lewitt, R. M. (1975). *Optik* **44,** 1–16.

Beck, V. (1977). *Ultramicroscopy* **2,** 351–360.

Beer, M., Frank, J., Hanszen, K.-J., Kellenberger, E. and Williams, R. C. (1975). *Q. Rev. Biophys.* **7,** 211–238.

Bénard, C. (1970a). *Phys. Rev.* **A2,** 2140–2153.

Bénard, C. M. (1970b). Particle beam fluctuations in quantum mechanics. *In* "Quantum Optics" (S. M. Kay and A. Maitland, eds), pp. 535–544. Academic Press, London and New York.

Beorchia, A. and Bonhomme, P. (1974). *Optik* **39,** 437–442.

Beran, M. and Parrent, G. B. (1963). *Nuovo Cim.* **27,** 1049–1065.

Beran, M. J. and Parrent, G. B. (1964). "Theory of Partial Coherence". Prentice-Hall, Englewood Cliffs, N.J.

Boersch, H. (1954). *Z. Phys.* **139,** 115–146.

Boersch, H. (1967). *Phys. Bl.* **23,** 393–404.

Bonhomme, P. and Laberrigue, A. (1969). *J. Microscopie* **8,** 795–798.

Bonhomme, P., Beorchia, A. and Bonnet, N. (1973). *C.r. hebd. Séanc. Acad. Sci., Paris* **B277,** 83–86.

Born, M. and Wolf, E. (1959). "Principles of Optics". Pergamon Press, Oxford. (Fifth and most recent ed., 1975.)

Bowring, I. M., Perlman, H. S., Troup, G. J. and McLaren, A. C. (1971). *Phys. Lett.* **34A,** 275–276.

Brandt., G. B. (1969). *Appl. Opt.* **8,** 1421–1429.

Burge, R. E. (1973). *J. Microscopy* **98,** 251–285.

Burge, R. E. and Dainty, J. C. (1976). *Optik* **46,** 229–240.

Burge, R. E. and Scott, R. F. (1975). *Optik* **43,** 503–507.

Burge, R. E. and Scott, R. F. (1976). *Optik* **44,** 159–172.

Burge, R. E., Dainty, J. C. and Thom, J. (1976a). *In* "Developments in Electron Microscopy and Analysis" (J. A. Venables, ed.), pp. 221–224. Academic Press, London and New York.

Burge, R. E., Dainty, J. C. and Thom, J. (1976b). *Proc. 6th Eur. Cong. Electron Microscopy, Jerusalem* **1,** 256–258.

Carter, W. H. and Wolf, E. (1975). *J. opt. Soc. Am.* **65,** 1067–1071.

Carter, W. H. and Wolf, E. (1977). *J. opt. Soc. Am.* **67,** 785–796.

Chiu, W. and Glaeser, R. M. (1977). *Ultramicroscopy* **2,** 207–217.

Cittert, P. H. van (1934). *Physica* **1,** 201–210.

Collier, R. J., Burckhardt, C. B. and Lin, L. H. (1971). "Optical Holography". Academic Press, New York and London.

Cowley, J. M. (1969). *Appl. Phys. Lett.* **15,** 58–59.

Cowley, J. M. (1975a). *J. Phys.* **D8,** L77–79.

Cowley, J. M. (1975b). Contrast in high-resolution bright-field and dark-field images of thin specimens. *In* "Physical Aspects of Electron Microscopy and Microbeam Analysis" (B. M. Siegel, ed.), pp. 3–15. Wiley, New York and London.

Cowley, J. M. (1975c). A comparison of scanning and fixed beam high-voltage electron microscopy. *In* "Physical Aspects of Electron Microscopy and Microbeam Analysis" (B. M. Siegel, ed.), pp. 17–28. Wiley, New York and London.

Cowley, J. M. (1976a). *Proc. 34th Annual Meeting EMSA, Miami Beach,* pp. 466–467.

Cowley, J. M. (1976b). *Ultramicroscopy* **2,** 3–16.

Crewe, A. V. (1970). *Q. Rev. Biophys.* **3,** 137–175.

Crewe, A. V. and Saxon, J. [sic] (1971). *Proc. 29th Annual Meeting EMSA, Boston,* pp. 12–13.

Crewe, A. V. and Wall, J. (1970). *Optik* **30,** 461–474.

Crewe, A. V., Langmore, J. P. and Isaacson, M. S. (1975). Resolution and contrast in the scanning electron microscope. *In* "Physical Aspects of Electron Microscopy and Microbeam Analysis" (B. M. Siegel, ed.), pp. 47–62. Wiley, New York and London.

Dainty, J. C. (1973). *Opt. Commun.* **7,** 129–134.

Dainty, J. C. (1976a). *Prog. Opt.* **14,** 1–46.

Dainty, J. C., ed. (1976b). "Laser Speckle and Related Phenomena". Springer, Berlin and New York.

Dainty, J. C. (1976c). Stellar speckle interferometry". *In* "Laser Speckle and Related Phenomena" (J. C. Dainty, ed.), pp. 255–280. Springer, Berlin and New York.

De, M. and Basuray, A. (1972). *Opt. Acta* **19,** 307–318 and 523–531.

Dekkers, N. H. and Lang, H. de (1974). *Optik* **41,** 452–456.

Dekkers, N. H. and Lang, H. de (1977). *Philips Tech. Rev.* **37,** 1–9.

Dekkers, N. H., Lang, H. de and Mast, K. D. van der (1976). *J. Microsc. Spectrosc. Electron.* **1**, 511–512.

DeVelis, J. B., Parrent, G. B. and Thompson, B. J. (1966). *J. opt. Soc. Am.* **56**, 423–427.

Dowell, W. C. T. and Goodman, P. (1976). *Optik* **45**, 93–96.

Downing, K. H. (1975). *Optik* **43**, 199–203.

Drahoš, V. and Delong, A. (1964). *Opt. Acta* **11**, 173–181.

Drahoš, V. and Delong, A. (1970). *Proc. 7th int. Cong. Electron Microscopy, Grenoble* **2**, 147–148.

Drahoš, V. and Delong, A. (1971). *Czech. J. Phys.* **B21**, 604–613.

Düker, H. (1955). *Z. Naturf.* **10a**, 256.

Dupouy, G. and Perrier, F. (1970). *Proc. 7th int. Cong. Electron Microscopy, Grenoble* **1**, 129–130.

Dupouy, G., Perrier, F., Enjalbert, L., Lapchine, L. and Verdier, P. (1969). *C.r. hebd. Séanc. Acad. Sci., Paris* **B268**, 1341–1345.

Dutta, K. and Goodman, J. W. (1977). *J. Opt. Soc. Am.* **67**, 796–803.

Ehrenberg, W. and Siday, R. E. (1949). *Proc. phys. Soc.* **B62**, 8–21.

Engel, A. (1974). *Optik* **41**, 117–126.

Engel, A., Wiggins, J. W. and Woodruff, D. C. (1974). *J. appl. Phys.* **45**, 2739–2747.

Erickson, H. P. (1973). *Adv. Opt. Electron Microsc.* **5**, 163–199.

Erickson, H. P. and Klug, A. (1970a). *Ber. Bunsen. Ges. Phys. Chem.* **74**, 1129–1137.

Erickson, H. P. and Klug, A. (1970b). *Proc. 28th Annual Meeting EMSA, Houston*, pp. 248–249.

Erickson, H. P. and Klug, A. (1971). *Phil. Trans. R. Soc.* **B261**, 105–118.

Every, I. M. (1973). *J. Phys.* **A6**, 1375–1382.

Every, I. M. (1975). *J. Phys.* **A8**, 133–141.

Faget, J. and Fert, C. (1956). *C.r. hebd. Séanc. Acad. Sci., Paris* **243**, 2028–2029.

Faget, J. and Fert, C. (1957). *Cah. Phys.* **11**, 285–296.

Farago, P. S. and Sillitto, R. M. (1974a). *Phys. Lett.* **A47**, 481–482.

Farago, P. S. and Sillitto, R. M. (1974b). *Proc. R. Soc. Edinb.* **A71**, 305–321.

Favro, L. D. and Kuo, P. K. (1973). *Phys. Rev.* **A7**, 866–872.

Favro, L. D., Fradkin, D. M. and Kuo, P. K. (1970). *Nuovo Cim. Lett.* **4**, 1147–1150.

Favro, L. D., Fradkin, D. M. and Kuo, P. K. (1971a). *Phys. Rev.* **D3**, 2934–2937.

Favro, L. D., Fradkin, D. M., Kuo, P. K. and Rolnick, W. B. (1971b). *Appl. Phys. Lett.* **19**, 378–380.

Favro, L. D., Fradkin, D. M., Kuo, P. K. and Rolnick, W. B. (1973). Electron beams as carriers of optical coherence. *In* "Coherence and Quantum Optics" (L. Mandel and E. Wolf, eds), pp. 547–550. Plenum, New York.

Fellgett, P. B. (1953). *J. opt. Soc. Am.* **43**, 271–282.

Ferrier, R. P. (1969). *Adv. Opt. Electron Microsc.* **3**, 155–218.

Fert, C. (1961). Interférences en optique électronique et microscopie électronique interférentielle. *In* "Traité de Microscopie électronique" (C. Magnan, ed.), Vol. 1, pp. 356–366. Hermann, Paris.

Fertig, J. and Rose, H. (1977a). *Ultramicroscopy* **2**, 269–279.

Fertig, J. and Rose, H. (1977b). *Proc. 35th Annual Meeting EMSA, Boston*, pp. 192–193.

Ferwerda, H. A. (1976a). *Optik* **45**, 411–426.

Ferwerda, H. A. (1976b). *Proc. 6th Eur. Cong. Electron Microscopy, Jerusalem* **1**, 261–262.

Ferwerda, H. A. and Heel, M. G. van (1977). *Optik* **47**, 357–362.

Françon, M. and Mallick, S. (1967). *Prog. Opt.* **6**, 71–104.

Frank, J. (1973). *Optik* **38**, 519–536.

Frank, J. (1975a). *Optik* **43**, 103–109.

Frank, J. (1975b). *Proc. 33rd Annual Meeting EMSA, Las Vegas*, pp. 182–183.
Frank, J. (1976a). *Optik* **44**, 379–391.
Frank, J. (1976b). *Proc. 6th Eur. Cong. Electron Microscopy, Jerusalem* **1**, 97–98.
Frank, J., Bussler, P., Langer, R. and Hoppe, W. (1970). *Ber. Bunsen-Ges. Phys. Chem.* **74**, 1105–1115.
Frank, J., Salih, S. M. and Cosslett, V. E. (1974). *Proc. 8th int. Cong. Electron Microscopy, Canberra* **2**, 678–679.
Franke, G. (1966). *Optik* **23**, 20–25.
Franzen, W. and Porter, J. H. (1975). *Adv. Electron. Electron Phys.* **39**, 73–119.
Frieden, B. R. (1966). *J. Opt. Soc. Am.* **56**, 1355–1362.
Fujii, H. and Asakura, T. (1973). *Optik* **39**, 99–117 and 284–302.
Fujii, H. and Asakura, T. (1974). *Opt. Commun.* **12**, 32–38.
Gabor, D. (1948). *Nature* **161**, 777–778.
Gabor, D. (1949). *Proc. R. Soc. Lond.* **A197**, 454–487.
Gabor, D. (1951). *Proc. phys. Soc.* **B64**, 449–469.
Gabor, D. (1956). *Rev. mod. Phys.* **28**, 260–276.
Gabor, D. (1968/9). *Optik* **28**, 437–441.
Gamo, H. (1964). *Prog. Opt.* **3**, 187–332.
Gerchberg, R. W. and Saxton, W. O. (1972). *Optik* **35**, 237–246.
Gerchberg, R. W. and Saxton, W. O. (1973). Wave phase from image and diffraction plane pictures. *In* "Image Processing and Computer-aided Design in Electron Optics" (P. W. Hawkes, ed.), pp. 66–81. Academic Press, London and New York.
Glaser, W. (1952). "Grundlagen der Elektronenoptik". Springer, Vienna.
Glauber, R. J. (1969). Coherence and quantum detection. *In* "Quantum Optics" (R. J. Glauber, ed.), pp. 15–56. Academic Press, London and New York.
Glauber, R. J. (1970). Quantum theory of coherence. *In* "Quantum Optics" (S. M. Kay and A. Maitland, eds), pp. 53–125. Academic Press, London and New York.
Goldberger, M. L. and Watson, K. M. (1964). *Phys. Rev.* **B134**, 919–928.
Goldberger, M. L. and Watson, K. M. (1965). *Phys. Rev.* **B137**, 1396–1409.
Goldberger, M. L., Lewis, H. W. and Watson, K. M. (1963). *Phys. Rev.* **132**, 2764–2787.
Goldfarb, W., Krakow, W., Ast, D. and Siegel, B. (1975). *Proc. 33rd Annual EMSA Meeting, Las Vegas*, pp. 186–187.
Guigay, J. P., Wade, R. H. and Delpla, C. (1971). *In* "Electron Microscopy and Analysis" (W. C. Nixon, ed.), pp. 238–239 (*Proc. 25th Anniv. Meeting EMAG, Institute of Physics, Cambridge*). Institute of Physics, London.
Hadley, R., Lynch, D. W., Stanek, E. and Rosauer, E. A. (1971). *Appl. Phys. Lett.* **19**, 145–147.
Hahn, M. H. (1973). "Theoretische und experimentelle Untersuchungen zum Nachweis von Einzelatomen mit Durchstrahlungs-Elektronenmikroskopen". Dissertation, Düsseldorf.
Hahn, M. and Seredynski, J. (1974). *Proc. 8th int. Cong. Electron Microscopy, Canberra* **1**, 234–235.
Haine, M. E. and Dyson, J. (1950). *Nature* **166**, 315–316.
Haine, M. E. and Mulvey, T. (1950). *Proc. 1st int. Cong. Electron Microscopy, Paris*, pp. 120–125 (published in 1953).
Haine, M. E. and Mulvey, T. (1952). *J. opt. Soc. Am.* **42**, 763–773.
Hanszen, K.-J. (1970a). *Proc. 7th int. Cong. Electron Microscopy, Grenoble* **1**, 21–22.
Hanszen, K.-J. (1970b). *Optik* **32**, 74–90.
Hanszen, K.-J. (1971). *Adv. Opt. Electron Microsc.* **4**, 1–84.

Hanszen, K.-J. (1972a). *Optik* **35**, 431–444.

Hanszen, K.-J. (1972b). *Optik* **36**, 41–54.

Hanszen, K.-J. (1973a). Contrast transfer and image processing. *In* "Image Processing and Computer-aided Design in Electron Optics" (P. W. Hawkes, ed.), pp. 16–53. Academic Press, London and New York.

Hanszen, K.-J. (1973b). "Neuere theoretische Erkenntnisse und praktische Erfahrungen über die holographische Rekonstruktion elektronenmikroskopischer Aufnahmen". PTB-Bericht, APh-4.

Hanszen, K.-J. (1974a). "The relevance of dark-field illumination in conventional and scanning transmission electron microscopy". PTB-Bericht APh-7.

Hanszen, K.-J. (1974b). *Optik* **39**, 520–542.

Hanszen, K.-J. (1975). "In-line Holographie unter schräger Beleuchtung ohne Objektivapertur-Begrenzung", presented at the Berlin meeting of the Deutsche Gesellschaft für Elektronenmikroskopie in September 1975; see Hanszen (1976) and Hanszen and Ade (1976b).

Hanszen, K.-J. (1976). *Proc. 6th Eur. Cong. Electron Microscopy, Jerusalem* **1**, 95–96.

Hanszen, K.-J. and Ade, G. (1974a). "Problems and results of the optical transfer theory and of reconstruction methods in electron microscopy". PTB-Bericht APh-5.

Hanszen, K.-J. and Ade, G. (1974b). *Proc. 8th int. Cong. Electron Microscopy, Canberra* **1**, 196–197.

Hanszen, K.-J. and Ade, G. (1975). *Optik* **42**, 1–22.

Hanszen, K.-J. and Ade, G. (1976a). *Optik* **44**, 237–249.

Hanszen, K.-J. and Ade, G. (1976b). "Aspects of some image reconstruction and holographic methods in electron microscopy". PTB-Bericht APh-10.

Hanszen, K.-J. and Ade, G. (1976c). *Proc. 6th Eur. Cong. Electron Microscopy, Jerusalem* **1**, 446–447.

Hanszen, K.-J. and Ade, G. (1977). "A consistent Fourier optical representation of image formation in the conventional fixed beam electron microscope, in the scanning transmission electron microscope and of holographic reconstruction". PTB-Bericht APh-11.

Hanszen, K.-J. and Trepte, L. (1970). *Proc. 7th int. Cong. Electron Microscopy, Grenoble* **1**, 45–46.

Hanszen, K.-J. and Trepte, L. (1971a). *Optik* **32**, 519–538.

Hanszen, K.-J. and Trepte, L. (1971b). *Optik* **33**, 166–198.

Hanszen, K.-J., Rosenbruch, K.-J. and Sunder-Plassmann, F.-A. (1965). *Z. angew. Phys.* **18**, 345–350.

Hanszen, K.-J., Ade, G. and Lauer, R. (1972a). *Optik* **35**, 567–590.

Hanszen, K.-J., Lauer, R. and Ade, G. (1972b). *Optik* **36**, 156–159.

Harada, Y., Goto, T. and Someya, T. (1974). *Proc. 32nd Annual Meeting EMSA, St Louis*, pp. 388–389.

Hardy, D. F. (1974). *Proc. 8th int. Cong. Electron Microscopy, Canberra* **1**, 124–125.

Hauser, H. (1962). *Opt. Acta* **9**, 121–140 and 141–148.

Hawkes, P. W. (1973). Introduction to electron optical transfer theory. *In* "Image Processing and Computer-aided Design in Electron Optics" (P. W. Hawkes, ed.), pp. 2–14. Academic Press, London and New York.

Hawkes, P. W. (1974a). *Optik* **40**, 539–556.

Hawkes, P. W. (1974b). *Optik* **41**, 64–68.

Hawkes, P. W. (1976a). *Proc. 6th Eur. Cong. Electron Microscopy, Jerusalem* **1**, 259–260.

Hawkes, P. W. (1976b). *Optik* **46**, 357–359.

Hawkes, P. W. (1977a). *Optik* **47**, 453–467.
Hawkes, P. W. (1977b). *Optik* **48**, 253.
Hawkes, P. W. (1977c). *In* "Developments in Electron Microscopy and Analysis" (D. L. Misell, ed.). Institute of Physics, Bristol. pp. 123–126.
Hawkes, P. W. (1977d). *Optik* **49**, 149–161.
Heidenreich, R. D. (1964). "Fundamentals of Transmission Electron Microscopy". Wiley-Interscience, New York and London.
Heinemann, K. and Poppa, H. (1970a). *Appl. Phys. Lett.* **16**, 515–516.
Heinemann, K. and Poppa, H. (1970b). *Proc. 28th Annual Meeting EMSA, Houston,* pp. 538–539.
Hibi, T. (1974). *Proc. 8th int. Cong. Electron Microscopy, Canberra* **1**, 208–209.
Hibi, T. and Takahashi, S. (1969). *Z. angew. Phys.* **27**, 132–138.
Hibi, T. and Takahashi, S. (1970). *Proc. 7th int. Cong. Electron Microscopy, Grenoble* **1**, 43–44.
Hibi, T. and Takahashi, S. (1971). *J. Electron Microsc.* **20**, 17–22.
Hibi, T. and Yada, K. (1976). Electron inference microscope. *In* "Principles and Techniques of Electron Microscopy" (M. A. Hayat, ed.), vol. 6, pp. 312–343. Van Nostrand Reinhold, New York and London.
Hirt, A. and Hoppe, W. (1972). *Proc. 5th Eur. Cong. Electron Microscopy, Manchester,* pp. 12–13.
Hoch, H. (1976). "Berechnung der Stromdichte in Dunkelfeldabbildern von schwachen Phasenobjekten". Dissertation, Tübingen.
Hoch, H. (1977). *Optik* **47**, 65–85.
Hopkins, H. H. (1951). *Proc. R. Soc. Lond.* **A208**, 263–277.
Hoppe, W. (1974). *Naturwissenschaften* **61**, 239–249.
Hoppe, W. and Köstler, D. (1976). *Proc. 6th Eur. Cong. Electron Microscopy, Jerusalem* **1**, 99–104.
Hoppe, W., Langer, R. and Thon, F. (1970). *Optik* **30**, 538–545.
Hoppe, W., Köstler, D. and Sieber, P. (1974). *Z. Naturf.* **29a**, 1933–1934.
Hoppe, W., Köstler, D., Typke, D. and Hunsmann, N. (1975). *Optik* **42**, 43–56.
Hora, H. (1970). *Phys. stat. sol.* (b) **42**, 131–136.
Hora, H. (1975). *Nuovo Cim.* **26B**, 295–308.
Hora, H. (1977). *Phys. stat. sol.* (b) **80**, 143–147.
Howie, A. (1972). *Proc. 5th Eur. Cong. Electron Microscopy, Manchester,* 408–413.
Howie, A., Krivanek, O. L. and Rudee, M. L. (1973). *Phil. Mag.* **27**, 235–255.
Hutchison, J. L. (1976). *In* "Developments in Electron Microscopy and Analysis" (J. A. Venables, ed.), pp. 241–244. Academic Press, London and New York.
Jakeman, E. and Welford, W. T. (1977). *Opt. Commun.* **21**, 72–79.
Johansen, B. V. (1973). *Micron* **4**, 121–135.
Kano, Y. and Wolf, E. (1962). *Proc. phys. Soc.* **80**, 1273–1276.
Kiselev, A. G. and Sherman, M. B. (1976). *Optik* **46**, 55–60.
Kohler, D. and Mandel, L. (1973). *J. opt. Soc. Am.* **63**, 126–134.
Komoda, T. (1972). *Proc. 30th Annual Meeting EMSA, Los Angeles,* pp. 548–549.
Komrska, J. (1971). *Adv. Electron. Electron Phys.* **30**, 139–234.
Komrska, J. (1975). *Čs. Čas. Fyz.* **A25**, 1–13.
Komrska, J. and Lenc, M. (1970). *Proc. 7th int. Cong. Electron Microscopy, Grenoble* **1**, 67–68.
Komrska, J., Drahoš, V. and Delong, A. (1967). *Opt. Acta* **14**, 147–167.
Korobochko, Yu. S., Grachev, B. D. and Mineev, V. I. (1972). *Zh. Tekh. Fiz.* **42**, 2422–2424. (English transl. in *Sov. Phys. Tech. Phys.* **17**, 1880–1881.)

Krakow, W. (1976a). *In* "Developments in Electron Microscopy and Analysis" (J. A. Venables, ed.), pp. 261–264. Academic Press, London and New York.

Krakow, W. (1976b). *Proc. 34th Annual Meeting EMSA, Miami Beach*, pp. 566–567.

Krakow, W. (1977). *Proc. 35th Annual Meeting EMSA, Boston*, pp. 72–73.

Krakow, W. and Howland, L. A. (1976). *Ultramicroscopy* **2**, 53–67.

Krakow, W., Ast, D. G., Goldfarb, W and Siegel, B. M. (1976). *Phil. Mag.* **33**, 985–1014.

Krivanek, O. L. (1975). *Optik* **43**, 361–372.

Krivanek, O. L. (1976a). *Proc. 6th Eur. Cong. Electron Microscopy, Jerusalem* **1**, 263–264.

Krivanek, O. L. (1976b). *Proc. 6th Eur. Cong. Electron Microscopy, Jerusalem* **1**, 275–276.

Krivanek, O. L. and Howie, A. (1975). *J. appl. Cryst.* **8**, 213–219.

Ledinegg, E. (1967). *Z. Phys.* **205**, 25–34.

Leith, E. N. and Upatnieks, J. (1962). *J. opt. Soc. Am.* **52**, 1123–1130.

Leith, E. N. and Upatnieks, J. (1967). *Prog. Opt.* **6**, 1–52.

Lenz, F. (1965). *Lab. Invest.* **14**, 808–818.

Lenz, F. (1971). Transfer of image information in the electron microscope. *In* "Electron Microscopy in Material Science" (U. Valdrè, ed.), pp. 540–569. Academic Press, New York and London.

Lenz, F. (1972). *Z. Phys.* **249**, 462–464.

Lenz, F. (1973). Bildentstehung in der Raster-Transmissions-Elektronenmikroskopie. *In* "Höchstauflösung in der Elektronenmikroskopie", pp. 2–10. Proc. Kontron Seminar, Munich.

Lenz, F. (1976). *In* "Developments in Electron Microscopy and Analysis" (J. A. Venables, ed.), pp. 179–184. Academic Press, London and New York.

Lenz, F. and Wilska, A. P. (1966/7). *Optik* **24**, 383–396.

Lichte, H., Möllenstedt, G. and Wahl, H. (1972). *Z. Phys.* **249**, 456–461.

Linfoot, E. H. (1956). *J. opt. Soc. Am.* **46**, 740–752.

Linfoot, E. H. (1957). *Opt. Acta* **4**, 12–16.

Linfoot, E. H. (1960). "Qualitätsbewertung optischer Bilder". Vieweg, Braunschweig.

Linfoot, E. H. (1964). "Fourier Methods in Optical Image Evaluation". Focal Press, London and New York.

Loeffler, K. H. (1969). *Z. angew. Phys.* **27**, 145–149.

Loeffler, K. H. and Hudgin, R. H. (1970). *Proc. 7th int. Cong. Electron Microscopy, Grenoble* **2**, 67–68.

Maclachlan, M. E. C. (1977). *Optik* **47**, 363–364.

Mandel, L. (1963). *Prog. Opt.* **2**, 181–248.

Mandel, L. and Wolf, E. (1965). *Rev. mod. Phys.* **37**, 231–287.

Mandel, L. and Wolf, E. (1976). *J. Opt. Soc. Am.* **66**, 529–535.

Marathay, A. S. (1976). *Opt. Acta* **23**, 785–794 and 795–798.

Marchand, E. W. and Wolf, E. (1972a). *Opt. Commun.* **6**, 305–308.

Marchand, E. W. and Wolf, E. (1972b). *J. Opt. Soc. Am.* **62**, 379–385.

Marchand, E. W. and Wolf, E. (1974). *J. Opt. Soc. Am.* **64**, 1219–1226.

Marton, L. (1952). *Phys. Rev.* **85**, 1057–1058.

Marton, L., Simpson, J. A. and Suddeth, J. A. (1953). *Phys. Rev.* **90**, 490–491.

Marton, L., Simpson, J. A. and Suddeth, J. A. (1954). *Rev. Scient. Instrum.* **25**, 1099–1104.

Mast, K. D. van der (1975). "A Laser-heated Schottky Emission Gun for Electron Microscopy". Proefschrift, Delft.

Mast, K. D. van der, Barth, J. E. and Le Poole, J. B. (1974). *Proc. 8th int. Conf. Electron Microscopy, Canberra* 1, 120–121.
May, M. (1977). *J. Phys.* **E10**, 849–864.
McFarlane, S. C. (1975). *J. Phys.* **C8**, 2819–2836.
McFarlane, S. C. (1977/8). *Optik*, to be published.
McFarlane, S. C. and Cochran, W. (1975). *J. Phys.* **C8**, 1311–1321.
McLaren, A. C. and MacKenzie, W. S. (1976). *Phys. stat. sol.* (a) **33**, 491–495.
Mehta, C. L. (1965). *Nuovo Cim.* **36**, 202–205.
Mehta, C. L. (1968). *J. Opt. Soc. Am.* **58**, 1233–1234.
Menu, C. and Evrard, D. (1971). *C.r. hebd. Séanc. Acad. Sci., Paris* **B273**, 309–312.
Menzel, E. (1958). *Optik* **15**, 460–470.
Menzel, E. (1960). *In* "Optics in Metrology" (P. Mollet, ed.), pp. 283–293. Pergamon Press, Oxford.
Menzel, E., Mirandé, W. and Weingärtner, I. (1973). "Fourier-Optik und Holographie". Springer, Vienna and New York.
Mirandé, W. and Weingärtner, I. (1969). *Phys. Lett.* **28A**, 623–624.
Mirandé, W., Weingärtner, I. and Menzel, E. (1969). *Optik* **29**, 537–548.
Mirandé, W., Weingärtner, I. and Menzel, E. (1970). *Opt. Commun.* **1**, 315–318.
Misell, D. L. (1971a). *J. Phys.* **A4**, 782–797.
Misell, D. L. (1971b). *J. Phys.* **A4**, 798–812.
Misell, D. L. (1973a). *Adv. Electron. Electron Phys.* **32**, 63–191.
Misell, D. L. (1973b). *J. Phys.* **A6**, 62–78.
Misell, D. L. (1973c). *J. Phys.* **A6**, 205–217.
Misell, D. L. (1976). *J. Phys.* **D9**, 1849–1866.
Misell, D. L. (1977). *J. Phys.* **D10**, 1085–1107.
Misell, D. L. and Atkins, A. J. (1973). *J. Phys.* **A6**, 218–235.
Misell, D. L., Stroke, G. W. and Halioua, M. (1974). *J. Phys.* **D7**, L113–117.
Möllenstedt, G. and Düker, H. (1955). *Naturwissenschaften* **42**, 41.
Möllenstedt, G. and Düker, H. (1956). *Z. Phys.* **145**, 377–397.
Möllenstedt, G. and Jönsson, C. (1959). *Z. Phys.* **155**, 472–474.
Möllenstedt, G. and Wahl, H. (1968). *Naturwissenschaften* **55**, 340–341.
Munch, J. (1975). *Optik* **43**, 79–99.
Munch, J. and Zeitler, E. (1974). *Proc. 32nd Annual Meeting EMSA, St Louis*, pp. 386–387.
Nagata, F., Matsuda, T. and Komoda, T. (1975). *Jap. J. appl. Phys.* **14**, 1815.
Niehrs, H. (1973). *Optik* **38**, 44–63.
Nussenzveig, H. M. (1967). *J. Math. Phys.* **8**, 561–572.
Oberlin, A. (1977). *J. Microsc. Spectrosc. Electron.* **2**, 529–536.
Ohtsuki, M. and Zeitler, E. (1977). *Ultramicroscopy* **2**, 147–148.
O'Neill, E. L. (1963). "Introduction to Statistical Optics". Addison-Wesley, Reading (Mass.) and London.
Papoulis, A. (1965). "Probability, Random Variables and Stochastic Processes". McGraw-Hill, New York and London.
Parry, C. (1976). Speckle patterns in partially coherent light. *In* "Laser Speckle and Related Phenomena" (J. C. Dainty, ed.), pp. 77–121. Springer, Berlin and New York.
Parsons, J. R. and Hoelke, C. W. (1974). *Phil. Mag.* **30**, 135–143.
Peřina, J. (1972). "Coherence of Light". Van Nostrand-Reinhold, London.
Pfeiffer, L., Rousseau, D. L. and Hutson, A. R. (1972). *Appl. Phys. Lett.* **20**, 147–148.
Pozzi, G. (1977). *Optik* **47**, 105–107.

Reimer, L. (1967). "Elektronenmikroskopische Untersuchungs- und Präparations-methoden". Springer, Berlin and New York.

Riecke, W. D. (1964). *Z. Naturf.* **19a**, 1228–1230.

Riecke, W. D. (1972). *Proc. 5th Eur. Cong. Electron Microscopy, Manchester*, pp. 98–103.

Rocca, F. (1973). *Phys. Rev.* **D8**, 4403–4410.

Röhler, R. (1967). "Informationstheorie in der Optik". Wissenschaftliche Verlags-gesellschaft, Stuttgart.

Rose, H. (1974a). *Optik* **39**, 416–436.

Rose, H. (1974b). *Proc. 8th int. Cong. Electron Microscopy, Canberra* **1**, 212–213.

Rose, H. (1975). *Optik* **42**, 217–244.

Rose, H. (1977). *Ultramicroscopy* **2**, 251–267.

Rose, H. and Fertig, J. (1976). *Proc. 34th Annual Meeting EMSA, Miami Beach*, pp. 548–549.

Rose, H. and Fertig, J. (1977). *Proc. 35th Annual Meeting EMSA, Boston*, pp. 200–201.

Rosen, L. (1966). *Appl. Phys. Lett.* **9**, 337–339.

Saleh, B. E. A. (1974). *Opt. Commun.* **10**, 247–249.

Saxon, G. (1972a). *Optik* **35**, 195–210.

Saxon, G. (1972b). *Optik* **35**, 359–375.

Saxton, W. O. (1974). "Computer Techniques for Image Processing in Electron Microscopy". Dissertation, Cambridge.

Saxton, W. O. (1977). *Optik* **49**, 51–62.

Saxton, W. O. (1978). *Adv. Electron. Electron Phys. Suppl.* **10**, 289 pp.

Schaal, G., Jönsson, C. and Krimmel, E. F. (1966/7). *Optik* **24**, 529–538.

Schade, O. H. (1952). *J. Soc. Mot. Pict. Telev. Eng.* **58**, 181–222.

Schiske, P. (1968). *Proc. 4th Eur. Reg. Conf. Electron Microscopy, Rome* **1**, 145–146.

Schiske, P. (1973). Image processing using additional statistical information about the object. *In* "Image Processing and Computer-aided Design in Electron Optics" (P. W. Hawkes, ed.), pp. 82–90. Academic Press, London and New York.

Schwarz, H. (1968). *Bull. Am. Phys. Soc.* **13**, 897.

Schwarz, H. (1970). *Proc. 7th Cong. Electron Microscopy, Grenoble* **2**, 151–152.

Schwarz, H. (1971a). *Trans. NY Acad. Sci.* **33**, 150–162.

Schwarz, H. (1971b). *Appl. Phys. Lett.* **19**, 148.

Schwarz, H. (1972a). *Appl. Phys. Lett.* **20**, 148–149.

Schwarz, H. (1972b). Electron–photon interaction. *In* "Laser Interaction and Related Plasma Phenomena" (H. Schwarz and H. Hora, eds), pp. 209–225. Plenum, New York.

Schwarz, H. (1975). Detection and demodulation of electron beams modulated by high intensity lasers. *In* "Invited Papers, II Conference on Interactions of electrons with Strong Electromagnetic Field (Budapest, October 1975)" pp. 292–337. Central Research Institute for Physics, Budapest.

Schwarz, H. and Hora, H. (1969). *Appl. Phys. Lett.* **15**, 349–351.

Séverin, C., Genotel, D., Girard, M. and Laberrigue, A. (1971). *Rev. Phys. Appl.* **6**, 459–465.

Sieber, P. and Tonar, K. (1976). *Optik* **44**, 361–365.

Simpson, J. A. (1954). *Rev. Scient. Instrum.* **25**, 1105–1108.

Simpson, J. A. (1956). *Rev. mod. Phys.* **28**, 254–260.

Slansky, S. (1959). *J. Phys. Radium* **20**, 13S–14S.

Slansky, S. (1960). *Rev. Opt.* **39**, 555–577.

Slansky, S. (1962). *Opt. Acta* **9**, 277–294.

Slansky, S. and Maréchal, A. (1960). *C.r. hebd. Acad. Sci., Paris* **250**, 4132–4134.
Sonier, F. (1971). *J. Microscopie* **12**, 17–32.
Stoyanova, I. G. and Anaskin, I. F. (1968). *Proc. 4th Eur. Reg. Conf. Electron Microscopy, Rome* **1**, 161–162.
Stroke, G. W. and Halioua, M. (1972). *Optik* **35**, 50–65 and 489–508.
Stroke, G. W., Halioua, M., Saffir, A. J. and Evins, D. J. (1971a). *Proc. 29th Annual EMSA Meeting, Boston*, pp. 92–93.
Stroke, G. W., Halioua, M., Saffir, A. J. and Evins, D. J. (1971b). *In* "Scanning Electron Microscopy/1971" (O. Johari and I. Corvin, eds), pp. 57–64. IIT Research Institute, Chicago.
Stroke, G. W., Halioua, M., Thon, F. and Willasch, D. (1977). *Proc. IEEE* **65**, 39–62.
Thompson, B. J. (1965). *Jap. J. appl. Phys.* **4**, Suppl. 1, 302–307.
Thompson, B. J. (1969). *Prog. Opt.* **7**, 169–230.
Thomson, M. G. R. (1973). *Optik* **39**, 15–38.
Thomson, M. G. R. (1975). Resolution and image signal-to-noise ratio: a comparison between the conventional transmission electron microscope and the scanning transmission electron microscope. *In* "Physical Aspects of Electron Microscopy and Microbeam Analysis" (B. M. Siegel, ed.), pp. 29–45. Wiley, New York and London.
Thomson, M. G. R. and Zeitler, E. (1970). *Proc. 7th int. Cong. Electron Microscopy, Grenoble* **1**, 63–64.
Thon, F. (1971). Phase contrast electron microscopy. *In* "Electron Microscopy in Material Science" (U. Valdrè, ed.), pp. 570–625. Academic Press, New York and London.
Thon, F. and Willasch, D. (1972). *Optik* **36**, 55–58.
Tomita, H., Matsuda, T. and Komoda, T. (1970a). *Jap. J. appl. Phys.* **9**, 719.
Tomita, H., Matsuda, T. and Komoda, T. (1970b). *Proc. 7th int. Cong. Electron Microscopy, Grenoble* **1**, 151–152.
Tomita, H., Matsuda, T. and Komoda, T. (1972). *Jap. J. appl. Phys.* **11**, 143–149.
Tonomura, A. (1969). *J. Electron Microsc.* **18**, 77.
Tonomura, A. and Watanabe, H. (1968). *Nihon Butsuri Gakkai-shi* [*Proc. phys. Soc. Japan*] **23**, 683–684.
Tonomura, A., Fukuhara, A., Watanabe, H. and Komoda, T. (1968a). *Jap. J. appl. Phys.* **7**, 295.
Tonomura, A., Fukuhara, A., Watanabe, H. and Komoda, T. (1968b). *Proc. 4th Eur. Reg. Conf. Electron Microscopy, Rome* **1**, 277–278.
Troyon, M. (1977). *Optik* **49**, 247–251.
Typke, D. and Köstler, D. (1976). *Optik* **45**, 495–498.
Typke, D. and Köstler, D. (1977). *Ultramicroscopy* **2**, 285–295.
Typke, D., Hegerl, R. and Hunsmann, N. (1974). *Proc. 8th int. Cong. Electron Microscopy, Canberra* **1**, 198–199.
Ueha, S., Oshima, S. and Tsujiuchi, J. (1976). *Opt. Commun.* **18**, 488–491.
Veneklasen, L. H. (1976). *Optik* **44**, 447–468.
Vorob'ev, Yu. V. and Zhukov, V. A. (1974). *Izv. Akad Nauk SSSR (Ser. Fiz.)* **38**, 1375–1378. (English transl. in *Bull. Acad. Sci. USSR, Phys. Ser.* **38**, No. 7, 13–16.)
Voronin, Yu. M., Demenchenok, I. P., Mokhnatkin, A. V. and Khaitlina, R. Yu. (1972). *Izv. Akad. Nauk SSSR (Ser. Fiz.)* **36**, 1293–1296. (English transl. in *Bull. Acad. Sci. USSR, Phys. Ser.* **36**, 1154–1156.)
Wade, R. H. (1973). *Adv. Opt. Electron Microsc.* **5**, 239–296.

184   P. W. HAWKES

Wade, R. H. (1976a). *In* "Developments in Electron Microscopy and Analysis" (J. A. Venables, ed.), pp. 197–200. Academic Press, London and New York.
Wade, R. H. (1976b). *Optik* **45**, 87–91.
Wade, R. H. (1976c). *Phys. stat. sol.* (a) **37**, 247–256.
Wade, R. H. (1978). Holographic methods in electron microscopy. *In* "Computer Processing of Electron Micrographs" (P. W. Hawkes, ed.). Springer, Berlin.
Wade, R. H. and Frank, J. (1977). *Optik* **49**, 81–92.
Wahl, H. (1973). Bildebenen-Holographie mit Elektronen. *In* "Höchstauflösung in der Elektronenmikroskopie", pp. 86–113. Proc. Kontron Seminar, Munich.
Wahl, H. (1974). *Optik* **39**, 585–588.
Wahl, H. (1975). "Bildebenenholographie mit Elektronen". Habilitationsschrift, Tübingen, 63 pp.
Walther, A. (1968). *J. opt. Soc. Am.* **58**, 1256–1259.
Watanabe, H. and Tonomura, A. (1969). *Nihon Kessho Gakkai-Shi* [*J. Cryst. Soc. Japan*] **11**, 23–25.
Weingärtner, I., Mirandé, W. and Menzel, E. (1969a). *Optik* **29**, 87–104.
Weingärtner, I., Mirandé, W. and Menzel, E. (1969b). *Optik* **30**, 318–322.
Weingärtner, I., Mirandé, W. and Menzel, E. (1970). *Optik* **31**, 335–353.
Weingärtner, I., Mirandé, W. and Menzel, E. (1971). *Ann. Phys.* (*Leipzig*) **26**, 289–300
Willasch, D. (1973). "Versuche zur Kontrastverbesserung in der Elektronenmikroskopie durch Hellfeldabbildung mittels Phasenplatten und Dunkelfeldabbildung bei hohlkegelförmiger Beleuchtung". Dissertation, Tübingen.
Willasch, D. (1976). *In* "Developments in Electron Microscopy and Analysis" (J. A. Venables, ed.), pp. 185–190. Academic Press, London and New York.
Wolf, E. (1962). *Proc. phys. Soc.* **80**, 1269–1272.
Wolf, E. and Carter, W. H. (1975). *Opt. Commun.* **13**, 205–209.
Wolf, E. and Carter, W. H. (1976). *Opt. Commun.* **16**, 297–302.
Yada, K. and Hibi, T. (1968). *J. Electron Microsc.* **17**, 97–105.
Yada, K. and Hibi, T. (1969). *J. Electron Microsc.* **18**, 266–271.
Yada, K. and Hibi, T. (1970). *J. Microscopie* **9**, 833–844.
Zeitler, E. (1968). *Adv. Electron. Electron Phys.* **25**, 277–332.
Zeitler, E. (1975). *In* "Scanning Electron Microscopy/1975" (O. Johari and I. Corvin eds), pp. 671–677. IIT Research Institute, Chicago.
Zeitler, E. (1976). Scanning transmission electron microscopy. *In* "Electron Microscopy in Materials Science" (E. Ruedl and U. Valdrè, eds), pp. 1275–1301. EEC Press, Luxemburg.
Zeitler, E. and Thomson, M. G. R. (1970a). *Optik* **31**, 258–280.
Zeitler, E. and Thomson, M. G. R. (1970b). *Optik* **31**, 359–366.
Zernike, F. (1938). *Physica* **5**, 785–795.
Zimmermann, B. (1970). *Adv. Electron. Electron Phys.* **29**, 257–312.

The Phase Problem in Electron Microscopy

D. L. MISELL

*Biophysics Division, National Institute for Medical Research,
Mill Hill, London NW7 1AA, England*

I. Introduction

At low resolution (5–10 nm) it is possible to interpret in-focus electron micrographs of biological specimens in terms of the variation of mass thickness or density of the biological material. However, at high and medium resolution (0·5–5 nm) the appearance of the image depends critically on objective lens defocus. Image interpretation is no longer trivial because ideally the image should be corrected for microscope effects, such as defocus and spherical aberration, and the reconstructed image should be independent of electron-optical conditions. In-focus images are not ideal because the image is then distorted by spherical aberration, and usually images are recorded 50–100 nm underfocus in order partially to compensate for spherical aberration. Examination of a focus series of a thin crystal of graphite shows clearly the danger of interpreting the image in terms of a specimen structure (Johnson and Crawford, 1973), and it is well known that the image of a thin carbon film depends critically upon defocus (Thon, 1971): this latter phenomenon is used to determine optimum defocus for imaging biological specimens.

These experimental observations can only be explained by a theoretical model that considers the electron scattering by the specimen and the effect of defocus and spherical aberration as a wave-optical phenomenon. When we measure the intensity of the image, that is, the number of electrons incident on the detector (photographic plate or photomultiplier), we do not have all the information about the specimen structure. In wave-optics we require not only the intensity but the phase of the scattered electron beam. The only way to explain the observed images of a thin carbon film is to use both the amplitude and phase information. The phase problem in electron microscopy is the determination of phase angles from a set of image (or diffraction) plane intensity measurements; with this information we should be in a better position to interpret an image in terms of the specimen structure.

Image interpretation depends critically on the preservation of the specimen structure in the electron microscope, and ultimately, for biological materials in particular, the additional phase information may be uninformative about genuine high resolution detail because radiation damage or specimen stain causes large structural distortions (Beer et al., 1975). In general, the radiation dose cannot be reduced substantially (by a factor of a 100 or more) because a certain minimum number of electrons is required to give an image that can be seen by eye; for similar reasons the low contrast of unstained biological specimens necessitates the use of stains. The situation is dramatically improved by the use of crystalline specimens because the signal-to-noise ratio of a noisy low electron dose image can be improved by using the repeating nature of the specimen structure (Unwin and Henderson, 1975).

In this review we shall be examining various techniques of image reconstruction to extract the maximum information (amplitude and phase) from electron images, but these techniques should not be used to interpret high resolution detail which becomes evident as a result, unless there is good reason to assume structural integrity of the specimen to high resolution.

Many theoretical papers examining the phase problem state that the determination of the complex wavefunction (amplitude and phase) from intensity (amplitude) measurements is required to give a complete interpretation of the image. There is little explanation of how this complex wavefunction ψ relates to the object structure. In fact it is clear that ψ *cannot* necessarily be interpreted in terms of specimen structure for a thick specimen (Grinton and Cowley, 1971; Lipson and Lipson, 1972) or for a negatively stained specimen (Unwin, 1975). We can write the electron wavefunction immediately after the object as $\psi_o(\mathbf{r}) = 1 + \psi_s(\mathbf{r})$, where $\psi_s(\mathbf{r})$ describes the effect of the specimen on the incident electron beam and represents the projection of the specimen structure onto a plane (x, y) (the object plane) where $\mathbf{r} = (x, y)$; the unity represents the unscattered electron beam. We have neglected the effect of the thickness of the specimen (the z direction), and ψ_s can be interpreted as the projection of the potential distribution of the object $V(\mathbf{r}, z)$ onto a plane only if the specimen is thin (Cowley and Moodie, 1957; Cowley and Rees, 1958). For a thick specimen there are many complications such as multiple scattering of the incident electron beam, giving in effect a superposition of structural detail onto a plane; also in the case of a thick specimen, the top of the specimen will be imaged differently from the bottom of the specimen because of a defocus difference corresponding to the specimen thickness, t (Hanszen, 1971). These effects will be discussed in more detail in Section VII on the interpretation of phase information.

In the absence of lens aberrations the image intensity $j(\mathbf{r})$ at unit magnification ($\mathbf{r}_{\text{image}} = \mathbf{r}_{\text{object}}$) in bright-field microscopy

$$j(\mathbf{r}) = |\psi_o(\mathbf{r})|^2 = |1 + \psi_s(\mathbf{r})|^2$$
$$= 1 + 2|\psi_s(\mathbf{r})| \cos [\eta(\mathbf{r})] + |\psi_s(\mathbf{r})|^2 \qquad (1)$$

where we have written $\psi_s = |\psi_s| \exp (i\eta)$ in terms of an amplitude $|\psi_s|$ and a phase η, ($\exp i\eta = \cos \eta + i \sin \eta$). Evidently even if $|\psi_s| \ll 1$ in Eqn (1) we can determine only $|\psi_s| \cos \eta$, the real part of ψ_s, (denoted by Re ψ_s) from image intensity measurements. In the presence of lens aberrations and defocus, phase shifts are introduced into the Fourier transform of ψ_s and j can no longer be directly interpreted in terms of ψ_s or even $|\psi_s|$. Again this point is emphasized by a focus series of a biological specimen, where, subject to experimental limitations such as radiation damage, the apparent structure of the specimen in the image varies with defocus, and in extreme cases the contrast of a particular part of the image of a macromolecule may reverse as defocus is varied (Thon, 1971; Johnson and Crawford, 1973). The question we ask at this point is as follows: Assuming that the image can be corrected for lens aberrations, is information on only the real part of ψ_s, $|\psi_s|\cos\eta$, sufficient to tell us something about the specimen structure? In general the answer is no, but two approximations have been suggested and implemented in electron microscopy which avoid the phase problem for thin specimens (reviewed by Hanszen, 1971), namely, the weak phase approximation (Unwin and Henderson, 1975) and the weak phase–weak amplitude approximation (Erickson and Klug, 1971; Frank, 1972), corresponding to the assumption that $|\psi_s| \ll 1$ so that $|\psi_s|^2$ can be neglected in Eqn (1); these approximations and their limitations will be examined in Section II.

We can illustrate the importance of a knowledge of ψ_s, as opposed to knowing only $|\psi_s|$ or $|\psi_s|\cos\eta$, by referring to the classical phase problem in X-ray crystallography. In X-ray diffraction only the intensities of the diffraction spots can be measured, and the Fourier transform to give an electron density map does not have positional information on the locations of atoms or molecules unless the phases of the diffraction spots are known. The situation in electron microscopy is not so serious, because besides the electron diffraction pattern we can also record focus series of images, all nominally of the same structure. In order to show as simply as possible how the phase problem arises in X-ray crystallography, we consider a crystal which is composed of discrete identical atoms positioned at $\mathbf{r}_j$. Thus the electron density $\rho(\mathbf{r})$ can be written as a sum of point atoms $\delta(\mathbf{r} - \mathbf{r}_j)$, that is,

$$\rho(\mathbf{r}) = \sum_{j=1}^{j=n} \delta(\mathbf{r} - \mathbf{r}_j) \tag{2}$$

for a two-dimensional projection of the structure; this delta function δ has the property of being zero when $\mathbf{r} \neq \mathbf{r}_j$ and infinite when $\mathbf{r} = \mathbf{r}_j$ and so ρ gives a mathematical representation of a set of point atoms. The diffracted wave $F(\mathbf{v})$ in the direction $\mathbf{v}$ where $\boldsymbol{\theta} = \lambda\mathbf{v}$, ($\theta$ is the angle of scattering = twice the Bragg angle, and λ = the wavelength of the incident radiation) is given by the Fourier transform of $\rho(\mathbf{r})$:

$$F(\mathbf{v}) = \int \rho(\mathbf{r}) \exp(2\pi i \mathbf{v}.\mathbf{r}) \, d\mathbf{r}. \tag{3}$$

The Fourier transform of $\delta(\mathbf{r} - \mathbf{r}_j)$ is $\exp(2\pi i \mathbf{v}.\mathbf{r}_j)$ and $F(\mathbf{v})$ is then

$$F(\mathbf{v}) = \sum_{j=1}^{j=n} \exp(2\pi i \mathbf{v}.\mathbf{r}_j)$$

$$= |F(\mathbf{v})| \exp[i\omega(\mathbf{v})]. \tag{4}$$

Clearly, if we could measure $F(\mathbf{v})$, an inverse transform of $F(\mathbf{v})$ could be used to calculate $\rho(\mathbf{r})$. However, we can only measure the intensity $|F(\mathbf{v})|^2$

of the diffracted wave; from Eqn (4)

$$|F(\mathbf{v})|^2 = n + \sum_{\substack{j=1 \\ j \neq k}}^{j=n} \sum_{k=1}^{k=n} \cos\left[2\pi\mathbf{v}.(\mathbf{r}_j - \mathbf{r}_k)\right] \qquad (5)$$

that is, we can only determine the cosine part of the phase angle $2\pi\mathbf{v}.\mathbf{r}_j$. Now since $\cos(a) = \cos(-a)$ we cannot distinguish between an atom at $\mathbf{r}_j$ and one at $-\mathbf{r}_j$; if we only have a small number of atoms we can use trial and error, but for protein structures of several thousand atoms this is impossible. Also note that Eqn (5) gives information only on the relative positions of two atoms, $\mathbf{r}_j - \mathbf{r}_k$.

In one way this phase problem is similar to the phase problem in electron microscopy, where we can only determine $|\psi_s| \cos \eta$ as in Eqn (1), so that η can have either of two values $\pm\eta$. The importance of the phase information is further emphasized by the calculations of Ramachandran and Srinivasan (1961) and Srinivasan (1961), who put in the amplitudes $|F_A|$ from one structure A with the phases ω_B from a second structure B; although the peaks in the electron density map were not of the correct magnitude, the result of a Fourier transform of $|F_A| \exp(i\omega_B)$ gave essentially structure B. Similar calculations using random structure amplitudes $|F|$, or $|F| = $ constant with the correct phases ω, show clearly the importance of knowing ω to within 0.2 rad; the converse case where $|F|$ is known very accurately but ω is not known gave incorrectly positioned density peaks.

The phase problem has not been solved in X-ray crystallography although a number of refinement methods based on the Patterson map, the Fourier transform of $|F|^2$, have been developed (for example, Raman and Katz, 1967). Other computer refinement methods have been based on a physical constraint such as the positivity of $\rho(\mathbf{r})$ (Karle and Hauptman, 1964), and the equality of ρ and ρ^2 for point atom resolution (Sayre, 1952). It must be remembered that Eqns (2) and (5) are an over-simplification as a statement of the phase problem because a structure does not consist of either point atoms or identical atoms.

As mentioned previously the phase problem in electron microscopy is not so serious as in X-ray crystallography because additional experimental information is available (Hoppe, 1970, 1971) besides the electron diffraction data, and use can be made of image data with diffraction data (Gerchberg and Saxton, 1971, 1972), or of focus series (Schiske, 1968; Erickson and Klug, 1971; Misell, 1973a) leading to mathematical relations including the phase information. In addition for thin specimens, particularly for regular structures only one or two protein molecules thick, such as membranes, the phase problem has been solved indirectly by approximation. In this last example electron microscopy is able to give a structure where X-ray diffraction results are difficult to obtain because of the problem of preparing sufficiently large single crystals.

In addition to the multi-range approach of electron microscopy, we can consider the application of X-ray type refinement techniques to improve the phase determined from electron micrographs; there must be some doubt about the success of such refinement techniques since they nearly all assume that the electron density map is near atomic resolution (0·3 nm), whereas the electron micrograph of a biological material may display a resolution of only 0·5–1·0 nm even for unstained specimens under minimum radiation dose conditions.

It is possible that the determination of the phase from the image intensity of a perfect (aberration-free) micrograph would not give much more structural information than is given by $|\psi_s|$, but the phase of an aberrated image is required in order to correct the electron micrograph for the objective lens defects and defocus effects (Frank, 1974); in general there is not a simple relation between the image intensity $j(\mathbf{r}) = |\psi_i(\mathbf{r})|^2$, ψ_s (or $|\psi_s|$) and the lens aberrations, but there is a linear relation between the image wave-function $\psi_i(\mathbf{r})$ and ψ_s (Lenz, 1971a). In one case we know that the phase of the image wavefunction gives additional structural information, namely, in the electron microscopy of thin ferromagnetic films (Chapman, 1975a) where the phase of the object wavefunction $\psi_o(\mathbf{r}) = \exp[i\phi(\mathbf{r})]$ is related to the magnetic flux in the specimen.

It is emphasized that thin specimens should be used whenever possible with viable approximations for $|\psi_s| \ll 1$, rather than creating a phase problem by the use of thick specimens when $|\psi_s|^2$ may not be negligible. In such a case the value of ψ_s determined may not be interpreted in terms of specimen structure except at low resolution.

We examine in Section II the use of the weak phase approximation, and the weak phase–weak amplitude approximation (reviewed by Hanszen, 1971; Erickson, 1973; Frank, 1973a). We shall also give specimen thickness limits for the validity of these approximations for unstained and stained specimens. Even these approximate methods require at least two sets of information: either an electron diffraction pattern and an image or a pair of images taken at different defocus. We shall term these approximations indirect methods for solving the phase problem in contrast to direct methods (Section III) which make no assumption about the magnitude of ψ_s.

Direct methods require at least two sets of information: for example, electron diffraction and image data (Gerchberg and Saxton, 1971, 1972; Gerchberg, 1972)—Section IIIA, focus series images (Schiske, 1968; Misell, 1973a)—Section IIIB, bright-field and dark-field image pairs (Ansley, 1973; Frank, 1973c)—Section IIIC, and the use of complementary half-plane objective apertures (Hanszen, 1969; Hoppe et al., 1970)—Section

IIID. All these methods have some serious disadvantages such as the requirement of crystalline specimens or electron-optical problems (such as electrical
charging of a half-plane aperture). These methods, with the exception of the
half-plane aperture images, may not give unique phase solutions in bright-field
microscopy, and all methods completely neglect the contribution of inelastic
electron scattering to the total (elastic $+$ inelastic) image. The non-uniqueness
problem is examined in Section IV, where we consider how the phase solutions
from the direct methods can be restricted by the use of additional information
such as the finite size of the structure (Barrett *et al.*, 1971), the positivity of $V(\mathbf{r})$
(the projection of $V(\mathbf{r}, z)$) in a similar way to the use of positivity for electron
density $\rho(\mathbf{r})$ (Karle and Hauptman, 1964), squaring $V(\mathbf{r})$ (Sayre, 1952) assuming that the shape of $V(\mathbf{r})$ is similar to $V^2(\mathbf{r})$, and the use of mathematical
relations between the phases and the structure factors for centrosymmetric
structures (Hosemann and Bagchi, 1962). We also strongly recommend the
use of the approximate (indirect) phase determination methods as a first
approximation in the use of the more general direct methods of Section
III; this procedure will also give some indication as to the real validity of
approximations such as the weak phase approximation, when we can compare
approximate and "exact" solutions for the object wavefunction.

We examine briefly optical methods for solving the phase problem in
electron microscopy and relate electron images taken under various electron-
optical conditions to their corresponding analogues in optical holography
(Section V) such as in-line holography (Gabor, 1949, 1951; Goodman,
1968) for normal bright-field electron micrographs, off-axis holography
(Leith and Upatnieks, 1962) for electron microscopy with tilted illumination,
and single-sideband holography (Lohmann, 1956; Bryngdahl and Lohmann,
1968) for half-plane aperture images. This comparison of electron images
with various types of holograms gives another way of looking at the phase
problem in electron images, namely, the problem of separating the conjugate "twin" images in a micrograph (Lohmann, 1974; Misell, 1974) such
as occurs in holography. We consider also in Section V possible optical
analogues of the mathematical reconstruction schemes given in Section II
(Stroke and Halioua, 1973a, b; Burge and Scott, 1975, 1976) and Section
III (Bryngdahl and Lohmann, 1968).

Phase determination will be subject to error due to many factors such
as radiation damage (Beer *et al.*, 1975), specimen preparation (Unwin,
1975), instrumental factors (electrical charging of the aperture, photographic noise, limited coherence of the incident electron beam) and inelastic
electron scattering (Burge, 1973). We examine in Section VI how these
factors will distort the information we can gain on the specimen structure,
and discuss ways of minimizing some of the detrimental effects of these
experimental problems.

All the techniques for determining the object wavefunction ψ_o will only reflect the biological structure in so far as the specimen structure is preserved in the harsh environment of the electron microscope. We are interested only in information that can be interpreted in terms of the structure of the biological material. Radiation damage clearly destroys high resolution detail (0·5 nm) rapidly (Beer et al., 1975; Unwin and Henderson, 1975), so that any image of a biological specimen contains more reliable low resolution detail (1–2 nm) than high resolution information. The danger in image reconstruction is that the less reliable high resolution detail will be given more weight in the image reconstruction than is warranted by the limitations imposed by radiation damage. Also, negatively stained specimens may appear to have a resolution of 2 nm, as judged by optical diffraction of negatively stained crystals, but even at 2 nm resolution the image reconstruction may bear little relation to the native biological material (Unwin, 1975). With these limitations in mind, in Section VII we try to relate the image to the object structure, and examine the effect of specimen thickness on the interpretation of the object wavefunction in terms of the projection of the potential $V(\mathbf{r}, z)$ in the specimen (Lynch et al., 1975). This gives definite experimental conditions for the interpretation of ψ_o or ψ_s in terms of specimen structure and gives an indication of the importance of phase information.

We conclude this review (Section VIII) with an evaluation of the various methods for phase determination together with an assessment of phase refinement techniques as used in X-ray crystallography and optics. We also summarize situations where the knowledge of phase leads to additional structural information, such as thin crystalline specimens and unstained protein molecules.

There are other situations where phase information may not be essential such as heavy atom labelled macromolecules, negatively stained specimens and thick specimens. In the case of resolving single heavy atoms in normal bright-field microscopy the interference between the unscattered and scattered waves can lead to a complex image (Engel et al., 1974), whereas the scanning transmission electron microscope (STEM), used in its normal mode with an annular detector (Crewe, 1971) gives an image free from interference effects (Engel et al., 1974), and an image intensity proportional to the electron scattering factor squared $|f(\boldsymbol{\theta})|^2$ of the particular atom. Heavy atom discrimination in the STEM then depends on the dependence of $|f(\boldsymbol{\theta})|^2$ on atomic number Z (Raith, 1968), and there seems to be little advantage in using a conventional transmission electron microscope (CTEM) to determine the complex electron scattering factor $f(\boldsymbol{\theta}) = |f(\boldsymbol{\theta})| \exp[i\eta(\boldsymbol{\theta})]$ (Raith, 1968) because the Z dependence of the phase angle η is similar to that of $|f|$ (Section VII).

II. INDIRECT METHODS FOR SOLVING THE PHASE PROBLEM

A physical description of the interaction of the incident electron beam with the specimen is provided by the phase object approximation (Molière, 1947; Cowley and Moodie, 1957). In this model the potential distribution $V(\mathbf{r}, z)$ in the specimen affects the incident electron wave just as the refractive index affects a light wave in optics. The specimen thickness t is divided into n slices each of thickness $\Delta z = t/n$, where the potential $V(\mathbf{r}, z_n)$ in the nth slice can be considered constant through the thickness Δz of the slice (Cowley and Moodie, 1957; Cowley and Rees, 1958). Thus the phase shift produced by the specimen slice Δz at z_1 is $-\sigma V(\mathbf{r}, z_1)\Delta z$, where $\sigma = 2\pi me\lambda/h^2 = \pi/\lambda E_0$ with $E_0 =$ incident electron energy; the negative sign implies a phase retardation of the electron wave with respect to an electron wave that passes through a hole in the specimen. Hence we can write the transmitted electron wave through slice z_1 as $\exp\left[-i\sigma V(\mathbf{r}, z_1)\Delta z\right]$ and this wave is incident on slice z_2, which produces a further phase shift $-\sigma V(\mathbf{r}, z_2)\Delta z$. After n slices, the resultant transmitted electron wave is

$$\psi_o(\mathbf{r}) = \exp\left[-i\sigma V(\mathbf{r}, z_1)\Delta z\right] \exp\left[-i\sigma V(\mathbf{r}, z_2)\Delta z\right]$$
$$\ldots \exp\left[-i\sigma V(\mathbf{r}, z_n)\Delta z\right] \qquad (6)$$

which can be rewritten as

$$\psi_o(\mathbf{r}) = \exp\left[-i\sigma \sum_{z_1}^{z_n} V(\mathbf{r}, z_n)\Delta z\right]. \qquad (7)$$

Now $\sum_{z_1}^{z_n} V(\mathbf{r}, z_n)\Delta z$ is just the sum of all the different potential elements in the z direction, and in the limit as Δz becomes very small (n becomes very large) we can write the sum as an integral over the specimen thickness t, that is,

$$\psi_o(\mathbf{r}) = \exp\left[-i\phi(\mathbf{r})\right] \qquad (8)$$

where

$$\phi(\mathbf{r}) = \sigma \int_0^t V(\mathbf{r}, z)\, \mathrm{d}z. \qquad (9)$$

Thus the overall effect of the specimen on the electron beam is represented by a phase shift $-\phi$ proportional to the projection of the potential distribution of the specimen onto a two-dimensional plane, $\mathbf{r} = (x, y)$, in the specimen (Lenz, 1971a).

In order to arrive at this simple result of the phase object approximation we have neglected several factors, which make result (9) incorrect. Firstly we have assumed coherent illumination, that is a plane wavefront corresponding to a collimated (parallel) electron beam in the CTEM; in Fig. 1

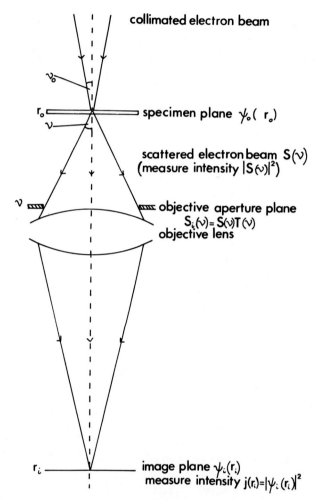

collimated electron beam

specimen plane $\psi_o(\ r_o)$

scattered electron beam $S(\nu)$
(measure intensity $|S(\nu)|^2$)

objective aperture plane
$S_i(\nu) = S(\nu)T(\nu)$
objective lens

image plane $\psi_i(r_i)$
measure intensity $j(r_i) = |\psi_i(r_i)|^2$

FIG. 1. The various planes in a conventional transmission electron microscope.

the angle of illumination $\beta(=v_0\lambda)$ is small, corresponding to the use of a small condenser aperture. We will discuss the effect of partially coherent illumination on the image later in this section and in more detail in Section VIC.

Secondly we have ignored the effect of specimen thickness on ψ_o; in simple terms an electron scattered at the top of the specimen will have a different phase from an electron which is scattered at the bottom of the specimen (Hanszen, 1971); in the phase object approximation this is referred to as the Fresnel propagation factor (Cowley and Moodie, 1957) between different slice elements of the specimen. Yet another way of looking at the thickness effect in electron microscopy is in terms of the defocus difference $\Delta f = t$ of images formed from the top and the bottom of the specimen. We shall discuss the thickness effect in more detail and the limitations it imposes on the interpretation of an electron micrograph in Section VII, but for the present it is sufficient to remember that $\psi_o(\mathbf{r})$ cannot necessarily be interpreted as the projection of the object potential onto a plane except in the case of a thin specimen.

Lastly the phase object approximation does not naturally include the effect of inelastic scattering. In one sense inelastic electron scattering depletes the elastic scattering, so that ψ_o, which represents only the elastic scattering effects, is decreased in amplitude; but this is not to say that inelastically scattered electrons are lost. In fact, particularly in the case of unstained specimens, they contribute a significant proportion of electrons to the image (Burge, 1973). Inelastically scattered electrons can be considered to form an image completely independently of the elastic wave, because the inelastic scattering, as a result of its essential incoherence, does not interfere with the elastic wave. In addition it has been shown that inelastic scattering is a non-local phenomenon and so the inelastic image represents only a low resolution map of the specimen (Isaacson et al., 1974). Thus we can consider an inelastic image as superimposed incoherently (that is, intensities are added) on an elastic image. We shall therefore ignore here the indirect effect of the inelastic scattering on $\psi_o(\mathbf{r})$, and, omitting any detailed analysis of inelastic images, simply consider the inelastic image to form an undesirable low resolution background. This is true provided that we do not record electron micrographs too far underfocus, when the inelastic image can give a resolution comparable to the elastic image resolution (Misell, 1975). We write the object wavefunction as (Grinton and Cowley, 1971)

$$\psi_o(\mathbf{r}) = \exp\left[-i\phi(\mathbf{r})\right] \exp\left[-\epsilon(\mathbf{r})\right] \qquad (10)$$

$$= \exp\left[-i\phi(\mathbf{r}) - \epsilon(\mathbf{r})\right]$$

where $\exp\left[-\epsilon(\mathbf{r})\right]$ represents the attenuation of the amplitude of the elastic wave by inelastic scattering. The intensity (amplitude squared) of the inelastic scattering is then $[1 - \exp(-2\epsilon)]$. The ϵ term *does not* represent the scattering of electrons outside the objective aperture because in a correct wave-optical theory this type of loss of electrons is accounted for by an integration of the scattering over the objective aperture (see below).

We now proceed to the calculation of the scattered or diffracted wave in the direction $\mathbf{v}$. We prefer to use the spatial frequency $\mathbf{v}$ to the angle of scattering θ because $1/\mathbf{v}$ can be interpreted directly in terms of resolution, independent of electron wavelength λ; of course, θ and $\mathbf{v}$ are related by $\theta = \lambda\mathbf{v}$ for small angles of scattering ($\sin\theta = \theta$), so that $|\mathbf{v}| = \theta/\lambda$.

Formally, the scattered wave in the back focal plane of the objective lens $S(\mathbf{v})$ is calculated from the two-dimensional Fourier transform of the object wavefunction $\psi_o(\mathbf{r})$ (Lenz, 1971a)

$$S(\mathbf{v}) = \int \psi_o(\mathbf{r}) \exp\ (2\pi i\mathbf{v}.\mathbf{r})\ d\mathbf{r}. \tag{11}$$

Experimentally we can only determine the intensity of the diffraction pattern $|S(\mathbf{v})|^2$; for a crystalline specimen $|S(\mathbf{v})|^2$ consists of discrete spots corresponding to the periodicity of the crystalline lattice. As is the case in X-ray crystallography, measurement of $|S(\mathbf{v})|$ only does not enable $\psi_o(\mathbf{r})$ to be calculated. The diffracted or scattered intensity is normally observed in the back focal plane (diffraction plane) of the objective lens. For imaging we usually use this plane to describe the effect of an objective aperture and lens defects, including defocusing, on the object wavefunction ψ_o. The effect of spherical aberration, coefficient C_s, and defocusing, Δf, is described by the deviation of the electron wavefront from the ideal spherical wavefront. The wave aberration function $W(\mathbf{v})$ depends on the spatial frequency $\mathbf{v}$ (Scherzer, 1949; Lenz, 1971a):

$$W(\mathbf{v}) = \frac{C_s v^4 \lambda^4}{4} - \frac{\Delta f v^2 \lambda^2}{2} \tag{12}$$

so that electrons scattered at large angles, corresponding to high resolution detail (large v), are more seriously affected by spherical aberration. Equation (12) excludes other aberrations such as axial astigmatism, which can be accurately corrected in modern electron microscopes; if present, a small amount of axial astigmatism can be corrected by computer processing (Frank, 1973a). The convention used here is that $\Delta f > 0$ corresponds to underfocus of the objective lens. Underfocus of the objective lens is used to cancel partially the spherical aberration effect in $W(\mathbf{v})$; overfocus ($\Delta f < 0$) leads to an increase in $W(\mathbf{v})$ and so is not recommended in electron microscopy. The phase difference between electrons scattered in different directions $\mathbf{v}$ is given by $2\pi W(\mathbf{v})/\lambda = \gamma(\mathbf{v})$; and since electrons at larger $\mathbf{v}$ are retarded in phase with respect to electrons at $\mathbf{v} = 0$, we represent the effect of the lens defects by

$$T(\mathbf{v}) = \exp\ [-i\gamma(\mathbf{v})]B(\mathbf{v}) \tag{13}$$

where $T(\mathbf{v})$ is called the transfer function of the electron microscope. $B(\mathbf{v})$ is the objective aperture function, which is unity for the open parts of the aperture and zero for the opaque parts. $B(\mathbf{v})$ therefore represents the fact that all electrons scattered at angles larger than $\alpha = \theta_{\max}$, the semi-angle subtended by the objective aperture at the specimen, are stopped by the aperture and do not contribute to the image. The maximum spatial frequency $v_{\max} = \alpha/\lambda$ determines the best resolution that can be achieved in the image $1/v_{\max}$; for example, if $\alpha = 0\cdot01$ rad, $v_{\max} = 2\cdot7$ nm^{-1} for 100 keV electrons and the resolution in the image cannot be better than $1/v_{max}$ $= 0.37$ nm. The use of an aperture function to describe the removal of electrons from the scattered electron beam, effectively gives an amplitude attenuation of ψ_o; this should not be confused with the attenuation effect of $\exp(-\epsilon)$ in Eqn (10). We view the effect of the objective aperture not as producing aperture or scattering contrast (Erickson and Klug, 1971), but as limiting the resolution of the final image because of the elimination of scattering with spatial frequencies greater than v_{max}. This statement may seem to imply that electron micrographs should be recorded with a large objective aperture. This is not true for two reasons: spherical aberration effects increase as v^4 and so high resolution information is seriously affected by spherical aberration to such an extent that no amount of image processing can correct completely for the defect; and secondly there is no point in recording high frequency (large angle) information if it does not arise from the specimen structure—high resolution information from the specimen substrate or from an extensively damaged specimen can only add to the noise in the final electron image and mask useful, perhaps lower resolution, structural information.

The effect of the transfer function on the object transform $S(\mathbf{v})$ is calculated by multiplying $S(\mathbf{v})$ by the transfer function (Lenz, 1971a) to give an image wavefunction transform (Fig. 1):

$$S_i(\mathbf{v}) = S(\mathbf{v})\,T(\mathbf{v}). \tag{14}$$

An inverse Fourier transform of $S_i(\mathbf{v})$ gives the image wavefunction $\psi_i(\mathbf{r})$ as a convolution of the object wavefunction $\psi_o(\mathbf{r})$ with an instrumental resolution function $G(\mathbf{r}) = F^{-1}[T(\mathbf{v})]$, the inverse Fourier transform of $T(\mathbf{v})$; that is

$$\psi_i(\mathbf{r}) = \int \psi_o(\mathbf{r}')G(\mathbf{r}-\mathbf{r}')\,\mathrm{d}\mathbf{r}'$$
$$= \psi_o(\mathbf{r})*G(\mathbf{r}) \tag{15}$$

where an asterisk * denotes a convolution of two functions, ψ_o and G in this case.

Clearly if we could measure ψ_i we could determine ψ_o from Eqn (15) or Eqn (14) provided that we know the electron microscope resolution function G. However, we can only measure the image intensity $j(\mathbf{r}) = |\psi_i(\mathbf{r})|^2$ (Fig. 1):

$$j(\mathbf{r}) = |\psi_o(\mathbf{r})*G(\mathbf{r})|^2 \tag{16}$$

and it is generally impossible to solve this equation for ψ_o, because the Fourier transform of Eqn (16) is not separable into an object-dependent term $S(\mathbf{v})$ and an instrumental term $T(\mathbf{v})$ as is possible in Eqn (14). This provides the motivation in conventional transmission microscopy for considering approximate models for ψ_o, derived from Eqn (10), which enable $j(\mathbf{r})$ to be linearly related to $\phi(\mathbf{r})$ and to $\epsilon(\mathbf{r})$.

We could consider using incoherent illumination in the CTEM (conventional transmission electron microscope), when the expression for $j(\mathbf{r})$ becomes a simple convolution of $|\psi_o(\mathbf{r})|^2$ with $|G(\mathbf{r})|^2$, but, in essence, information on $|\psi_o(\mathbf{r})|^2$ is only information on ϵ since $|\exp(-i\phi)| = 1$; in addition, if the scattering is weak, the image contrast under incoherent imaging conditions is very low, particularly for unstained biological specimens. These two factors make the use of incoherent imaging in the CTEM unacceptable in biological electron microscopy, despite the fact that there is no phase problem and a complete absence of complex electron interference effects as occur in normal transmission electron microscopy.

Image formation in the STEM (scanning transmission electron microscope) can be treated in a similar way to the CTEM (Crewe, 1971) but now the electron collector geometry (Fig. 2) determines whether the imaging is coherent or incoherent (Engel *et al.*, 1974; Misell, Stroke and Halioua,

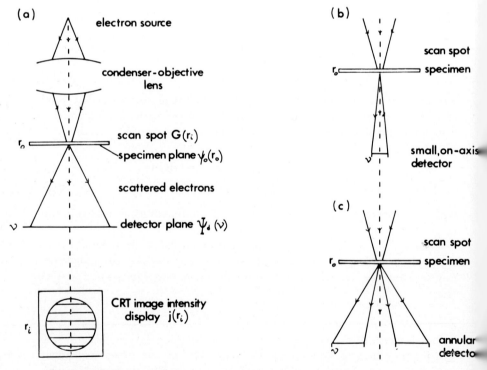

FIG. 2. The various planes in a scanning transmission electron microscope with (a) a full detector, (b) a small on-axis detector and (c) an annular detector.

1974). In the case of the STEM the resolution function $G(\mathbf{r})$ represents the profile of the scan spot, depending on the C_s and Δf of the condenser-objective lens in the same way as $G(\mathbf{r})$ for the CTEM objective lens, and this spot is modified by the object wave-function $\psi_o(\mathbf{r})$ (Fig. 2a). If a small on-axis detector is used (Fig. 2(b)), then the imaging is coherent and described by Eqns (15) and (16). However, such a small detector is an inefficient collector of the scattered electrons, and normally the STEM is operated with an annular detector (Fig. 2c) which is able to collect large-angle scattering, and allows the unscattered and small-angle inelastically scattered electrons to pass through a hole in the centre of the detector. Thus an effective separation of elastic and inelastic scattering can be achieved for thin specimens. However, because the detector collects most of the elastic scattering, irrespective of its spatial frequency $\mathbf{v}$, we lose information on the phase of the scattered electron beam. In this case image formation in the STEM corresponds to incoherent imaging (Misell, Stroke and Halioua, 1974)

$$j(\mathbf{r}) = |\psi_o(\mathbf{r})|^2 * |G(\mathbf{r})|^2 \qquad (17)$$

where $\mathbf{r}$ now represents the position of the scan spot on the specimen. This is a simplification because the detector is not infinite and has a hole in its centre; thus phase contrast or interference effects as in coherent imaging conditions do contribute to the image (Cowley, 1975) but far less than in the case of the CTEM. In imaging biological structures we shall see (Section IIA) that the STEM has certain disadvantages as compared to the CTEM, because of the differences in the normal imaging in the two microscopes: coherent conditions for the conventional microscope, Eqn (16), and incoherent conditions for the scanning microscope, Eqn (17).

A. Weak Phase Approximation Using Electron Diffraction Data

In the weak phase approximation we assume that the specimen is so thin that the phase shift ϕ in exp $[-i\phi(\mathbf{r})]$ is appreciably less than unity and, in addition, we neglect the effect of inelastic scattering on ψ_o, that is, exp $[-\epsilon(\mathbf{r})] \simeq 1$. This latter approximation works very well in the crystalline case as will be discussed below. Thus we write the object wavefunction in terms of the expansion of exp $(-i\phi)$:

$$\psi_o(\mathbf{r}) \simeq 1 - i\phi(\mathbf{r}) - \phi^2(\mathbf{r})/2 + \ldots \qquad (18)$$

where we neglect all terms containing ϕ^2 and higher powers of ϕ. This assumption leads to a linear relationship between the image intensity $j(\mathbf{r})$ and $\phi(\mathbf{r})$ for coherent illumination in the CTEM.

It is necessary to examine the conditions under which we can neglect $\phi^2/2$ in comparison to ϕ in Eqn (18). In order to obtain an indication of the magnitude of ϕ we will suppose that $V(\mathbf{r}, z)$ does not change in the z direction; thus

$$\phi(\mathbf{r}) = \sigma \int_0^t V(\mathbf{r}, z) \, \mathrm{d}z \simeq \sigma t V(\mathbf{r}). \qquad (19)$$

In order to calculate ϕ we require to know $V(\mathbf{r})$ for typical specimens. In the case of unstained biological specimens the mean value of $V(\mathbf{r})$, V_m, is about 4 volts, whereas for negatively stained specimens V_m is about 16 volts (Grinton and Cowley, 1971); these figures are approximate but they will give an indication of the specimen thickness limits for which $\phi^2/2$ can be neglected. At 100 keV ($\lambda = 3 \cdot 7$ pm) $\phi = 7 \cdot 73 \times 10^{-3} \, V_m t$, where t is in nm and V_m in volts. In Table I we show the values of ϕ and $\phi^2/2$, together

TABLE I

Variation of the phase shift ϕ with specimen thickness t

t (nm)	Unstained ($V_m = 4$ V)			Stained ($V_m = 16$ V)		
	ϕ (rad)	$\phi^2/2$	R	ϕ (rad)	$\phi^2/2$	R
5	0·16	0·01	0·08	0·62	0·19	0·31
10	0·31	0·05	0·15	1·24	0·77	0·62
15	0·46	0·11	0·23	1·86	1·72	0·93
20	0·62	0·19	0·31	2·47	3·06	1·24
25	0·77	0·30	0·39	3·09	4·78	1·55
30	0·93	0·43	0·46	3·71	6·88	1·86
40	1·24	0·77	0·62	4·95	12·2	2·47
50	1·55	1·20	0·77	6·18	19·1	3·09

ϕ is compared to $\phi^2/2$ for unstained and negatively stained specimens. The column labelled R gives the ratio of the second order term $\phi^2/2$ to the first order term ϕ.

with their ratio R, for a specimen thickness range 5–50 nm for both unstained and negatively stained materials. Clearly if we can accept a 30% error in ϕ (and hence $V(\mathbf{r})$) the thickness limits are about 15 nm for unstained specimens and less than 5 nm for stained specimens. So it is almost certain that stained specimens or those consisting of a large quantity of high atomic number atoms, cannot be used in the weak phase approximation, but images of such specimens may be analysed, at least approximately, by the weak phase–weak amplitude approximation (Section IIB).

The diffracted wave is the Fourier transform of ψ_o:

$$S(\mathbf{v}) = \delta(\mathbf{v}) - i\Phi(\mathbf{v}) \qquad (20)$$

where Φ is the two-dimensional Fourier transform of ϕ; the delta function

$\delta(\mathbf{v})$ represents the intense unscattered beam at zero angle of scattering. The electron diffraction intensities for $\mathbf{v} \neq 0$ are then given by

$$I(\mathbf{v}) = |S(\mathbf{v})|^2 = |\Phi(\mathbf{v})|^2 = \Phi_r^2(\mathbf{v}) + \Phi_i^2(\mathbf{v}) \qquad (21)$$

where Φ_r and Φ_i are respectively the real and imaginary parts of Φ. Since for a crystalline lattice $I(\mathbf{v})$ will reflect the periodicity of the lattice, the transform will be discrete rather than continuous. Inelastic scattering, which has been omitted from Eqn (21), will mainly form a diffuse background in the diffraction pattern because of the non-localized nature of inelastic scattering. The effect of this scattering will therefore largely be eliminated if measurements of the transform are confined to the region of the reciprocal lattice points; in this way the inelastic scattering between reciprocal lattice points is eliminated.

The image transform S_i is obtained by multiplying Eqn (20) by the transfer function $T(\mathbf{v}) = \exp\left[-i\gamma(\mathbf{v})\right]B(\mathbf{v})$. Thus

$$S_i(\mathbf{v}) = \delta(\mathbf{v}) \exp\left[-i\gamma(\mathbf{v})\right]B(\mathbf{v}) - i\Phi(\mathbf{v}) \cos\left[\gamma(\mathbf{v})\right]B(\mathbf{v})$$
$$- \Phi(\mathbf{v}) \sin\left[\gamma(\mathbf{v})\right]B(\mathbf{v}). \qquad (22)$$

In bright-field microscopy $B(\mathbf{v}) = 1$ for $|\mathbf{v}| \leqslant v_{\max}$ and zero for $|\mathbf{v}| > v_{\max}$.

The image wavefunction $\psi_i(\mathbf{r})$ in bright-field is then calculated from an inverse transform of Eqn (22):

$$\psi_i(\mathbf{r}) = 1 - i\phi(\mathbf{r}) * q'(\mathbf{r}) - \phi(\mathbf{r}) * q(\mathbf{r}) \qquad (23)$$

where q and q' are respectively the inverse Fourier transforms of $\sin(\gamma)B$ and $\cos(\gamma)B$. The image intensity in bright-field microscopy $j(\mathbf{r})$ is calculated from $|\psi_i(\mathbf{r})|^2$ neglecting terms in ϕ^2:

$$j(\mathbf{r}) = 1 - 2\phi(\mathbf{r}) * q(\mathbf{r}). \qquad (24)$$

Thus the image intensity j is linearly related to ϕ and Eqn (24) can be solved for ϕ subject to certain limitations. Normally in order to determine ϕ we calculate the Fourier transform of the image intensity because the convolution becomes a multiplication:

$$J(\mathbf{v}) = \delta(\mathbf{v}) - 2\Phi(\mathbf{v}) \sin\left[\gamma(\mathbf{v})\right]B(\mathbf{v}). \qquad (25)$$

The delta function can be eliminated by omitting the $\mathbf{v} = 0$ term of the transform, so that

$$\Phi(\mathbf{v}) = -J(\mathbf{v})/2 \sin\left[\gamma(\mathbf{v})\right]B(\mathbf{v}) \qquad (26)$$

can be evaluated. Now from Eqns (12) and (13) we can see that $\sin\gamma$ depends on Δf and C_s, and $\sin\gamma$ will have values of zero whenever $\gamma = n\pi$ (n is an integer); also note that we cannot define Φ beyond $\mathbf{v} = v_{\max}$ because $B(\mathbf{v}) = 0$ for $|\mathbf{v}| > v_{\max}$. Since $J(\mathbf{v})$ has noise components (for example, photographic noise), the division of J by a small value of $\sin\gamma$ can lead to a large increase in the noise; so the ideal phase contrast transfer function would be $\sin\gamma = 1$ and we can nearly achieve this condition over a limited

202   D. L. MISELL

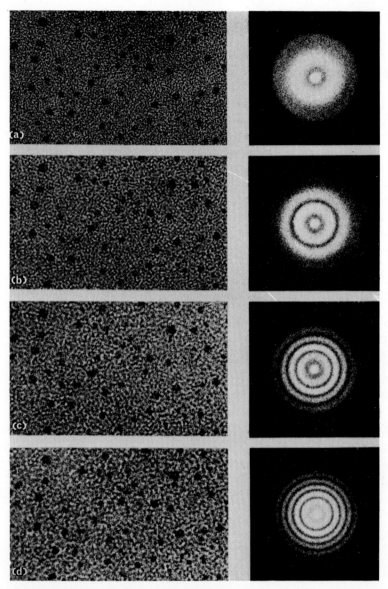

FIG. 3. Focus series of a thin carbon film (with gold particles as a focus aid) with optical diffractograms for (a) optimum defocus, (b) 150 nm, (c) 210 nm and (d) 250 nm under focus. Image magnification $M = 870\,000$ (scale 10 mm $\equiv$ 11·5 nm) and incident electron energy $E_0 = 125$ keV; in the diffraction pattern 10 mm $\equiv 2$·6 nm^{-1}. (P. Sieber, unpublished.)

resolution range by choosing Δf to be about 100 nm underfocus for $C_s = 2$ mm. Of course, we need a means for determining Δf and hence sin γ; the determination of Δf and C_s can be made using the substrate background in the image (Thon, 1971). In the image transform of the substrate $\Phi \simeq$ constant for an amorphous film, and J is proportional to sin γ. Thus the measurement of the transform J or its intensity $|J|^2$ will give a set of rings with positions of zero (or near zero) value corresponding to sin $\gamma = 0$ (Thon, 1971). As an example Fig. 3 shows a focus series of carbon together with the corresponding optical transforms $|J|^2 \propto \sin^2\gamma$. Optimum defocus, Δf_{opt}, corresponds to Fig. 3(a) giving the most uniform transform whereas larger defocus values give an increasing number of frequency gaps in sin γ from Fig. 3(b), 150 nm underfocus, to Fig. 3(d), 250 nm underfocus.

Ideally, images should be recorded at optimum defocus, but practical problems, such as minimizing the exposure of the specimen to the electron beam, mean that images are often taken at substantially larger underfocus values than Δf_{opt} (Unwin and Henderson, 1975). It will be noticed that the intensity of the optical transforms falls off as v increases; this is due to the limited coherence of the electron beam which in this case essentially multiplies J by a Gaussian factor exp $(-bv^4)$ falling rapidly to zero for large spatial frequencies (Hanszen and Trepte, 1971). The rate of decay of this coherence envelope depends on the angle of specimen illumination β, the spatial coherence, and the energy spread of the incident electron beam E_f, the chromatic coherence. From the positions of the zeros of $|J|^2 \propto \sin^2\gamma$ we can determine C_s and Δf (Frank, 1972) for use in Eqn (26). Figure 4 shows the calculated curves for the radial dependence of $\sin^2\gamma$ on Δf corresponding to the optical transforms of Fig. 3, including the effects of limited source coherence ($\beta = 5 \times 10^{-4}$ rad, $E_f = 1$ eV), with a value of $C_s = 1.9$ mm. Note that axial astigmatism, specimen drift and electrical charging of the specimen will show in the optical transform as a distortion of the rings; as can be seen from Fig. 3 the focus series is almost completely free of these image defects to a resolution of about 0.3 nm ($v_{max} = 3$ nm^{-1}).

In principle, in order to calculate Φ from Eqn (26) we require only one micrograph but in practice because of the zeros of sin γ we require at least two micrographs taken at different defocus, so as to be able to reconstruct Φ without any frequency gaps (Schiske, 1968). Unwin and Henderson (1975) use several micrographs in the analysis of their images of unstained purple membrane and choose from a particular image only those $J(\mathbf{v})$ values significantly removed from the zeros of the sin $[\gamma(\mathbf{v})]$ for that image.

In the case of a crystalline specimen, which gives a discrete electron diffraction pattern, Unwin and Henderson (1975) give a very good method for correcting the image of a weak phase object for lens defects without requiring the actual value of sin $[\gamma(\mathbf{v})]$, requiring only the positions of

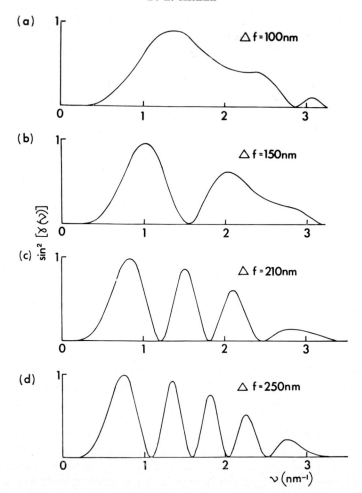

FIG. 4. Theoretical results for the intensities $\sin^2[\gamma(\nu)]$ of the optical transforms of the carbon film series in Fig. 3. Coherence envelope on $\sin^2 \gamma$ corresponds to an illumination angle of $\beta = 5 \times 10^{-4}$ rad with a thermal energy spread of $E_f = 1$ eV.

zeros of $\sin \gamma$. From the electron diffraction pattern we can determine $|\Phi| = (\Phi_r^2 + \Phi_i^2)^{\frac{1}{2}}$ whilst the phase angle of $\Phi = \Phi_r + i\Phi_i$ can be determined from the micrograph transform, Eqn (25); since

$$J(\mathbf{v}) \propto \Phi_r(\mathbf{v}) \sin [\gamma(\mathbf{v})] + i\Phi_i(\mathbf{v}) \sin [\gamma(\mathbf{v})] \qquad (27)$$

FIG. 5. Electron diffraction pattern from purple membrane: (a) high-angle pattern, scale 10 mm $\equiv 0.6$ nm^{-1}; (b) low-angle pattern, scale 10 mm $\equiv 0.3$ nm^{-1} $E_0 = 100$ keV. (Unwin and Henderson, 1975.)

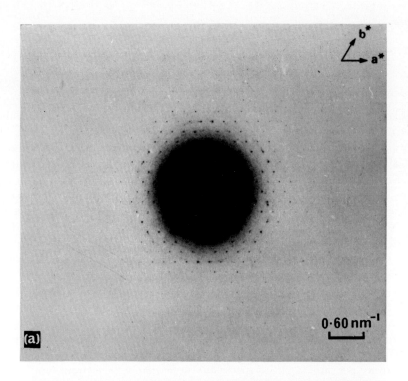

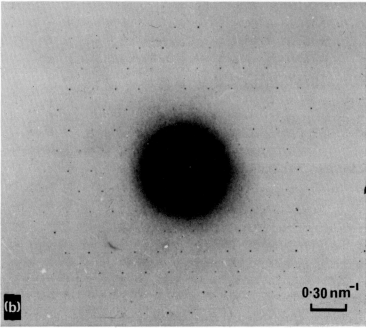

Fig. 5. (For legend see facing page.)

dividing the imaginary part of J by its real part gives the phase angle:

$$\omega = \tan^{-1}\left(\frac{\Phi_i \sin \gamma}{\Phi_r \sin \gamma}\right) = \tan^{-1}\left(\frac{\Phi_i}{\Phi_r}\right). \tag{28}$$

ω is just the phase angle of Φ in $\Phi = |\Phi| \exp (i\omega)$ independent of the value of $\sin \gamma$. Thus we can calculate Φ free from lens aberrations by using $|\Phi|$ from the electron diffraction data, and ω from a transform of the micrograph. There are, however, two limitations: (a) at zeros of the transfer function there is no information in the image transform on either Φ_r or Φ_i; (b) there are ambiguities in the phase angle ω because neither the sign of Φ_r nor Φ_i is known; only the sign of Φ_i/Φ_r is known, so that sign reversals of $\sin \gamma$ can give values for the angle ω in one of two quadrants. This latter problem is avoided by changing the sign of the amplitude $|\Phi|$ whenever $\sin \gamma$ is negative. The problem of the zeros is solved by the use of several micrographs at varying defocus.

Figure 5 shows high-angle (Fig. 5a) and low-angle (Fig. 5b) electron diffraction patterns from unstained purple membrane (a protein–lipid complex about 5 nm thick). Because of the absence of stain and the low radiation dose used, the diffraction spots in some cases extend to 3 nm^{-1} (0·3 nm resolution). The image at a corresponding low dose (about 100 electrons per nm^2 area of specimen; note that 6·2 electrons nm$^{-2} \equiv 1$ coulomb m^{-2}) is statistically noisy with a mean optical density on the photographic plate of only 0·1, and the structure cannot be visually distinguished from the background (Unwin and Henderson, 1975). However, because of the periodic nature of the purple membrane, the Fourier transform of the electron micrograph is discrete and the non-periodic noise can be filtered out. Figure 6(a) shows a quadrant of an optical transform of a purple membrane micrograph, indexed as in the electron diffraction pattern. Thus from the diffraction pattern, Fig. 5, we determine $|\Phi|$ and from the image transform we determine the phase angle, ω, of Φ; a second normal dose image of the purple membrane (and its carbon substrate) gave the transform shown in Fig. 6(b); this transform may be used to determine the zeros of $\sin \gamma$ and the sign of $\sin \gamma$, which alternates between positive and negative values between zeros. In order to improve the accuracy of ω, the hexagonal symmetry of the lattice is used to make threefold related phases the same. The error in the phase of Φ was estimated as $\pm 10°$ (about 0·15 rad) to a spatial frequency of 1·4 nm^{-1} (0·7 nm resolution), which is quite accurate by X-ray diffraction standards. It should be noted that

Fig. 6. Optical transform quadrants of purple membrane micrographs taken in bright-field microscopy: (a) low dose image, (b) high dose image; scale 10 mm $\equiv$ 0·12 nm^{-1}, $E_0 = 100$ keV. (Unwin and Henderson, 1975.)

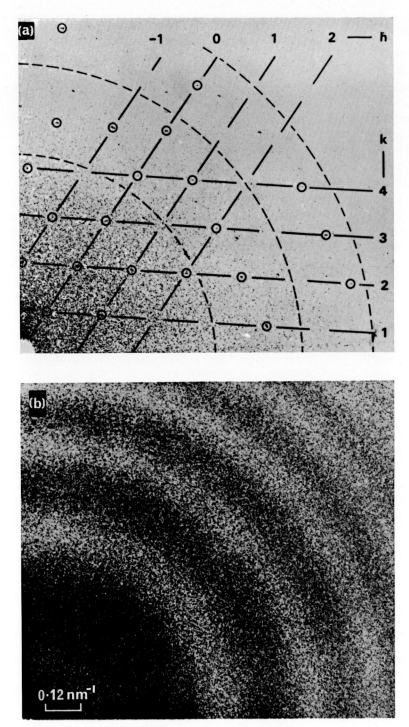

FIG. 6. (For legend see facing page.)

although in the weak phase approximation the phase ϕ should be small (less than unity), this does not mean that the phase of Φ is small; in fact ω can have values between 0 and 2π as in X-ray crystallography. The reason for the inferior resolution of the image (0·7 nm) as compared to the diffraction pattern (0·3 nm) arises from instrumental problems (for example, stray magnetic fields) for recording images at relatively low magnifications of 40 000× (Unwin and Henderson, 1975). Thus although the amplitudes, $|\Phi|$, are known to 0·3 nm resolution, the phases, ω, are known to only 0·7 nm resolution.

The projected map of purple membrane is obtained by an inverse transform of Φ; Fig. 7 shows the two-dimensional projection $\phi(\mathbf{r})$ of purple membrane to 0·7 nm resolution; this map can be interpreted as the projection of the potential distribution for a specimen only about 5 nm thick. The high density regions in the contour map of purple membrane indicate protein in mainly α-helical form, while the low density region comprises relatively unstructured lipid and glucose (used as a replacement for the water in the membrane system).

In the case of non-periodic specimens, we do not have electron diffraction data, and in the absence of periodicity we have no way of averaging the statistically noisy image arising from a low electron dose. Although the weak phase approximation can be used within the thickness limitations indicated by Table I, it is unlikely that high resolution information on non-periodic biological specimens will be obtained.

Dark-field microscopy of weak phase objects does not seem to be very useful because of the increased electron dose required to obtain an image with the same signal to noise ratio as in bright-field microscopy. In addition, the phase shift ϕ is not linearly related to the dark-field image intensity (Cowley, 1973; Hoch, 1973); in the diffraction plane, Eqn (22), the aperture function $B(\mathbf{v})$ is now zero at $\mathbf{v} = 0$ corresponding to an axial dark-field stop in the objective aperture intercepting the unscattered electron beam:

$$S_i(\mathbf{v}) = -i\Phi(\mathbf{v}) \exp\left[-i\gamma(\mathbf{v})\right]B(\mathbf{v}). \tag{29}$$

The image wavefunction $\psi_i(\mathbf{r})$ is given by the inverse Fourier transform of Eqn (29):

$$\psi_i(\mathbf{r}) = -i\phi(\mathbf{r}) * G(\mathbf{r}) \tag{30}$$

and the image intensity in dark-field is

$$j(\mathbf{r}) = |\phi(\mathbf{r}) * G(\mathbf{r})|^2. \tag{31}$$

This non-linear equation cannot in general be solved for ϕ even in the weak phase approximation unless some simplifying assumptions are made (Cowley, 1973) or the structure has a centre of symmetry (Hosemann and Bagchi, 1962). There is the additional problem in dark-field microscopy of

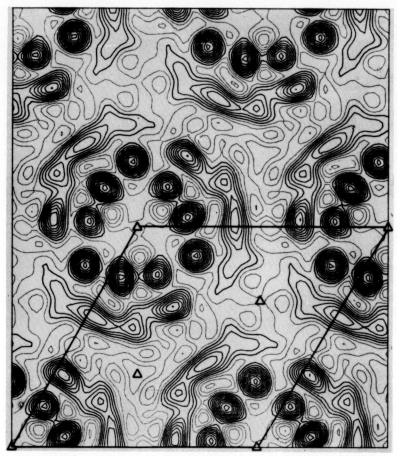

FIG. 7. Contour map of the projected structure of purple membrane at 0·7 nm resolution. Positive contours are indicated by thicker lines; the positive peaks are due to high concentrations of scattering material (protein). Low density regions indicated by thinner lines are due to lipid and glucose. Unit cell dimensions are 6·2 nm × 6·2 nm. (Unwin and Henderson, 1975.)

determining C_s and Δf, because the transform of a dark-field image gives a uniform transform with little indication of defocus variations (Thon, 1971).

Finally in this section we compare the performance of the CTEM in bright-field and the STEM under normal dark-field operating conditions for the examination of weak phase objects. In the CTEM the image intensity is proportional to 2ϕ neglecting the effect of lens defects, Eqn (24), whereas in the STEM using an annular detector the image intensity is proportional to $|\psi_o|^2 = \phi^2$, Eqn (17). If we consider a lipid–protein complex about 5 nm thick, such as purple membrane, then the intensity differences in the CTEM depend on $2(\phi_p - \phi_l)$, whilst in the STEM they depend on $\phi_p^2 - \phi_l^2$. The ability to distinguish in the image between protein, ϕ_p, and lipid, ϕ_l, depends on the magnitude of these differences and the number of electrons detected; image noise either in the photographic plate or the electron detector depends on the square root of the number of electrons detected. A simple approximation gives ϕ^2 proportional to the fraction of elastic scattering from the specimen for a beam of unit intensity, because $|\psi_o|^2 = |1 - i\phi|^2 = 1 + \phi^2$ represents approximately the unscattered plus elastically scattered intensity. For a thickness of 5 nm of lipid (density 1000 kg m^{-3}), $\phi_l^2 \simeq 0.004$, $2\phi_l \simeq 0.13$, and for a corresponding thickness of protein (density 1350 kg m^{-3}) $\phi_p^2 \simeq 0.006$, $2\phi_p \simeq 0.16$ for an objective aperture or electron detector aperture corresponding to a semi-angle of 0.01 rad at 100 keV. There is little point in using a larger annular detector than this, because at larger angles the spatial frequency $|\mathbf{v}| > 2.7$ nm^{-1} (0.37 nm resolution) and any higher angle scattering collected by the detector is unlikely to contain genuine structural information on the protein–lipid complex.

For an incident electron beam of intensity n_0 electrons nm^{-2} at the specimen, the differences between the protein and lipid in the intensity detected in the image are $2n_0(\phi_p - \phi_l)$ for the CTEM and $n_0(\phi_p^2 - \phi_l^2)$ in the STEM, whilst the noise in both images will be proportional to the square root of the number of electrons detected in the image. In the CTEM the total number of electrons detected in bright-field is virtually n_0. The signal-to-noise ratio in the case of the CTEM will be $2n_0(\phi_p - \phi_l)/n_0^{\frac{1}{2}}$, that is, $S/N = 0.22$ for a low dose image with $n_0 = 100$. In the ideal case the STEM annular detector would record only elastic scattering and the unscattered/inelastically scattered electrons pass undetected through the centre of the annular detector; then for $n_0 = 100$, $n_0(\phi_p^2 - \phi_l^2) = 0.16 \pm 1.03$ ($S \pm N$ or $S/N = 0.16$). This demarcation cannot be made exactly, because if the detector angle a is the same as the angle of illumination β, a significant proportion of elastically scattered electrons will pass through the centre of the detector. But making the detector hole small means that unscattered electrons will be collected on the annulus with the signal, and thus add to the background noise as in bright-field microscopy. In the case of a full detector the S/N would be zero; it is clear that, because of the low intensity of the elastic scattering (ϕ^2) for a thin specimen, we should avoid collecting even a small fraction of the unscattered beam in the STEM. The S/N for differentiation between the protein and lipid will be between zero and 0.16; taking a compromise figure of $S/N = 0.08$ for $n_0 = 100$, the electron dose has to be increased to 800 electrons nm^{-2} in the STEM to give a comparable S/N to the CTEM; this is a substantial increase in radiation dose for biological materials.

These calculations say nothing about the resolution in the image because we have only considered the gross elastic scattering within a spatial frequency range 0–$2\cdot7$ nm^{-1}. A complete calculation would require the resolution of the elastic scattering into a series of specific spatial frequency intervals, for example, the contribution of the 2 nm object detail to the image is different from that of the 1 nm detail. However, we believe that the above figures reflect a clear advantage of the CTEM over the STEM for thin unstained biological specimens. Of course, the signal-to-noise ratio in the CTEM is not good but this can be improved by the averaging techniques discussed above for a periodic structure (Unwin and Henderson, 1975). Note also that $2n_0(\phi_p - \phi_l)$ and $n_0(\phi_p^2 - \phi_l^2)$ will be reduced by the effects of lens aberrations, scattering from the specimen substrate, inelastic scattering, and the limited efficiency of the detection system. Thus in the CTEM the above figure for S/N may be reduced to about $0\cdot1$, so that an averaging over about 1000 unit cells of specimen will be needed for a final S/N of 3. This advantageous situation for the CTEM is completely reversed when we consider the resolution (and S/N) of single heavy atoms on a carbon substrate (see Section VIID).

These figures given for a comparison of the CTEM with the STEM also reflect the necessity to use phase contrast microscopy for imaging thin biological specimens rather than to use incoherent imaging conditions in the CTEM, where the signal-to-noise ratio in the image will be extremely low.

B. *Weak Phase–Weak Amplitude Approximation Using Two Electron Micrographs*

The next step in improving the analysis of electron microscope images is to take account of the effect of inelastic scattering on the object wavefunction; the weak phase–weak amplitude approximation corresponds to the expansion of Eqn (10) to first order in ϕ and ϵ (Hanszen, 1971):

$$\psi_0(\mathbf{r}) \simeq 1 - i\phi(\mathbf{r}) - \epsilon(\mathbf{r}). \tag{32}$$

We know the thickness limits for which this expansion is valid for ϕ (see Table I) and Table II gives a comparison of ϵ with $\epsilon^2/2$ calculated from the fraction of inelastic scattering $[1 - \exp(-2\epsilon)]$ for a specimen of thickness t. In order to simplify the results we have assumed that the inelastic scattering is independent of Z and therefore the same for unstained and stained specimens. It can be seen that the restriction on thickness for ϵ is much less serious than the thickness limit for ϕ. Thus for a 20% error in ϵ the specimen can be as thick as 50 nm, but then the error in ϕ would be very large. However, we think that the weak phase–weak amplitude approxi-

TABLE II

Variation of the amplitude term ϵ with specimen thickness t

	Unstained and stained		
t (nm)	ϵ	$\epsilon^2/2$	R
5	0·032	0·0005	0·02
10	0·064	0·002	0·03
15	0·096	0·005	0·05
20	0·13	0·009	0·07
25	0·16	0·013	0·08
30	0·19	0·019	0·10
40	0·25	0·033	0·13
50	0·33	0·053	0·16

ϵ is compared to $\epsilon^2/2$ for both unstained and stained specimens; the inelastic scattering is assumed to be the same in both cases. R is the ratio of the second order term $\epsilon^2/2$ to the first order term ϵ.

mation can actually be applied to thicker specimens than the weak phase approximation alone. This is because in the expansion of Eqn (10) we can combine the real ϵ term with the real second order term in ϕ, $\phi^2/2$ as $-(\epsilon + \phi^2/2)$. In this case, provided the specimen thickness is small enough to neglect other second order terms in ϕ and ϵ, such as $\phi\epsilon$, we can extend the thickness limit for the expansion of Eqn (10) to about 25 nm for unstained and 10 nm for stained specimens. However, we cannot now interpret the ϵ term in Eqn (32) in terms of the amplitude attenuation of ψ_o, because we have included a significant contribution from $\phi^2/2$.

In a similar way to the case of the weak–phase approximation, we can calculate the diffracted wave to be

$$S(\mathbf{v}) = \delta(\mathbf{v}) - i\Phi(\mathbf{v}) - E(\mathbf{v}) \tag{33}$$

and the intensity of the diffracted wave is $(\mathbf{v} \neq 0)$

$$|S(\mathbf{v})|^2 = |\Phi(\mathbf{v})|^2 + |E(\mathbf{v})|^2. \tag{34}$$

The effect of the microscope transfer function $T(\mathbf{v})$, Eqn (13), on $S(\mathbf{v})$ gives the transform of the image wavefunction $S_i(\mathbf{v})$. The final result for the image intensity $j(\mathbf{r})$ is obtained by calculating the inverse Fourier transform of S_i, $\psi_i(\mathbf{r})$, and taking the modulus squared of the image wavefunction, $|\psi_i(\mathbf{r})|^2$. The image intensity $j(\mathbf{r})$ is again linearly related to $\phi(\mathbf{r})$ and $\epsilon(\mathbf{r})$ (Erickson and Klug, 1971; Frank, 1972):

$$j(\mathbf{r}) = 1 - 2\phi(\mathbf{r}) * q(\mathbf{r}) - 2\epsilon(\mathbf{r}) * q'(\mathbf{r}) \tag{35}$$

where terms in ϕ^2 and ϵ^2 have been neglected. Since Eqn (35) contains two unknown functions, ϕ and ϵ, we cannot solve it for either, and at least a second micrograph taken at a different defocus, thus varying the resolution functions q and q', is required to determine ϕ and ϵ (Ferwerda and Hoenders, 1975). The determination of ϕ and ϵ using Eqn (35) is again best made using the Fourier transform of the image intensity $j(\mathbf{r})$. For two images $j_1(\mathbf{r})$ and $j_2(\mathbf{r})$ recorded at defocus values of Δf_1 and Δf_2 respectively, the image transforms are:

$$J_1(\mathbf{v}) = \delta(\mathbf{v}) - 2\Phi(\mathbf{v}) \sin [\gamma_1(\mathbf{v})]B(\mathbf{v}) - 2E(\mathbf{v}) \cos [\gamma_1(\mathbf{v})]B(\mathbf{v})$$

and (36)

$$J_2(\mathbf{v}) = \delta(\mathbf{v}) - 2\Phi(\mathbf{v}) \sin [\gamma_2(\mathbf{v})]B(\mathbf{v}) - 2E(\mathbf{v}) \cos [\gamma_2(\mathbf{v})]B(\mathbf{v}).$$

We assume, as in all cases involving the recording of more than one micrograph, that the specimen structure (defined by ϕ and ϵ) does not change between images. This is, of course, a severe limitation since radiation damage, an important factor for biological specimens, will certainly alter the structure of ϕ. In the applications of Eqn (36) to electron microscopy, either negatively stained specimens (Erickson and Klug, 1971) or positively stained specimens (Frank, 1972) were used well beyond the minimum radiation dose; there is evidence in both these cases that the specimen had reached a stable (if low resolution) structure.

From Eqn (36) the transforms Φ and E can be calculated (Schiske, 1968; Frank, 1972)

$$\Phi(\mathbf{v}) = \frac{J_1(\mathbf{v}) \cos [\gamma_2(\mathbf{v})] - J_2(\mathbf{v}) \cos [\gamma_1(\mathbf{v})]}{2 \sin [\gamma_2(\mathbf{v}) - \gamma_1(\mathbf{v})]B(\mathbf{v})}$$

and (37)

$$E(\mathbf{v}) = \frac{-J_1(\mathbf{v}) \sin [\gamma_2(\mathbf{v})] + J_2(\mathbf{v}) \sin [\gamma_1(\mathbf{v})]}{2 \sin [\gamma_2(\mathbf{v}) - \gamma_1(\mathbf{v})]B(\mathbf{v})}$$

where the delta function $\delta(\mathbf{v})$ at $\mathbf{v} = 0$ has been omitted from the transform. There are, however, severe limitations in using only two micrographs, namely the zeros of $\sin (\gamma_2 - \gamma_1)$ whenever $\gamma_2 - \gamma_1 = n\pi$, when both Φ and E are indeterminate. In fact, whenever $\sin (\gamma_2 - \gamma_1) = \sin (\pi \Delta f \lambda v^2)$ (where $\Delta f = \Delta f_2 - \Delta f_1$) attains small values, the division in Eqn (37) can give large and spurious features in the ϕ and ϵ calculated from an inverse transform of Eqn (37). Erickson and Klug (1971) and Frank (1972) use at least four micrographs to avoid this problem, using only those spatial frequencies for which $\sin (\pi \Delta f \lambda v^2)$ is significantly different from zero. A theoretical assessment of the weak phase–weak amplitude approximation which may lead to a practical improvement in the reconstruction method indicated in Eqns (36) and (37) has been given by Ferwerda and Hoenders (1975).

The practical analysis of micrographs in the weak phase–weak amplitude approximation is similar to that given for the weak phase object. In the application to negatively stained catalase crystals (Erickson and Klug,

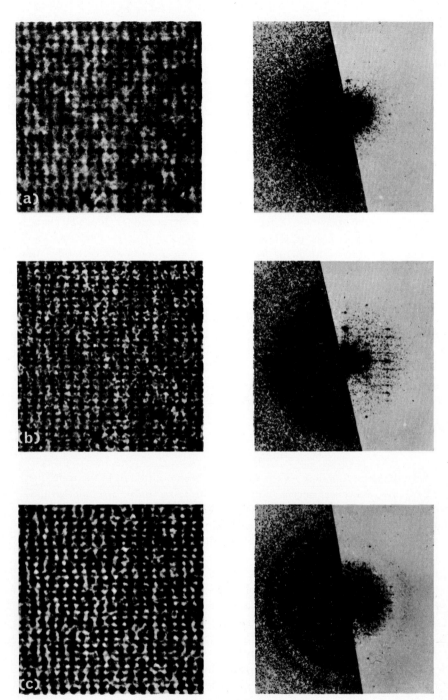

Fig. 8. (For legend see facing page.)

1971), a focus series is recorded (Fig. 8). An optical transform of the specimen substrate, which is assumed to behave as a weak phase object gives the electron-optical parameters C_s and Δf_n, the defocus for the nth image of the focus series, from the positions of the zeros of the transfer function $\sin \gamma_n$. The optical diffraction patterns showing the effect of defocus are shown in one half of the results in Fig. 8; the second half of the pattern shows the optical diffraction spots from the images of the catalase lattice. Because the crystal is negatively stained the diffraction spots extend only to about $0 \cdot 4$ nm^{-1} ($2 \cdot 4$ nm resolution). Having determined the appropriate transfer functions $\sin \gamma_n$ and $\cos \gamma_n$ for each micrograph, Eqn (36) is solved to give Φ and E using only those transform values $J_n(\mathbf{v})$ that do not fall near the zeros of either $\sin \gamma_n$ or $\cos \gamma_n$. The reconstructed result for ϕ, calculated from an inverse transform of Φ is shown in Fig. 9 (Erickson and Klug, 1971). As for the case of the purple membrane, the signal-to-noise ratio in the reconstruction can be improved by sampling the image transform only at reciprocal lattice points (the diffraction spots); this corresponds to an averaging of the non-periodic noise in the image by using the periodic nature of the specimen. Ideally the results in Fig. 9 should be independent of defocus after image processing; the fact that they are not identical reflects the errors involved in determining defocus and correcting the images over a large focus range, about 1400 nm (Erickson and Klug, 1971). Also, images taken at different defocus will almost certainly have different contributions from second order terms that have been neglected in this approximation.

In the case of the weak phase--weak amplitude object we are unable to use the electron diffraction data, because although we can determine the amplitude of the diffraction pattern $|\Phi(\mathbf{v})|^2 + |E(\mathbf{v})|^2$, Eqn (34), we cannot easily determine the phase angle $\omega(\mathbf{v}) = \tan^{-1}[(\Phi_i + E_i)/(\Phi_r + E_r)]$ from the image transforms, Eqn (36).

As in Section IIA a comparison of the CTEM and STEM for the weak phase--weak amplitude approximation, shows that the radiation damage, for a given signal to noise in the image, favours the CTEM. This is because the image intensity in the STEM is dependent on $|\psi_o(\mathbf{r})|^2 \simeq [\epsilon^2(\mathbf{r}) + \phi^2(\mathbf{r})]$, whereas in the CTEM the relationship between the image intensity and the object structure is linear, although not a very attractive linear equation. Also although it is possible to separate the effects of ϕ and ϵ from a focus

---

FIG. 8. The bright-field images of negatively stained catalase and the corresponding optical diffraction patterns at different defocus: (a) 80 nm, (b) 540 nm and (c) 1450 nm underfocus. Image magnification $M = 350\,000$ (10 mm $\equiv$ 29 nm), $E_0 = 80$ keV. The scale in the optical diffraction pattern is 10 mm $\equiv 0 \cdot 3$ nm^{-1}. (Erickson and Klug, 1971.)

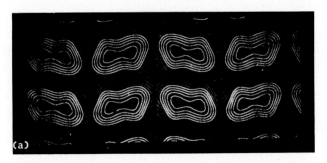

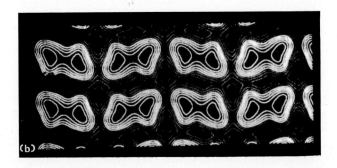

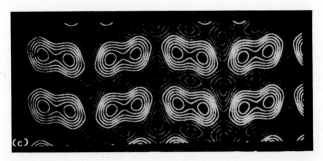

FIG. 9. Noise filtered, averaged images reconstructed from computer calculated Fourier transforms of catalase images, corrected for lens aberrations and defocus. (a) 80 nm, (b) 540 nm and (c) 1450 nm underfocus. $M = 2\,000\,000$ (10 mm $\equiv$ 5 nm) $E_0 = 80$ keV. (Erickson and Klug, 1971.)

series in the CTEM, it is difficult to determine how to separate ϕ^2 and ϵ^2 in the incoherent image intensity equation

$$j(\mathbf{r}) = [\phi^2(\mathbf{r}) + \epsilon^2(\mathbf{r})] * |G(\mathbf{r})|^2 \qquad (38)$$

for the STEM (Misell, Stroke and Halioua, 1974) even using a focus series to vary the resolution function for the scan spot, $G(\mathbf{r})$.

Consideration of dark-field microscopy of a weak phase–weak amplitude object again leads to a result for the image intensity that is difficult to evaluate, except in simple cases (Cowley, 1973).

Mention should be made of a suggestion by Hoppe (1970) for determining ϕ and ϵ from a single defocus image, recorded with and without a $\pi/2$ carbon phase plate in the objective aperture plane. The carbon phase plate has a small hole in its centre to allow the unscattered electron beam to pass through without being phase shifted. In the absence of the phase plate the image intensity is given by Eqn (35), but with the $\pi/2$ phase plate in place the phase of the microscope transfer function is changed by $\pi/2$; thus in the second image $\sin(\gamma + \pi/2)$ becomes $\cos\gamma$, and $\cos(\gamma + \pi/2)$ becomes $-\sin\gamma$. The image intensity $j_p(\mathbf{r})$ with a $\pi/2$ phase plate is then:

$$j_p(\mathbf{r}) = 1 - 2\phi(\mathbf{r}) * q'(\mathbf{r}) + 2\epsilon(\mathbf{r}) * q(\mathbf{r}). \qquad (39)$$

Equations (35) and (39) can be solved in a similar way to the method used for a focus series of electron micrographs. There are, however, many practical problems in using a carbon phase plate, namely, making the centre hole small enough for the scattered electrons at small angles to be phase shifted, and the more serious effect of scattering of electrons by the phase plate itself (Badde and Reimer, 1970; Thon, 1971). A $\pi/2$ carbon phase plate has a thickness of about 25 nm, which will scatter 30% of the electrons inelastically and 10% elastically; thus about 40% of the elastic scattering from the specimen will be subsequently scattered in the phase plate, with a resultant reduction in image contrast.

We have treated indirect methods of phase determination in detail for several reasons: firstly to establish the basic equations for image formation, including the effects of lens aberrations, leading to a physical interpretation of $\phi(\mathbf{r})$ and $\epsilon(\mathbf{r})$; secondly we believe that such approximations are essential to the success of the direct methods given in Section III. In many cases an approximate solution for the object wavefunction $\psi_o(\mathbf{r}) \simeq 1 - i\phi(\mathbf{r}) - \epsilon(\mathbf{r})$ will avoid the problem of just guessing an initial set of phase solutions.

The weak phase–weak amplitude approximation has been extended to include second order terms in ϵ and ϕ (Erickson, 1973), but the resulting equations are very complex and difficult to solve. If, after applying the weak phase–weak amplitude approximation to a set of micrographs there are reasons to suppose that ϕ and ϵ are too large for the neglect of ϵ^2 and $\phi\epsilon$, then the main alternative is to use one of the direct methods of Section III, which do not make any assumptions about the magnitude of the scattered electron wave ψ_s.

III. Direct Methods for Solving the Phase Problem

In this section we examine methods for determining the complex object wavefunction $\psi_o(\mathbf{r}) = 1 + \psi_s(\mathbf{r})$ from intensity measurements in both bright-field and dark-field microscopy. No assumptions will be made about the magnitude of ψ_s, nor shall we try to interpret the results we obtain for ψ_s. We hope that ψ_s will give us more information on the specimen structure than we could determine from just the image intensity; but the veracity of the correlation between ψ_s and structure will depend on several factors including radiation damage, electron optical factors, as well as specimen thickness (see Sections VI and VII). Direct methods are to be preferred to the indirect methods of Section II whenever there is doubt about the validity of the linear approximations, rather than to attempt to extend the approximations to second order terms of doubtful meaning; such additional terms will evidently give better fits of the theory to experimental data just because of an increase in the number of fitting parameters available.

The methods examined in this section make only the assumption of the validity of the basic imaging equations given in Section II, that is, the sequence $\psi_o(\mathbf{r}) \rightarrow S(\mathbf{v}) \rightarrow S_i(\mathbf{v}) \rightarrow \psi_i(\mathbf{r}) \rightarrow j(\mathbf{r})$ (Eqns (11), (14), (15), (16)); we neglect the direct contribution of inelastic electron scattering to the diffraction plane and image plane intensities because it cannot be adequately included. We can assess the effect of the inelastic scattering on image contrast and resolution in a qualitative way, but we cannot eliminate its effect on ψ_s (derived from elastic scattering only). We also assume coherent illumination of the specimen; except for the linear equations considered in Section II, partially coherent illumination leads to a complicated relation between the object and image wavefunction (Frank, 1973b); partial coherence is again a factor that can be qualitatively assessed but in general cannot be corrected.

In order to simplify the mathematics for this section we shall consider the determination of ψ_s from intensity measurements in the absence of lens defects (including defocus), except when the method depends on these factors, such as in the two defocus method (Section IIIB). In mathematical terms the problem of determining $\psi_i(\mathbf{r})$ from $j(\mathbf{r})$ is the same as determining $\psi_o(\mathbf{r})$ or $\psi_s(\mathbf{r})$ from $|\psi_o(\mathbf{r})|$, the essential difference being that $\psi_i(\mathbf{r})$ is $\psi_o(\mathbf{r})$ modified by the microscope resolution function $G(\mathbf{r})$, Eqn (15). Thus if we can determine ψ_i from the image intensity, we can correct ψ_i for lens defects by solving the convolution integral

$$\psi_i(\mathbf{r}) = \psi_o(\mathbf{r}) * G(\mathbf{r}) \tag{40}$$

for $\psi_o(\mathbf{r})$. Normally $\psi_o(\mathbf{r})$ is determined from the Fourier transform of $\psi_i(\mathbf{r})$, $S_i(\mathbf{v})$:

$$S_i(\mathbf{v}) = S(\mathbf{v}) \, T(\mathbf{v}) \tag{41}$$

or

$$S(\mathbf{v}) = S_i(\mathbf{v})/\exp\left[-i\gamma(\mathbf{v})\right]B(\mathbf{v}) \tag{42}$$

followed by an inverse Fourier transform of $S(\mathbf{v})$ to give $\psi_o(\mathbf{r})$. In fact the deconvolution represented by Eqn (42) is ideal because we divide by a function $\exp\left[-i\gamma(\mathbf{v})\right]$ whose modulus is unity for $|\mathbf{v}| < v_{max}$ (Frank, 1974; Spence, 1974), rather than the division by a $\sin\left[\gamma(\mathbf{v})\right]$ in the weak phase, or weak phase–weak amplitude approximations, Eqns (26) and (37) respectively.

The measurement of $|\psi_o|^2$ corresponds to the determination of only the real part of the scattered electron wavefunction, $\psi_s(\mathbf{r}) = |\psi_s(\mathbf{r})| \exp\left[i\eta(\mathbf{r})\right]$. In bright-field microscopy:

$$|\psi_o(\mathbf{r})|^2 = 1 + 2|\psi_s(\mathbf{r})| \cos\left[\eta(\mathbf{r})\right] + |\psi_s(\mathbf{r})|^2$$

or
$$\tag{43}$$

$$|\psi_o(\mathbf{r})|^2 = 1 + 2\,\mathrm{Re}\left[\psi_s(\mathbf{r})\right] + \mathrm{Re}^2\left[\psi_s(\mathbf{r})\right] + \mathrm{Im}^2\left[\psi_s(\mathbf{r})\right]$$

where Re and Im denote respectively the real and imaginary parts of $\psi_s(\mathbf{r})$. In dark-field microscopy, where the unscattered wave is intercepted, $\psi_o(\mathbf{r})$ is simply:

$$|\psi_o(\mathbf{r})|^2 = |\psi_s(\mathbf{r})|^2 = \mathrm{Re}^2\left[\psi_s(\mathbf{r})\right] + \mathrm{Im}^2\left[\psi_s(\mathbf{r})\right] \tag{44}$$

so that we only determine $|\psi_s(\mathbf{r})|$ in dark-field. For completeness we relate the $\psi_o(\mathbf{r}) = 1 + \psi_s(\mathbf{r})$ to the expression for $\psi_o(\mathbf{r})$ derived from the phase object approximation, Eqn (10), that is

$$1 + \psi_s(\mathbf{r}) \equiv \exp\left[-i\phi(\mathbf{r}) - \epsilon(\mathbf{r})\right] \tag{45}$$

which gives the phase angle ϕ as

$$\tan\phi \equiv -|\psi_s| \sin\eta/(1 + |\psi_s| \cos\eta) \tag{46a}$$

and the amplitude term $\exp(-\epsilon)$ as

$$\exp(-\epsilon) = (1 + 2|\psi_s| \cos\eta + |\psi_s|^2)^{\frac{1}{2}}. \tag{46b}$$

In the case of the weak phase–weak amplitude approximation ($\tan\phi \simeq \phi$, $\exp(-\epsilon) \simeq 1 - \epsilon$, and $|\psi_s| \ll 1$), we obtained a simple relationship between ϕ, ϵ and ψ_s:

$$\phi \equiv -|\psi_s| \sin\eta \text{ and } \epsilon \equiv |\psi_s| \cos\eta. \tag{47}$$

The preference for using $\psi_o = 1 + \psi_s$ to the phase grating approximation is because of the ease with which we can express the bright-field image intensity in terms of ψ_s as compared to the use of exponential terms.

The direct methods which we examine in this section are as follows: firstly, the use of diffraction data $|S(\mathbf{v})|$ and image data $|\psi_s|$ to determine either S or ψ_s (Section IIIA; Gerchberg and Saxton, 1971, 1972), which has been applied to negatively stained catalase (Gerchberg, 1972) and magnetic films (Chapman, 1975a, b); the method requires a crystalline specimen and in principle will work in bright-field and dark-field microscopy although the method has not been applied to the latter case. The second method involves the use of two images recorded at different defocus, using the mathematical relation between the two image wavefunctions ψ_1 and ψ_2 for a defocus difference Δf between the images (Section IIIB; Misell, 1973a, b; Schiske, 1975); the two defocus method does not require crystalline specimens, and has not been applied experimentally in either bright-field or dark-field microscopy. The third method uses a bright-field image and a dark-field image taken under identical electron–optical conditions (Section IIIC; Ansley, 1973; Frank, 1973c); the method would seem to be best applied to crystalline specimens because of the lack of uniqueness of the phase solution, but has not been applied to experimental data. The last method, involving the use of complementary half-plane objective apertures (Section IIID; Hanszen, 1969, 1973; Hoppe *et al.*, 1970), is sometimes referred to as single-sideband holography (for example, Bryngdahl and Lohmann, 1968) because of the similarity of the images to this type of optical hologram (see Section V). The half-plane aperture method is also similar to the optical analogue of Schlieren microscopy (Zernike, 1942; Belvaux and Vareille, 1971) used for making phase objects visible with a knife edge to cut-off one half of the optical Fourier transform of the object. The half-plane aperture method for phase determination has been applied to bright-field images of uranium-labelled DNA (Downing and Siegel, 1975), although the technique may prove to be more successful in the case of crystalline specimens.

The principal advantage that the half-plane aperture technique has over all the other methods given above is that an approximate phase solution can be determined directly from the bright-field image intensity (with the half-plane objective aperture in place). All the other methods require initial guesses for the phase, which cannot be assessed from intensity measurements only. Hence we stress the importance of the approximations detailed in Section II for giving at least some indication of the phase of ψ_s, η (see Eqn (47)).

A. *Electron Diffraction and Electron Image Data*

The method of Gerchberg and Saxton (1971, 1972) uses the Fourier transform relationship between the diffracted wave $S(\mathbf{v})$ and the object wavefunction $\psi_o(\mathbf{r})$. The proposition of Gerchberg and Saxton (GS) is that measurements of $|S(\mathbf{v})|$ and $|\psi_o(\mathbf{r})|$ are sufficient to determine both the wavefunctions. In its final form the GS algorithm is an iterative method, where we guess a set of phases for S, $\omega_1(\mathbf{v})$ and calculate an initial approximation for the diffracted wave from the electron diffraction intensities $I(\mathbf{v})$, that is,

$$S_1(\mathbf{v}) = |S(\mathbf{v})| \exp [i\omega_1(\mathbf{v})] \qquad (48)$$

where $|S(\mathbf{v})| = I^{\frac{1}{2}}(\mathbf{v})$.

An inverse Fourier transform of this $S_1(\mathbf{v})$ will give an object wave-function of the form:

$$\psi_1(\mathbf{r}) = |\psi_1(\mathbf{r})| \exp [i\eta_1(\mathbf{r})] \qquad (49)$$

where both the amplitudes $|\psi_1|$ and the phases η_1 are incorrect. However, we know the correct amplitudes $|\psi_o(\mathbf{r})|$ from image intensity measurements, so that we can replace $|\psi_1|$ by the correct amplitudes $|\psi_o|$ derived from $j^{\frac{1}{2}}$; the approximate phases η_1 are retained and we calculate the transform of $|\psi_o(\mathbf{r})| \exp [i\eta_1(\mathbf{r})]$. The diffracted wave will now have incorrect amplitudes but these are replaced by the correct amplitudes $|S|$ and the calculated phases ω_1 are retained. This iteration between diffraction and image plane measurements is continued until the differences between the actual diffracted amplitudes and those calculated by successive iterations attain some small value. The differences will in general never become zero because of the errors in the intensity measurements. In fact even with test diffraction and image plane intensities the difference between the actual amplitudes $|S(\mathbf{v})|$ and the final calculated diffraction amplitudes $|S_c(\mathbf{v})|$

$$\sum_{\mathbf{v}} (|S(\mathbf{v})| - |S_c(\mathbf{v})|)^2 = R \qquad (50)$$

will not always be zero. This is because, although the GS algorithm can be shown never to diverge (Gerchberg and Saxton, 1972), there is no reason why S_c (or ψ_c) should always converge to S (or ψ_o). In many cases the sum of squares in Eqn (50), R, reaches a certain value which will not decrease in subsequent iterations. The practical problem is in deciding what value of R is acceptable when the experimental data are subject to error.

An important practical point is that S and ψ_o should correspond to measurements from the same area of specimen so that the Fourier transform relation between S and ψ_o is valid. Since this is virtually impossible for amorphous or non-crystalline specimens, the technique is limited to crystal-line specimens, where the repeating nature of the specimen structure makes the correspondence between S and ψ_o a relatively easy condition to satisfy. Lens aberrations, including defocus, can be included in the GS algorithm simply by multiplying the transform $S_1(\mathbf{v})$ in Eqn (48) by the appropriate transfer function $T(\mathbf{v}) = \exp [-i\gamma(\mathbf{v})]B(\mathbf{v})$ for the image; the reverse operation for calculating $S_1(\mathbf{v})$ from the image wavefunction Eqn (49) would involve the division of the image transform by $T(\mathbf{v})$. The correction of the image wavefunction for lens defects is made under ideal conditions because the divisor, $\exp [-i\gamma(\mathbf{v})]B(\mathbf{v})$ of the image transform has a modulus of unity and the noise is not amplified as happens in the deconvolution given in Section II, where we divide by sin γ.

In the application of the GS algorithm to crystalline specimens, there are two practical points: firstly the actual diffraction and image plane intensity measurements should be normalized so that:

$$\int |S(\mathbf{v})|^2 \, d\mathbf{v} = \int |\psi_o(\mathbf{r})|^2 \, d\mathbf{r} \qquad (51)$$

that is, the total number of electrons detected in the diffraction and image planes should be identical. This physical requirement corresponds to the application of Parseval's theorem to two functions that are Fourier transform pairs, S and ψ_o in this case. Secondly, the image intensity should be measured (scanned) at the correct steps in $\mathbf{r} = (x, y)$ so that the transform of ψ_o corresponds to the spacing of the diffraction spots. If the highest order diffraction spot corresponds to a spatial frequency of v_m, then the image should be sampled at $1/2v_m$ when a fast Fourier transform is used to calculate the transform. Of course, if the image magnification is M this sampling corresponds to a scan step of $M/2v_m$ on the densitometer used to digitize the micrograph. For example, if the highest order diffraction spot corresponds to $v_m = 2$ nm^{-1} (0·5 nm resolution), at unit magnification the image should be sampled at 0·25 nm, and at an image magnification of 40 000 the image should be sampled at 10 μm steps. In practice, it is usually impossible to scan the image at the exact steps required and it is necessary to interpolate the image lattice onto a new lattice that corresponds exactly to the spacings observed in the diffraction pattern. Oversampling the image with a smaller step is, in any case, preferred to undersampling.

Scanning the image so that the transform is sampled only at reciprocal lattice points has the advantage that non-periodic noise and a substantial fraction of inelastic scattering may be eliminated from the transform.

Figure 10 shows an example of the application of the GS algorithm to a negatively stained catalase crystal specimen (Gerchberg, 1972). The original image and the corresponding electron diffraction pattern are shown in Fig. 10(a) and Fig. 10(e) respectively. Because the specimen is negatively stained the diffraction pattern only extends to about 0·5 nm^{-1} (2 nm resolution). Figure 10(b) shows the "averaged" image of the catalase specimen, obtained by simple Fourier filtering of the original bright-field image, Fig. 10(a) (Gerchberg, 1972), and it is this "averaged" image that is used in the algorithm. The image phases were initially chosen to be a set of random numbers between $\pm \frac{1}{2}$ rad, although they are in general chosen from a random set between $\pm \pi$. The final result for the phase distribution across the image, corrected for lens aberrations, is shown in Fig. 10(c), after 20 iterations, corresponding to an R which is only 1·6% of the total intensity in the diffraction plane. However, since the intensity

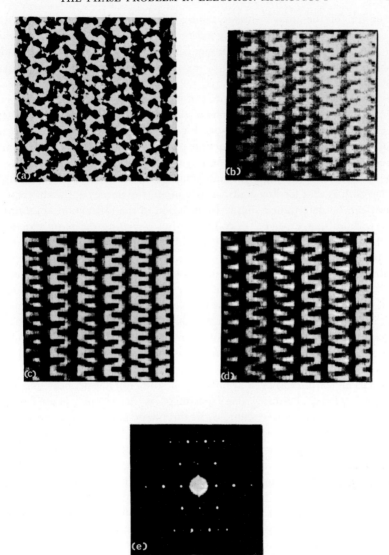

Fig. 10. Application of the diffraction-image plane method to a bright-field image and an electron diffraction pattern of negatively stained catalase: (a) original image ($M = 860\,000$, 10 mm $\equiv$ 11·6 nm), (b) averaged image, (c) image phase distribution determined from (b) and electron diffraction pattern, (d) image phase distribution determined from a blank image and electron diffraction pattern, and (e) electron diffraction pattern (10 mm $\equiv$ 0·2 nm^{-1}). (Gerchberg, 1972.)

modulation of the image (image contrast) seems to be low, only a few percent, this is not a particularly good result. It is evident that the appearance of the original "averaged" image, Fig. 10(b), is similar to the result for the phase distribution, Fig. 10(c), except for mis-registration of about a half-unit cell.

Because the contrast of the original in-focus image is so small, Gerchberg (1972) reasons that the modulations of the image intensity have very little effect on the final phase distribution. Figure 10(d) shows the result for the phase distribution when the diffraction pattern is used with a *blank* image of the correctly scaled uniform intensity, Eqn (51); in essence it is the same as the result obtained using a genuine image. The implication of Gerchberg's (1972) result is that for low contrast specimens, the phases of the diffraction pattern can be determined simply by iteration of the diffraction amplitudes $|S(\mathbf{v})|$ with an image $|\psi_o(\mathbf{r})| = $ constant, thus obviating the requirement to record two images. It is true that the ideal (aberration-free) image of a pure phase object, $\psi_o(\mathbf{r}) = \exp[-i\phi(\mathbf{r})]$, would have a uniform intensity distribution $|\psi_o|^2 = 1$, but there is considerable doubt that the diffraction amplitudes alone would determine a correct set of phases $\phi(\mathbf{r})$ (Schiske, 1974). We consider the uniqueness problem of the GS algorithm in more detail in Section IV, but at present we can only state that there seems to be no reason why the algorithm should converge to a correct set of phases, when the initial phase distribution used corresponds to a set of random phases between $\pm\pi$.

The GS algorithm has been applied to one-dimensional periodic magnetic structures where, because the specimen is a strong phase object $\psi_o = \exp[-i\phi]$, the phase shifts, ϕ, in the image can be several multiples of π (Chapman, 1975a, b). For a ferromagnetic film the magnetic flux distribution B_x is proportional to $d\phi/dx$ and there is some theoretical justification for using as an initial approximation for $d\phi/dx$ a sinusoidal variation in x, for example, $[\sin(ax)]^{\frac{1}{2}}$; the parameter a is estimated from the image. Again only the diffraction plane intensities are used with a blank image, but in this case there is some justification; because of the relatively large periodicity of the magnetic structure ($\sim$30 nm), the diffraction pattern is restricted to small angles $\sim 10^{-4}$ rad ($v < 3 \ \mu m^{-1}$), so that the image intensity is almost unaffected by spherical aberration, C_s, defocus, Δf, or the aperture function, $B(\mathbf{v})$. Then the image intensity of a strong phase object is the same as $|\psi_o(\mathbf{r})|^2$ for coherent illumination ($\exp[-i\gamma(\mathbf{v})]B(\mathbf{v}) = 1$ over the frequency spectrum $\mathbf{v}$ of the object). The success of the GS algorithm in this case can be ascribed to a considerable amount of information on physically acceptable solutions for B_x and hence ϕ. Chapman (1975a) describes some modifications to the original GS algorithm that take account of the errors in the diffraction amplitudes, and estimates phase errors of about 0·2 rad in a ϕ variation as large as 10 π rad.

Both these applications of the GS algorithm show the inadequacy of the approximations used in Section II; in the case of the catalase specimen the phase variation across the specimen was about 2 rad and for the magnetic specimens ϕ sometimes exceeds $10\,\pi$ (Chapman, 1975b)—see Table I.

B. *Two Images Recorded at Different Defocus*

The two defocus method depends on the mathematical relationship between two image wavefunctions $\psi_1(\mathbf{r})$ and $\psi_2(\mathbf{r})$ derived from the same object function $\psi_o(\mathbf{r})$ at defocus values of Δf_1 and Δf_2 respectively (Misell, 1973a). Although the method for determining the phase of ψ_o from the amplitudes $|\psi_1|$ and $|\psi_2|$ is essentially similar to the GS algorithm, the two defocus method relies implicitly on the modulation of the image intensity; the GS algorithm may work on low contrast images but the two defocus method is unlikely to produce useful results in this case unless the specimen has a regular structure to permit an averaging of the noise in the images.

The two image wavefunctions ψ_1 and ψ_2 are related to the object wavefunction ψ_o by their respective resolution functions G_1 and G_2 for coherent illumination:

$$\psi_1(\mathbf{r}) = \int \psi_o(\mathbf{r}')G_1(\mathbf{r} - \mathbf{r}')\,\mathrm{d}\mathbf{r}'$$

and

$$\psi_2(\mathbf{r}) = \int \psi_o(\mathbf{r}')G_2(\mathbf{r} - \mathbf{r}')\,\mathrm{d}\mathbf{r}'. \tag{52}$$

The relationship between ψ_1 and ψ_2 depends upon the defocus difference $\Delta f = \Delta f_2 - \Delta f_1$. This relationship is most easily derived by taking the Fourier transforms of ψ_1 and ψ_2, $S_1(\mathbf{v})$ and $S_2(\mathbf{v})$ respectively:

$$S_1(\mathbf{v}) = S(\mathbf{v})\,T_1(\mathbf{v})$$

and

$$S_2(\mathbf{v}) = S(\mathbf{v})\,T_2(\mathbf{v}). \tag{53}$$

Hence

$$S_1(\mathbf{v}) = S_2(\mathbf{v})\,T_1(\mathbf{v})/T_2(\mathbf{v}). \tag{54}$$

Since $T(\mathbf{v}) = T_1(\mathbf{v})/T_2(\mathbf{v}) = \exp\left[-i\gamma_1(\mathbf{v})\right]/\exp\left[-i\gamma_2(\mathbf{v})\right]$ we find that $T(\mathbf{v}) = \exp\left[-i\pi\Delta f v^2 \lambda\right]$ independent of C_s and other lens defects, such as axial astigmatism. Thus the relationship between ψ_1 and ψ_2 is in terms of a convolution:

$$\psi_1(\mathbf{r}) = \psi_2(\mathbf{r}) * G(\mathbf{r}) \tag{55}$$

where $G(\mathbf{r})$ is the inverse Fourier transform of $T(\mathbf{v})$. From Eqn (54) we can see that the difference between the Fourier spectra of ψ_1 and ψ_2 corresponds to a phase shift of $-\pi\Delta f v^2 \lambda$. The differences between ψ_1 and ψ_2 should be sufficiently large so that we have some hope of using the respective image intensity measurements $j_1 = |\psi_1|^2$ and $j_2 = |\psi_2|^2$ to determine ψ_1 and ψ_2 in the presence of noise; test calculations show that $\Delta f = 100$ nm is optimum, because larger defocus differences cause large changes in the character of the inelastic image (Misell, 1975), which we have neglected completely. We note that in order to solve Eqn (55) for either ψ_1 or ψ_2 we require only the defocus difference Δf; however, if we are to determine ψ_o from Eqn (52), we need to know the resolution function G_1 or G_2 and the appropriate C_s and defocus, Δf_1 or Δf_2. This essential requirement of precise values for the electron-optical parameters, particularly for high spatial frequencies (T depends on $\Delta f v^2$), probably limits the two defocus method to bright-field images, where C_s and Δf can be determined accurately (± 10 nm) from the optical transform of the *thin* substrate image.

The iteration scheme is similar to that of the GS algorithm: initial phases are assigned to the image amplitude $|\psi_1|$ and ψ_2 is calculated from Eqn (54) (computationally faster) or Eqn (55); the amplitudes of this ψ_2 will be incorrect because the phase information is incorrect and the next step is to replace these amplitudes with the correct set $|\psi_2|$ retaining the generated phase set. ψ_2 is then used to calculate ψ_1 using the resolution function $G'(\mathbf{r})$ corresponding to $\Delta f_1 - \Delta f_2$. The iteration is continued until the sum

$$\sum_{\mathbf{r}} (|\psi_1(\mathbf{r})| - |\psi_1'(\mathbf{r})|)^2 = R \tag{56}$$

for the differences between the actual amplitude $|\psi_1|$ and the calculated amplitude $|\psi_1'|$ attains some small value. As with the GS algorithm the assessment of the R value is difficult; although we know that the iteration scheme outlined above cannot diverge (R increases), there is no reason why it should converge. Test calculations, in fact, show that the results obtained for ψ_1 and ψ_2 depend on the initial phase guesses—certain random number sequences produce a small R value with correct ψ_1 and ψ_2 while other sequences produce a variety of incorrect solutions for ψ_1 and ψ_2 with small and large R values. Thus the two defocus method cannot be recommended as an independent phase determination method; the use of the weak phase–weak amplitude approximation of Section IIB (also using a focus series) to calculate reasonable approximations to ψ_1 and ψ_2 is required.

In the practical application of the two defocus method $|\psi_1|$ and $|\psi_2|$ should correspond to identical areas of the specimen, and should be normalized so that

$$\int |\psi_1(\mathbf{r})|^2 \, d\mathbf{r} = \int |\psi_2(\mathbf{r})|^2 \, d\mathbf{r}. \tag{57}$$

The number of electrons in each image is then the same, the only difference being the spatial distribution of the intensities due to the defocus difference.

There are several practical problems with the two defocus method; namely the difficulty in aligning two images taken at different defocus to an accuracy of about one-half the final resolution required in ψ_o (Frank, 1973a), and the serious effect of a relatively small contribution to the image from inelastic scattering on the phase solution for ψ_o (Misell, 1973b). These problems and the noise problem are less serious in the case of images of crystalline specimens which can be aligned very accurately using the discrete nature of the Fourier transforms of j_1 and j_2; also by using the discrete transform a large fraction of the inelastic scattering can be eliminated (see Section II). The fundamental assumption of the two defocus method is that the two images are of the same object and differ only in defocus. Even if the first image is taken under minimal radiation conditions, the second image will differ substantially because of the increased radiation dose to the specimen, particularly at high resolution (Unwin and Henderson, 1975). The problem here is that we cannot move to a new specimen area because we are not certain of the identity of the two areas, particularly for asymmetric molecules. This problem is not so serious for crystalline specimens or partially organized arrays of biological molecules, but even then we may have to take account of focus gradients that occur between areas of specimen separated by several tens of microns.

C. Bright-Field and Dark-Field Images

The bright-field/dark-field method uses the differences between the image intensity distributions $|\psi_o|^2$ for the two electron-optical situations (Ansley, 1973; Frank, 1973c). The bright-field image intensity (in the absence of lens aberrations) is

$$j_{BF}(\mathbf{r}) = |1 + \psi_s(\mathbf{r})|^2$$
$$= 1 + 2|\psi_s(\mathbf{r})| \cos [\eta(\mathbf{r})] + |\psi_s(\mathbf{r})|^2 \qquad (58)$$

while in the idealized dark-field image obtained by using an objective aperture centre stop to intercept the unscattered electrons (the unity in Eqn (58)):

$$j_{DF} = |\psi_s(\mathbf{r})|^2. \qquad (59)$$

Hence the difference between the two intensities

$$j_{BF} - j_{DF} = 1 + 2|\psi_s(\mathbf{r})| \cos [\eta(\mathbf{r})] \qquad (60)$$

can be used to calculate $|\psi_s|$ cos η and we can determine cos η because we know $j_{DF} = |\psi_s|^2$. However, η can have one of two values at every point in the image, $\pm\eta$, since cos $\eta = \cos(-\eta)$. Thus for n image points there are 2^n possible sets of phase solutions for $\eta(\mathbf{r})$. Frank (1973c) suggests that most of these solutions can be eliminated by the use of the smoothness (analyticity) of ψ_s; even this idea has problems whenever $\eta = 0$ or π, although it may be possible to eliminate this ambiguity by using the band-limited (finite transform) nature of ψ_s (see Section IV; Walther, 1963).

However, apart from the gross ambiguity of the solutions for ψ_s, there are several serious practical objections to the use of the bright-field/dark-field method in electron microscopy. Firstly, it is impossible to devise a dark-field stop which will only stop the sharply defined unscattered beam, and low spatial frequencies from the object structure will also be intercepted. Also, using axial dark-field often causes image distortion as a result of electrical charging of the centre stop; thus in this case the dark-field image will be affected by a different transfer function from that in the bright-field image. Tilted dark-field microscopy is no better because the asymmetric optics mean that the Fourier spectrum of j_{DF} will be completely different from the symmetric bright-field intensity j_{BF}.

A second problem is that the contribution of the inelastic scattering j_{In} to the total image intensity will be different in dark-field and bright-field; in the former case the centre stop will intercept a large proportion of the inelastic scattering. Thus $j_{BF} - j_{DF}$ will include a term which corresponds to the difference between the inelastic image intensity distributions.

Thirdly, it is difficult to see how we can scale the intensities of the two images and then align them accurately because of the essential differences between the appearance of bright-field and dark-field images. As in the two defocus method we also have the radiation damage problem when we record more than one image from a given specimen area; in fact, it has become rather worse because, in order to obtain a given signal-to-noise ratio in a dark-field image, the radiation dose may have to be increased by a factor of at least ten as compared with a bright-field image.

The main merit of this method is its mathematical simplicity and the absence of a need to solve iteratively a set of equations.

D. *Complementary Half-Plane Aperture Images*

The basic idea of using half-plane apertures is the use of a semicircular aperture to transmit only one-half of the diffracted wave to the image plane. The idea is not new and has been used in Schlieren microscopy (Zernike, 1942; see Goodman, 1968 for references) for increasing the contrast of a phase object and for phase determination in optics (Lohmann, 1956; Belvaux and Vareille, 1971). The suggestion that the idea should be tried in electron microscopy came from Hanszen (1969) and the analysis of such images was given by Hoppe *et al.* (1970). In electron microscopy we cannot use an exactly semicircular aperture in the diffraction plane because of the problem of electrical charging of the aperture edge by the intense unscattered beam (Thon, 1971; Hanszen, 1973). Thus we use an aperture with an indentation at the centre large enough to transmit the whole of the central beam (Fig. 11). Because we lose one-half of the spatial frequency information with a single half-plane aperture (Fig. 11a where

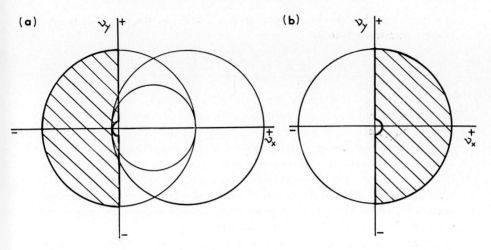

FIG. 11. Complementary semicircular (half-plane) apertures used in the back focal plane (diffraction plane) of the objective lens with (a) negative half frequency plane, (b) positive half frequency plane excluded by the aperture (shaded). Also in (a) are shown the positions of the normal circular objective aperture; the smaller aperture corresponding to the same maximum semi-angle as the half-plane aperture and the large aperture that has the same diameter as the half-plane aperture.

the half-plane $v_x < 0$ is cut off by the aperture), we need, in general, to record a second image with the complementary half-plane aperture, Fig. 11(b), where now only the $v_x < 0$ half-plane contributes to the image. The incentive for the use of such elaborate apertures is that in bright-field microscopy (where the centre beam is unattenuated) we can determine ψ_s without any ambiguity in its phase η, provided that the image contrast is not too high (see below; Misell, Burge and Greenaway, 1974). We consider again the equation for the image intensity for coherent illumination with the half-plane aperture in place:

$$j_+(\mathbf{r}) = 1 + 2 \operatorname{Re}\,[\psi_+(\mathbf{r})] + \operatorname{Re}\,{}^2[\psi_+(\mathbf{r})] + \operatorname{Im}\,{}^2[\psi_+(\mathbf{r})] \qquad (61)$$

where the subscript $+$ refers to the use of the positive half-plane aperture (transmitting $v_x > 0$), Fig. 11(a), and ψ_+ represents the scattered wave-function ψ_s derived by using only half of the Fourier spectrum $S(\mathbf{v})$ (for $v_x > 0$ in this case). Now in normal bright-field microscopy we can only determine $\operatorname{Re}\,[\psi_s]$ even if we are able to neglect the non-linear terms $\operatorname{Re}^2 \psi_s$ and $\operatorname{Im}^2 \psi_s$. However, for the half-plane aperture image, there is an exact mathematical relationship between the real and imaginary parts of a function, in this case ψ_+, whose Fourier transform, $S(\mathbf{v})$ is zero in one half of the Fourier plane (for example, Peřina, 1972), that is, $S(v_x, v_y) = 0$ for

$v_x < 0$. Thus the imaginary part of ψ_+, Im ψ_+ is the one-dimensional Hilbert transform of Re ψ_+ :

$$\text{Im}\left[\psi_+(x,y)\right] = \frac{1}{\pi} \int_{-\infty}^{+\infty} \frac{\text{Re}\left[\psi_+(z,y)\right]}{z-x}\,\mathrm{d}z \qquad (62)$$

where the Cauchy principal value of the integral is to be taken; in practice this last statement means that care should be taken in evaluating the integral near the singularity $z = x$, and for numerical evaluation the integral should be rewritten in a more suitable form (Misell and Greenaway, 1974a). There is an alternative Fourier transform version of Eqn (62) (Saxton, 1974) which increases the computational speed for evaluating Eqn (62); we shall defer a detailed discussion of the Fourier transform technique until Section V, where the relationship between half-plane aperture images and single-sideband holograms will be examined.

We now examine the way in which ψ_+ can be determined from Eqns (61) and (62). If we could neglect the non-linear terms in Eqn (61) we could determine from j_+ the value of Re $[\psi_+(x,y)]$. Then Eqn (62) would give the imaginary part of $\psi_+(x,y)$, and we could calculate the complex function $\psi_+ = \text{Re}\,\psi_+ + i\,\text{Im}\,\psi_+$. Similarly using a second complementary half-plane image for $v_x < 0$, we could determine Re ψ_- and Im ψ_- (the Hilbert transform equation has a change in sign for $v_x < 0$). Hence the complete wavefunction $\psi_s = \psi_+ + \psi_-$ could be determined (Misell, Burge and Greenaway, 1974). In most practical cases the contribution from the squared terms is less than 20–30% of 2Re ψ_+, and we shall assume that from Eqn (61) we can calculate a good approximation to Re ψ_+ by neglecting the squared terms: 2Re $\psi_+ \simeq j_+ - 1$. Evidently the Im ψ_+, calculated from Eqn (62) using an integral over Re ψ_+, will also be in error, but now we can calculate a good approximation to Re$^2\,\psi_+ + \text{Im}^2\,\psi_+$ to use in Eqn (61). We can therefore systematically correct Re ψ_+ for the non-linear terms by repeating this correction. There is a slight problem in the case of Re $\psi_+ \simeq 0$, when the main contribution to j_+ will arise from Im$^2\,\psi_+$, but this has little effect on Im ψ_+ derived from an integral over all real values, Eqn (62). The computational tests on the Hilbert transform method (Misell and Greenaway, 1974a) show that for contributions from the non-linear terms of up to 40% of 2Re ψ_+ this method gives correct amplitude and phase information. Figure 12 shows a comparison of image contrast (defined as the mean variation in the image intensity/background intensity) with the contribution from non-linear squared terms. It is clear from Fig. 12 that for contrast values of 0·6 (60%) then Re$^2\,\psi_+ + \text{Im}^2\,\psi_+$ satisfies the condition that the non-linear terms should be less than 0·4. This would seem to satisfy most practical situations in biological electron microscopy, where the image contrast is usually less than 0·2 (20%). Above

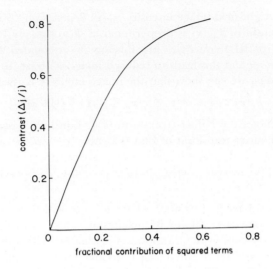

FIG. 12. The average contribution from the squared terms to the image intensity in bright-field microscopy for an image contrast $\Delta j/j$. $E_0 = 100 \text{ keV}, v_{max}; = 2 \cdot 7 \text{ nm}^{-1}$ ($\alpha = 0 \cdot 01$ rad).

a contribution of $0 \cdot 5$ from the non-linear terms Re ψ_+ does not converge to a stable value, and the corresponding phase solution is completely in error. The success of the Hilbert transform method depends on determining the phase angle of ψ_+, η_+, to within a fraction of a radian; the method may, however, work if η_+ is only in the correct quadrant, because the signs of Re ψ_+ and Im ψ_+ are still correct.

In certain cases we do not require both half-plane aperture images. The simplest case is that of a weak phase object $\psi_o(\mathbf{r}) \simeq 1 - i\phi(\mathbf{r})$; if we determine $\phi_+(\mathbf{r})$ from a single half-plane image, we can calculate $\phi_-(\mathbf{r})$ from the property of the Fourier transform of the *real* function ϕ, namely $\Phi(\mathbf{v}) = \Phi^\dagger(-\mathbf{v})$, where † denotes the complex conjugate of a function. The Fourier transform of $\phi_+(x,y)$ is zero for $v_x < 0$: $\Phi(v_x, v_y) = 0$ for $v_x < 0$, but since we know that $\Phi^\dagger(-v_x, -v_y) = \Phi(v_x, v_y)$, we can then generate $\Phi^\dagger$ for $v_x < 0$; knowing the complex number $(a + ib)$ or its complex conjugate $(a - ib)$ enables ϕ to be determined for all spatial frequencies less than v_{max}, the maximum spatial frequency transmitted by a circular objective aperture of the same diameter as the half-plane aperture. In view of the practical problems of using half-plane apertures the reader may question the interest in the analysis of a weak phase object. The simple advantage of using the half-plane image for a weak phase object is the improved image contrast over normal bright-field microscopy, although considerable care must be taken in interpreting such images (Scales, 1974).

The normal bright-field image intensity $j_{\mathrm{BF}}(\mathbf{r})$ depends on $2\phi(\mathbf{r}) * q(\mathbf{r})$ and its Fourier transform $J_{\mathrm{BF}}(\mathbf{v})$ is proportional to $\Phi(\mathbf{v}) \sin [\gamma(\mathbf{v})](|\mathbf{v}| < v_{\max})$; thus certain spatial frequencies are missing or attenuated in the image whenever $\gamma \simeq n\pi$ and this leads to reduced image contrast. In the case of a half-plane image, we can show that the image intensity is (Scales, 1974)

$$j_{+}(\mathbf{r}) = 1 - \phi(\mathbf{r}) * q(\mathbf{r}) + q'(\mathbf{r}) * [\mathrm{HT}\, \phi(\mathbf{r})] \qquad (63)$$

where HT denotes the Hilbert transform of ϕ, Eqn (62) using ϕ instead of Re ψ_{+}. The Fourier transform of Eqn (63) is:

$$J_{+}(\mathbf{v}) = \delta(\mathbf{v}) - \Phi(\mathbf{v}) \sin [\gamma(\mathbf{v})] - i\Phi(\mathbf{v}) \cos [\gamma(\mathbf{v})] \frac{v_x}{|v_x|} \qquad (64)$$

where $v_x/|v_x| = 1$ for $v_x > 0$ and -1 for $v_x < 0$. Whenever $\sin \gamma = 0$, the $\cos \gamma$ term in Eqn (64) attains its maximum value, so that there are no spatial frequency gaps in the transform of j_{+}, because either Φ or $i\Phi$ is non-zero. Thus the contrast in the image is greater than in normal bright-field microscopy. A more physical interpretation of Eqn (63) is obtained by using an approximation for the last term in the equation, namely that $1/x \approx \delta'(x)$ the derivative of the Dirac delta function $\delta(x)$. The essential result is that the Hilbert transform of ϕ becomes (Hoppe, 1971)

$$\frac{1}{\pi} \int \frac{\phi(z,y)}{z-x}\, \mathrm{d}z \simeq \frac{1}{\pi} \int \delta'(z-x)\phi(z,y)\, \mathrm{d}z = \frac{1}{\pi} \frac{\partial \phi}{\partial x} \qquad (65)$$

that is, the derivative of ϕ in the x-direction. Thus even if the phase shift ϕ is small, its derivative is probably quite large and the dominant term in Eqn (63) will be $q'(\mathbf{r}) * 1/\pi \partial \phi/\partial x$. The image will then have sharpened features in one direction (the x-direction). The direction in which we see these sharpened features will of course depend on the orientation of the half-plane aperture with respect to the specimen and this is the problem in directly interpreting the half-plane aperture image of a weak phase object; thus it would be wiser to determine ϕ_{+} from such an image using the Hilbert transform Eqn (62) or Eqn (64) and the relationship $\Phi(\mathbf{v}) = \Phi^{\dagger}(-\mathbf{v})$ to give the complete function ϕ. Figure 13 shows the half-plane image of a negatively stained bacteriophage; the subunits of the phage tail obviousiy have enhanced contrast as compared to a normal bright-field image of bacteriophage, and the overall appearance is that of a metal-shadowed specimen. In fact the use of half-plane apertures, usually approximated by using a normal circular aperture with tilted illumination (Fig. 11), has been called optical shadowing (Haydon and Lemons, 1972; Scales, 1974) by analogy with the similar effects observed in images of biological specimens shadowed from one direction by metal evaporation. The same technique has also been called topographical imaging (Cullis and Maher, 1975).

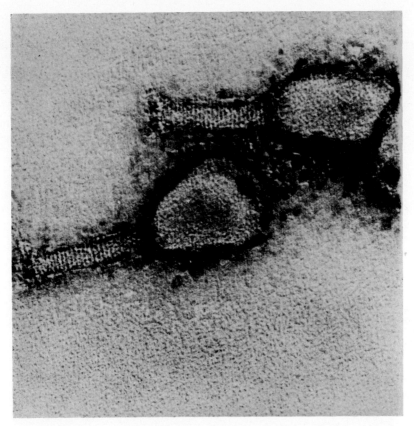

Fig. 13. Half-plane (single-sideband) image of a negatively stained bacteriophage. $M = 500\,000$ (10 mm $\equiv$ 20 nm) $E_0 = 100$ keV. (W. H. J. Andersen, unpublished.)

In addition to the case of a weak phase object we require only one half-plane image to completely evaluate ψ_s when the specimen has a centro-symmetric structure: then $\psi_+(x, y) = \psi_-(-x, -y)$, or when the specimen has a mirror plane: then $\psi_+(x, y) = \psi_-(-x, y)$. It should be noted, however, that the centrosymmetry of ψ_s does not mean that ψ_+ is centrosymmetric. In fact half-plane images display considerable asymmetry.

As an alternative to the use of Hilbert transforms, half-plane aperture images have been mathematically treated using the weak phase–weak amplitude approximation (Lenz, 1971b; Downing and Siegel, 1975). This analysis does not seem to add to the general analysis of half-plane images given above, and we still require two complementary half-plane aperture images to evaluate $\phi(\mathbf{r})$ and $\epsilon(\mathbf{r})$. However, the final result is interesting; for aberration-free images the sum and difference of the half-plane image intensities are (Hoppe, 1971; Downing and Siegel, 1975):

$$
\left.
\begin{aligned}
j_+(\mathbf{r}) + j_-(\mathbf{r}) &\equiv 2\epsilon(\mathbf{r}) \\
j_+(\mathbf{r}) - j_-(\mathbf{r}) &\equiv 2\phi(\mathbf{r}) * 1/\pi x
\end{aligned}
\right\}. \tag{66}
$$

Hence the sum of the two aligned images gives the absorption term, which includes a term in $\phi^2/2$ for a non-weak phase object (see Section IIB), whereas the difference, when corrected for the convolution effect of $1/x$, will give ϕ. The corresponding analysis including lens aberrations does not simplify to give a separation of ϵ and ϕ, and the half-plane aperture images

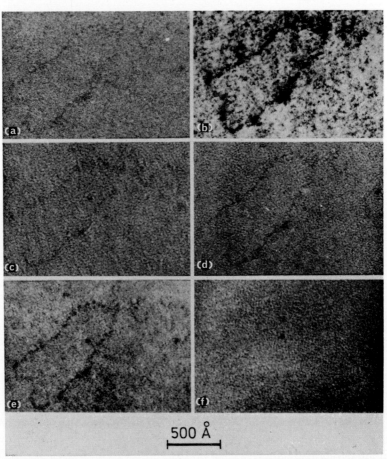

FIG. 14. Images of uranyl stained DNA: (a) normal bright-field image, (b) dark-field image (tilted illumination), (c) and (d) complementary single-sideband images, (e) sum of two images (heavy components), and (f) difference of two images (weak components). $M = 300\,000$ (10 mm $\equiv$ 33 nm), $E_0 = 100$ keV. (Downing and Siegel, 1975.)

must be first corrected for lens aberrations and other distortions in the image (Spence, 1974). As an example of the application of Eqn (66) Fig. 14 shows (a) normal bright-field, (b) tilted dark-field, (c) and (d) complementary half-plane aperture images of uranyl stained DNA (Downing and Siegel, 1975). Because none of the images corresponds to minimum radiation conditions it is unlikely that the biological structure (DNA) is preserved and the images are essentially of the stain. If the stain forms a thin layer of heavy atoms on a carbon substrate, we should expect the summed image to show mainly the unstructured inelastic contribution from the carbon and stain (ϵ) while the difference image should show the high resolution elastic contribution from the stain (ϕ). However, the results shown in Fig. 14(e) and (f) exhibit the reverse effect. The only viable explanation of this effect is that the term in $\phi^2/2$ in the expansion of exp $[-i\phi(\mathbf{r})]$ is greater than ϕ, but this would require a layer of stain about 20 nm thick, rather larger than normally occurs with stained DNA specimens.

Until this point we have only given the merits of recording half-plane images, but when we examine the practical problems in implementing the method we may conclude that the half-plane image technique will never become a routine technique in biological electron microscopy. Firstly the Hilbert transform relation between Re ψ_+ and Im ψ_+ is exactly valid only if we exclude the whole of the negative half-plane ($v_x < 0$). Clearly with an indentation at the centre of the aperture large enough to allow the unscattered beam to be transmitted, small-angle elastic scattering and nearly all the inelastic scattering will contribute to the image; also the complementary half-plane apertures must be exactly aligned in the diffraction plane of the electron microscope so that we do not have contributions from the $v_x < 0$ plane to the nominally $v_x > 0$ image. Calculations show that the half-plane apertures must be aligned to within 2 μm with a centre hole of no more than 2–4 μm in size, in order that the final result for ψ_s be acceptable (an average phase error of less than 0·2 rad); thus the incident electron beam divergence should be less than 5×10^{-4} rad and the rotational alignment of the complementary half-plane apertures should be accurate to 2–5° (Misell and Greenaway 1974a). A second problem arises from the electrical charging of the aperture edge which causes astigmatism; but, as can be seen from the half-plane images in Figs 13 and 14(c), the images are naturally streaked, although they may not in fact be astigmatic. It is very important to know the transfer function so that the image wavefunction determined can be corrected for lens defects and defocusing to give ψ_s. This is not possible for half-plane images; as can be seen from the Fourier transform J_+, Eqn (64), for a weak phase object, an optical transform of a half-plane image would give an intensity distribution $|J_+|^2$ which depends on both sin γ and cos γ. Such an optical transform would show very little modulation due to spherical aberration and defocus effects because the $\cos^2 \gamma$ ring pattern would be superimposed on a complementary $\sin^2 \gamma$ profile. This is in fact the principle advantage of the half-plane image: that all spatial frequencies are present in the image transform with a weighting of unity (Lenz, 1971b). Figure 15 shows an optical simulation of

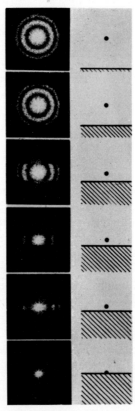

FIG. 15. Optical simulation showing the effect of the objective aperture edge position on the optical diffraction pattern of a carbon film. (Hanszen, 1973.)

the effect of a half-plane aperture on the optical transform of a "carbon" substrate (Hanszen, 1973). In the normal bright-field situation (left-hand side of Fig. 15) the optical transform shows the normal $\sin^2 \gamma$ behaviour; as the aperture edge is moved closer to the central spot the transform is progressively cut-off in the x-direction, until it becomes a bright central spot of uniform intensity; the streak in the y-direction is due to imperfections of the aperture edge. Results as illustrative as this optical simulation of the effect of the half-plane aperture on the optical transform of a carbon image are very difficult to obtain in the electron microscope, because of electrical charging of the aperture as a result of contamination (Thon, 1971). The lack of dependence of the transform of the half-plane image on defocus makes the correction of the image wavefunction (determined from the Hilbert transform relations) to give ψ_s rather difficult. Gross astigmatism caused by electrical charging of the aperture will, however, show in the optical transform of a half-plane image.

The next major problem is the alignment of the complementary wavefunctions ψ_+ and ψ_-, and in practice alignment is best made in Fourier space since the respective transforms should vanish for $v_x < 0$ and $v_x > 0$. In practice the dividing line between the transforms is not definite because the noise and the inelastic scattering contribute to both frequency half-planes. In fact the best way of aligning the transforms of the half-plane images seems to be from the line structure that shows in the transforms due to the imperfections of the aperture edge (Downing and Siegel, 1973, 1975) although alignment is also possible using optical correlation against a normal bright-field image. Finally there is the radiation damage problem as a result of recording two images of the same specimen.

To conclude this section we shall show that the Hilbert transform method is of very little use for phase determination in dark-field microscopy. If we use a half-plane objective aperture with a centre stop or a displaced circular aperture of the appropriate diameter (see Fig. 11), then the Hilbert transform relationship, Eqn (62), between the real and imaginary parts of ψ_+ is still valid; but, we no longer have an approximation to Re ψ_+ because the dark-field image intensity in the absence of lens aberrations depends on $|\psi_+|^2$. Thus the Hilbert transform relation could only become the basis of an iterative scheme, where we guess Re ψ_+ then calculate Im ψ_+ from Eqn (62), and the comparison of Re$^2 \psi_+$ + Im$^2 \psi_+$ with $|\psi_+|^2$ would form the basis of a refinement. However, such iterative schemes cannot work because Re $\psi_+ = |\psi_+| \cos \eta_+$ is the same for $\pm \eta_+$, and there are 2^n solutions for ψ_+ all giving the same image intensity $|\psi_+|^2$. A second type of Hilbert transform relates the phase angle η_+ to the logarithm of $|\psi_+|$ (Wolf, 1962; Peřina, 1972):

$$\eta_+(x, y) = \frac{1}{\pi} \int_{-\infty}^{+\infty} \frac{\ln |\psi_+(z, y)|}{z - x} \, dz. \qquad (67)$$

This relation can evidently be evaluated from image intensity measurements alone to give a phase angle η_+. Unfortunately this phase angle is correct only if ψ_+ is never zero. When there are zeros in ψ_+, the logarithmic term in Eqn (67) becomes singular (infinite), in which case the phase determined is only a minimal phase (Wolf, 1962; Roman and Marathay, 1963; Nussenzveig, 1967), which bears little relation to the correct phase (Misell and

Greenaway, 1974b). So we conclude that in dark-field the half-plane image technique is no more successful than preceding methods in providing a unique solution for ψ_s.

However, the logarithmic form of the Hilbert transform has been applied to the consideration of a bright-field image where the object wavefunction can be written as $1 + \psi_+(\mathbf{r})$ (Burge et al., 1974). In this case the equation becomes:

$$\chi_+(x, y) = \frac{1}{\pi} \int_{-\infty}^{+\infty} \frac{\ln |1 + \psi_+(z, y)|}{z - x}\, \mathrm{d}z \qquad (68)$$

where χ_+ is the phase angle of $1 + \psi_+$ and not that of ψ_+; the two phases can be easily related; $|1 + \psi_+|^2$ is just the ideal image intensity in bright-field j_+, Eqn (61). The difference between Eqns (67) and (68) is that the bright-field background prevents the occurrence of singularities in the logarithmic term unless $|\psi_+| \geqslant 1$. Calculations show that $|\psi_+| \geqslant 1$ corresponds to about 50% scattering of the incident electron beam by the specimen and also corresponds to the situation where the iterative Hilbert transform method, based on Eqns (61) and (62), fails to converge (Misell and Greenaway, 1974b). However, the advantage in using Eqn (68) is that the solution for the phase is non-iterative provided that $|\psi_+|$ is less than the background intensity; in bright-field microscopy the contrast rarely exceeds 0·2 and so it is unlikely that $|\psi_+|$ will exceed the background (unscattered) contribution to the image.

There is one possible ambiguity in the phase $\chi_+(x, y)$, that is, the addition of a linear phase term $2\pi \bar{v} x$, where $\bar{v}$ is a constant (Burge et al., 1974). In test calculations (Misell and Greenaway, 1974b) on images of single atoms this phase ambiguity did not occur. In general linear phase errors can be eliminated by taking the Fourier transform of ψ_+, when the transform will be displaced by $-\bar{v}$ in the x-direction, v_x.

IV. UNIQUENESS OF THE PHASE SOLUTION

The problem of the uniqueness of the phase $\phi(\mathbf{r})$ (or $\eta(\mathbf{r})$) of the wavefunction $\psi_o(\mathbf{r})$ (or $\psi_s(\mathbf{r})$) as determined from measurements of $|\psi_o(\mathbf{r})|$ (or $|\psi_s(\mathbf{r})|$) can be stated as follows. Given a series of measurements of $|\psi_o|$, is it possible to reconstruct only a single set of phases ϕ (O'Neill and Walther, 1963)? Clearly, if there are several possible solutions for ϕ at each image point $\mathbf{r}$ we cannot expect to interpret the results for the wavefunction $\psi_o = |\psi_o| \exp(-i\phi)$. There is a simple example where we can see that the measurement of $|\psi_o|$ alone will not distinguish between two different wavefunctions: $\exp(-\epsilon) \exp(-i\phi_1)$ and $\exp(-\epsilon) \exp(-i\phi_2)$; the aberration-free image (with no objective aperture) of either of these wavefunctions has an intensity $j = |\psi_o|^2 = \exp(-2\epsilon)$. However, with a restricting aperture in the Fourier plane certain spatial frequencies are omitted $(B(\mathbf{v}) = 0)$ from the image plane, and these Fourier components missing from the image do depend on the phase terms $\exp(-i\phi_1)$ and $\exp(-i\phi_2)$ (Walther, 1963); in this case the two image intensities j_1 and j_2 will no longer be the same and there is a unique set of phases for a given image intensity distribution. This mathematical statement of the uniqueness problem does not assist in the practical determination of the phase distribution; the perfect (noise-free) image may have a mathematically unique result for ϕ, but this does not tell us how to determine ϕ numerically. In practice most of the methods in Section III can give a large number of numerical solutions for ψ_o or ψ_s, and there is no simple way of telling which solution is correct, unless we use other information about the object or its Fourier spectrum. This is even more relevant in the case of noisy images, where the criterion that the difference between the measured $|\psi_o|$ and calculated $|\psi_o|$ should be a minimum, may give little indication of whether a correct phase distribution has been calculated. The situation is improved if we have some *a priori* knowledge about the phase solution as in the case of half-plane aperture images (Section IIID), where we can determine good approximations to ψ_s by virtue of the mathematical relationship between the real and imaginary parts of ψ_s. However, in neither the diffraction/image plane (Section IIIA) nor two defocus methods (Section IIIB), is there any known reason why the method should converge to the correct phase solution. The bright-field/dark-field method (Section IIIC) intrinsically gives a non-unique set of phases, and these can only be distinguished if other information on ψ_s is available.

In this section we shall assume that there is a unique solution for ψ_o or ψ_s from a given set of intensity measurements; we shall be primarily interested in what types of non-uniqueness are produced by the direct methods detailed in Section III. We shall examine these problems in bright-field (Section IVA) and dark-field (Section IVB) microscopy. In the case of non-unique phase solutions, we examine how other information, such as the finite size of the object, may be used to reduce the number of solutions; and in the case of phase solutions which are only approximate, perhaps as a result of experimental error, we look at refinement techniques, such as are used in X-ray crystallography for improving the accuracy of the phase (Section IVC).

A. *Bright-Field Microscopy*

The diffraction plane/image plane method of Gerchberg and Saxton (1972) uses an initial set of phases derived from random numbers between $-\pi$ and π (Section IIIA). In addition to the obvious ambiguity that

$\phi = \phi + 2n\pi$ is a solution of their equations, $\phi = \phi + \phi_o$, where ϕ_o is an arbitrary constant, is also a solution. These two types of ambiguity may not be important because we are principally interested in the variation of ϕ across the specimen. A much more serious ambiguity in the phase of ψ_o occurs for a specimen whose diffraction pattern or image is centrosymmetric; then both $\psi_o = |\psi_o| \exp\left[-i\phi\right]$ and its complex conjugate $\psi_o^\dagger = |\psi_o| \exp\left[+i\phi\right]$ are possible solutions. In the case of an aberration-free image, whether we determine ϕ or $-\phi$ is immaterial; but when a correction has to be applied for lens aberrations this difference is important. If the Fourier transform of the image wavefunction ψ_i is $S_i(\mathbf{v})$ then the transform of $\psi_i^\dagger$ is $S_i^\dagger(-\mathbf{v})$; the division of the image transform by $\exp\left[-i\gamma(\mathbf{v})\right]$ in order to correct for lens defects will then give two completely different solutions for the object wavefunction ψ_o. There are also problems if the modulus of $\psi_o \simeq$ constant for a low contrast specimen, when the method can give the phase ϕ of ψ_o nearer to 2π instead of zero; this may lead to discontinuities in the solution for the object wavefunction. Generally the diffraction-image plane method will not give a unique solution for ϕ for a weak phase object. In the image of a weak phase object, $\psi_o = 1 + \psi_s$, the intensity distribution is essentially $1 + 2\mathrm{Re}\,\psi_s$ since $|\psi_s|^2 \ll 1$; thus the information in the image is confined to $\mathrm{Re}\,\psi_s = |\psi_s| \cos\eta$ with a negligible contribution from the $|\psi_s|^2$ term. Thus when we calculate the transform of the image amplitude, we have information only on $\cos\eta$; the transform can have one of two values at each spatial frequency $S(\mathbf{v})$ or $S^\dagger(-\mathbf{v})$, and diffraction plane intensity measurements $|S(\mathbf{v})|$ alone may not be sufficient to distinguish between these two possible solutions. Hence in the case of a weak phase object the diffraction-image plane method will lead to 2^n solutions for ψ_s, any one of which may occur as the final result in the iteration procedure. One problem in assessing the validity of the phase solution for experimental data is that the residual for the differences between the observed and calculated intensities will never be zero. A non-zero residual may indicate an incorrect phase solution or may arise as a result of the errors in the intensity measurements. We are assuming that both the diffraction pattern and image contain identical spatial frequency information on the specimen structure, that is, $F[\psi_s(\mathbf{r})] \equiv S(\mathbf{v})$. Such would not be the case if the diffraction data contained higher resolution information than the image; in this case the higher resolution diffraction spots could not be phased since there is no information in the image at this resolution. Hence this high resolution information would contribute only as noise in the final result for ψ_s and should be omitted from the transforms.

In the application of the Gerchberg and Saxton algorithm to magnetic structures, Chapman (1975a, b) achieves improved convergence by taking account of the experimental errors in the diffraction plane intensity measurements. In addition not only does the image wavefunction correspond closely to the image of a pure phase object, $\psi_o = \exp{(-i\phi)}$, but there is *a priori* information about the functional form of ϕ.

A more mathematical treatment of the non-uniqueness of the phase solutions from the diffraction-image plane method is given by Schiske (1974).

In practice the two defocus method (Section IIIB; Misell, 1973a) would appear to suffer from all the phase ambiguities associated with the diffraction-image plane method, with one exception, namely that the two defocus method may give a unique solution using two images of a weak phase object. From one bright-field image we can determine Re ψ_1 for defocus Δf_1, and from the second image we can determine Re ψ_2 for defocus Δf_2; one image will give η in one of either of two quadrants as will the second image, but the mathematical relation between ψ_1 and ψ_2 for a defocus difference Δf, should eliminate either $\pm\eta$. Drenth *et al.* (1975) conclude from the analytic properties of ψ_s that the two defocus method should give a unique solution for ψ_s, whereas the phase solution from the Gerchberg and Saxton algorithm (1972) may not be unique. This does not, in practice, say that we shall always determine the correct phase solution from the two defocus method, because measurements are made at discrete points on noisy(non-analytic) images.

Schiske (1975) examines an algorithm for phase determination using two defocus images with additional information from the diffraction pattern; mathematically the solution for ψ_s seems to be unique but again the effect of measurement errors on the result for ψ_s has not been determined.

As with the Gerchberg and Saxton algorithm (1972), the two defocus method assumes that both images contain exactly the same spatial information on ψ_s. This condition is clearly difficult to satisfy for non-crystalline specimens, when the second image will invariably include less high resolution information on ψ_s. High resolution information on ψ_s that arises from using a high resolution image ψ_1 with a lower resolution image ψ_2 cannot be believed.

We have already mentioned the ambiguity in the phase solution obtained from the bright-field/dark-field image pair method (Section IIIC; Frank, 1973c). Because we determine only Re $\psi_s = |\psi_s| \cos\eta$ there are two values for ψ_s at each image point, and hence 2^n solutions for an image measured at n points; since n may be as large as 10^4–10^6 image points, there is an extremely large number of possible solutions for ψ_s. Other ambiguities in the phase solution arise as a result of the non-equivalence of the dark-field and bright-field optics. Thus $|\psi_s|^2$ determined from the dark-field image probably excludes low resolution (low angle) information on ψ_s because of the finite size of the dark-field stop in the objective aperture. Whereas both the diffraction-image plane and two defocus image intensities can be correctly scaled, it is difficult to see how this can be done between the bright-field and dark-field intensities, $1 + 2 \operatorname{Re} \psi_s + |\psi_s|^2$ and $|\psi_s|^2$ respectively. If identical incident electron doses are used, it is unlikely that $|\psi_s|^2$ can be determined with any accuracy because the signal-to-noise ratio will be very low as a result of the relatively few electrons detected in the dark-field image as compared with the bright-field image. Clearly this method can only be used with other information such as the smoothness or the band-limited nature of ψ_s (see Section IVC).

In the case of the half-plane aperture method (Section IIID), it is clear that in bright-field microscopy we can determine a very good approximation to both $\operatorname{Re} \psi_s$ and $\operatorname{Im} \psi_s$ (subscripts $+$ and $-$ now omitted for simplicity) using the bright-field image intensity and the Hilbert transform relation (Misell and Greenaway, 1974a), or its Fourier equivalent (Saxton, 1974), between $\operatorname{Re} \psi_s$ and $\operatorname{Im} \psi_s$. The uncertainty in ψ_s only becomes serious when the contribution from $|\psi_s|^2$ exceeds 0·4 of the value of $2 \operatorname{Re} \psi_s$, corresponding to an image contrast of greater than 60% (Misell and Greenaway, 1974a). Noise on the image intensity measurements does lead to errors in $\operatorname{Re} \psi_s$ and hence $\operatorname{Im} \psi_s$, but these errors do not cause any serious ambiguities in the phase of ψ_s, except when η is near zero or 2π, when errors result in discontinuities in η. Despite the practical problems in implementing the half-plane aperture method (see Section VI), this method is recommended for phase determination in bright-field microscopy, because the conditions for a valid phase solution are easily determined. Having calculated an approximate value for $\operatorname{Re} \psi_s$ from the bright-field image intensity, the calculation of $\operatorname{Im} \psi_s$ from a Hilbert transform of $\operatorname{Re} \psi_s$, will give an estimate of the value of $|\psi_s|^2$. If $|\psi_s|^2$ is comparable to $\operatorname{Re} \psi_s$ it is unlikely that a correct phase solution can be determined.

The logarithmic Hilbert transform relation in bright-field (Burge *et al.*, 1974) will also give a correct solution for the phase χ of $(1 + \psi_s)$, provided that the image contrast is less than about 70% (Misell and Greenaway, 1974b). Both the normal Hilbert transform and the logarithmic transform methods assume that the constant background (unity) can be found from the image. In the Hilbert transform the addition of a constant error c to $\operatorname{Re} \psi_s$ will make little difference to the value of $\operatorname{Im} \psi_s$ $(1/\pi \int_{-\infty}^{+\infty} c/(z-x) \, \mathrm{d}z = 0)$ but, of course, the phase of ψ_s will be incorrect, $\eta = \tan^{-1}[\operatorname{Im} \psi_s/(\operatorname{Re} \psi_s + c)]$; the same problem arises in the logarithmic Hilbert transform when an incorrect background determination in $|1 + \psi_s|$ will lead to errors in the phase of ψ_s. In practice we have found that the constant background can be determined to within $\pm 10\%$ by the calculation of the mean value of the image intensity; or equivalently, a Fourier transform of the image intensity will separate the constant background as a delta function $\delta(\mathbf{v})$ at $\mathbf{v} \approx 0$ from the rest of the Fourier spectrum $J(\mathbf{v})$ (see Section V).

B. *Dark-Field Microscopy*

The non-uniqueness of phase solutions derived from both the diffraction-image and two defocus methods is the same as in bright-field microscopy, but the radiation damage problem, giving non-equivalent images, is now more serious—for a given signal-to-noise ratio in the image dark-field microscopy requires an electron dose at the specimen as much as 30 times the electron dose in bright-field.

In addition to the uniqueness problems of the above two methods, the half-plane aperture method now fails completely to produce acceptable phase solutions (Misell and Greenaway, 1974b). Both the normal Hilbert transform and the logarithmic Hilbert transform (with $\ln |\psi_s|$) are still valid, but in the case of the normal Hilbert transform we are unable to derive an approximation to $\mathrm{Re}\ \psi_s$ since the dark-field intensity depends on $|\psi_s|^2$ only. Iterative methods based on an initial guess for $\mathrm{Re}\ \psi_s = |\psi_s| \cos \eta$ fail because the use of either $\pm\eta$ will give the same value for the Hilbert transform of $\mathrm{Re}\ \psi_s$, $\mathrm{Im}\ \psi_s$. Thus we have 2^n possible solutions for ψ_s. A second iterative scheme based on the algorithm of Gerchberg and Saxton (1972) uses the image plane intensity and the restriction that the Fourier transform of ψ_s must be zero for one half of the frequency plane, either $v_x > 0$ or $v_x < 0$, as well as being zero for $|\mathbf{v}| \geqslant v_{\max}$; this method, which does work in bright-field microscopy (see Section V), often converges, but rarely to the correct set of phases.

The logarithmic relation leads only to a minimal phase for ψ_s, which has little connection with the correct phase, except in the trivial case where ψ_s has no zeros in the complex plane (Wolf, 1962). The same problem of determining the phase from intensity measurements occurs in source coherence measurements, where the visibility of the interference fringes $|\gamma(\tau)|$ is related to the phase of the coherence function $\gamma(\tau)$, $\phi(\tau)$, by a logarithmic Hilbert transform (Peřina, 1972). In this case even though the Fourier transform of $\gamma(\tau)$, $g(v) (=0$ for $v < 0)$, the spectral distribution of the source, is real and positive the solution for ϕ can only be derived from a detailed knowledge of the functional behaviour of γ (Roman and Marathay, 1963; Nussenzveig, 1967). The equation for $\phi(\tau)$ includes a sum of terms which depend upon the number and the positions of the complex zeros of $\gamma(\tau)$ and these terms are usually significantly larger than the minimal phase $\phi_0(\tau)$ derived from the Hilbert transform of $\ln |\gamma(\tau)|$. In electron microscopy the ambiguity in the phase solution is even more serious because we cannot assume as in optics that the Fourier transform of $\psi_s(\mathbf{r})$, $S(\mathbf{v})$, is real and positive. Bates (1969) does, however, suggest that the use of other information, such as the finite extent of the source and the smoothness of the wavefunction, at least reduces the number of possible phase solutions (see Section IIIC; Bates and Napier, 1972).

C. *Use of Other Information to Restrict Phase Solutions*

We use additional information on the object structure either to assess the validity of a phase solution, such as obtained in the two defocus method, or to distinguish between a large number of phase solutions, as in the bright-field/dark-field method. In addition, we may be able to use this information to refine a phase solution which is in error due to noise in the original intensity measurements.

The first restriction we could use is that the Fourier transform of the object wavefunction ψ_o must be zero for $|\mathbf{v}| > v_{max}$, the maximum spatial frequency transmitted by the objective aperture. Incorrect phase solutions will not satisfy this condition (O'Neill and Walther, 1963); in the case of half-plane aperture images we can impose the restriction that the transform of ψ_s must be zero for either $v_x > 0$ or $v_x < 0$. This restriction that ψ_o and ψ_s are band-limited does not apply to the noise which is non-analytic, so that we can refine approximate phases by calculating the transform of ψ_o (or ψ_s), and set the transform values $S(\mathbf{v})$ to zero outside a certain spatial frequency range. A reverse transform will give a new wavefunction ψ_o' which is correctly band-limited, but has incorrect amplitudes $|\psi_o'|$; as in the Gerchberg and Saxton (1972) algorithm we now retain the new set of phases ϕ' but replace $|\psi_o'|$ by the correct amplitudes $|\psi_o|$. This refinement procedure is continued until the differences between $|\psi_o|$ and $|\psi_o'|$ become small; noise on the original phase solution is progressively reduced in each iteration (Gerchberg, 1974; de Santis and Gori, 1975). In practice, the band-limited constraint may not be significant for biological specimens, because the transform of ψ_o usually becomes small for values of $|\mathbf{v}|$ less than v_{max} due to the effects of radiation damage. The band-limited constraint may also be used to select one of a large number of phase solutions (Walther, 1963): only the correct phase set will give a transform $S(\mathbf{v}) = 0$ for $|\mathbf{v}| > v_{max}$; however, in the presence of noise, including the effects of radiation damage which limits the maximum spatial frequency in the image, it will not be possible to distinguish between several phase solutions. Whether this method will be successful can only be assessed by the similarity of the ψ_s determined from the phase solutions which do satisfy the band-limited criterion within experimental error. Frank (1973c) suggests the use of the smoothness of the phase function for ψ_o or ψ_s to distinguish between each of the two solutions at each image point in the bright-field/dark-field method. None of these constraints has been tried in electron microscopy, but in radio astronomy Bates and Napier (1972) have applied the band-limited constraint to inter-ferograms obtained from stars. In this case the one-dimensional temperature distribution of the light/radio source $T(x)$ is of finite extent; the modulus of the transform $t(v)$ of $T(x)$ is measured. Bates and Napier (1972) then compute from $|t(v)|$ the 2^n possible phase solutions for $t(v)$ that give a $T(x)$ of finite extent; the additional constraint that the temperature distribution $T(x)$ is real and positive assists in the distinction between the mathematically possible phase solutions. The experimental results (Bates and Napier, 1972) are sufficiently encouraging to recommend its application to electron microscopy; of course, the number of possible phase solutions is large in two dimensions, but Napier and Bates (1974) do suggest that within certain limitations all the phase solutions can be computed. Bates *et al.* (1976) suggest that the constraint $T^{\dagger}(x) = T(x) \geqslant 0$ is not necessary to the success of their method, and it should therefore be applicable to electron microscopy, where $S(\mathbf{v})$ is neither real nor positive.

These analytic constraints on ψ_o or its Fourier transform S are strong but the number of acceptable phase solutions increases as the constraints are relaxed by experimental conditions.

Other constraints on the phase solutions can be obtained from the mathematical relationships between the Fourier coefficients $S(\mathbf{v})$: for example, using the unitarity relationship for elastic scattering of electrons by a centrosymmetric crystal $(V(\mathbf{r}) = V(-\mathbf{r}))$, Boyce and Roberts (1974) derive a relationship between the imaginary part of $S(\mathbf{v})$ and a convolution of the complex $S(\mathbf{v})$:

$$\text{Im}\,[S(\mathbf{v})] = c \sum_{\mathbf{v}'} S(\mathbf{v}')S(\mathbf{v} - \mathbf{v}'). \qquad (69)$$

where c is a constant. Since the summation has an infinite number of terms, we cannot exactly satisfy Eqn (69) with a band-limited ψ_s, $S(\mathbf{v}) = 0$ for $|\mathbf{v}| > v_{max}$. Equation (69) cannot be used as a basis for determining the phase of $S(\mathbf{v})$, $\omega(\mathbf{v})$ because $\text{Im}\,S = |S| \sin \omega$ gives either of two solutions for the phase, ω and $\pi - \omega$. However, it can be used to aid in choosing acceptable phase solutions.

In X-ray crystallography similar analytic relationships between the Fourier coefficients (structure amplitudes $F(\mathbf{v})$ in X-ray crystallography) can be derived by imposing the constraint that the electron density $\rho(\mathbf{r})$ must be positive at atomic resolution (Karle and Hauptman, 1964), or that the electron density $\rho(\mathbf{r}) \equiv \rho^2(\mathbf{r})$ for a specimen comprising identical (equal) atoms at atomic resolution (Sayre, 1952, 1972, 1974). This similarity between $\rho(\mathbf{r})$ and $\rho^2(\mathbf{r})$ has also been used in a phase refinement technique which minimizes the sum of the differences $[\rho(\mathbf{r}) - \rho^2(\mathbf{r})]^2$ over the electron density map (Allegra and Colombo, 1974). In all cases the relationships between the $F(\mathbf{v})$, for example for $\rho \equiv \rho^2$ (Sayre, 1952)

$$\sum_{\mathbf{v}'} F(\mathbf{v}')F(\mathbf{v} - \mathbf{v}') = aH(\mathbf{v})F(\mathbf{v}) \qquad (70)$$

(where a = unit cell area, $H(\mathbf{v})$ is a shape factor for the change in atomic shape on squaring), extend over an infinite sum, and when only low resolution $F(\mathbf{v})$ are available, these methods do not work. A more physical explanation of the failure of the squaring method is that at low resolution (0·5–1·0 nm) individual atoms are not resolved, and squaring unresolved atomic groups will give peaks in the squared density map $\rho(\mathbf{r})$ in incorrect positions; thus ρ and ρ^2 are no longer equivalent. X-ray refinement techniques usually commence with an electron density map at 0·25–0·30 nm resolution, so that such techniques are viable (Barrett and Zwick, 1971; Sayre, 1974). However, electron microscope images at this resolution are unlikely to be achieved even for periodic specimens. Besides the problem of achieving *significant* contributions to the image from high resolution structural information due to radiation damage and instrumental limitations (Section VI), there is the more fundamental problem of a severe restriction on specimen thickness if the phase information is to be accurate at 0·25 nm resolution (see Section VII). There is also the difficulty of determining the absolute value of the projected potential $V(\mathbf{r})$, which is essential to the success of these X-ray refinement techniques.

Another X-ray method, which has also been used to extend the resolution of the phase information, is the use of the finite dimensions of the specimen (Barrett *et al.*, 1971). This is in one sense the reverse procedure to that of using the band-limited nature of ψ_o or ψ_s; if we have *a priori* knowledge of the specimen dimensions, for example, the radius r_0 of a cylindrical particle such as TMV (Barrett *et al.*, 1971), then the inverse Fourier transform of $S(\mathbf{v})$ should fall to zero outside the radius r_0. Thus $S(\mathbf{v})$ can be refined by retaining the phases generated by the cut-off at r_0 but the amplitudes are replaced by their correct values $|S|$. There are two reasons why this method had limited success: firstly, the particle does not have a sharp cut-off at r_0 but probably its density falls slowly to zero; secondly, the value of r_0 was determined from an electron micrograph of negatively stained TMV and in this case the large uncertainty (± 1 nm) in r_0 could generate incorrect phases.

We have detailed these mathematical techniques because they have been successfully applied in other branches of physics, and at least some of them may be relevant to improving the accuracy of phases determined by electron microscopy. We also strongly recommend the use of the results obtained by approximate methods, the weak phase, and the weak phase–weak amplitude approximations (Section II), either as a starting point for direct methods or as a check that the phase solutions are at least consistent with approximate solutions.

V. HOLOGRAPHY AND THE ELECTRON MICROSCOPE

The original incentive for holography arose from the resolution limit of the electron microscope (Gabor, 1949). The principle of holography is to produce an interference pattern between the scattered electron wave ψ_s and a reference beam, without using imaging lenses (Gabor, 1949, 1951). However, the coherence requirements for the electron beam were so severe that recording electron holograms with conventional electron sources required very long exposure times (Haine and Mulvey, 1952). The recent development of intense field emission sources has brought electron holography to the stage where it may compete in resolution with conventional microscopy (Munch, 1975). Several authors have examined methods for recording holograms in the electron microscope (Weingärtner et al., 1969, 1971; Hoppe et al., 1970) and discussed the problems of the reconstruction of ψ_s from the hologram. However, the purpose of this review is not to examine this aspect of phase determination, but rather to discuss how, in one sense, conventional electron microscope images can be considered as holograms. Here the reference beam is the unscattered wave which interferes with the elastically scattered wave, and the problem of determining ψ_s from image intensity measurements is the equivalent problem of separating the conjugate (twin) images in a hologram (Hanszen, 1969, 1973; Lohmann, 1974). A holographic analysis of an electron image not only gives an alternative way of looking at the phase problem, but also leads to improved computational or optical methods for the determination of ψ_s from image intensity measurements. As in the previous analysis we assume that the incident electron beam is coherent and consider the problem of determining ψ_s from an aberration-free image; as stated previously the determination of the image wavefunction from the image intensity is equivalent to the problem of determining ψ_s from $|\psi_o|^2$.

A. *Normal Bright-Field Microscopy*

In normal bright-field microscopy we consider the image intensity distribution that arises from the interference of the unscattered wave (in the direction $\mathbf{v} = 0$) with a scattered wave $\psi_s(\mathbf{r})$ (in the direction $\mathbf{v}$). The image intensity $j(\mathbf{r}) = 1 + 2\mathrm{Re}\,\psi_s(\mathbf{r}) + |\psi_s(\mathbf{r})|^2$ may be rewritten in terms of ψ_s and its complex conjugate $\psi_s^\dagger$:

$$j(\mathbf{r}) = 1 + \psi_s(\mathbf{r}) + \psi_s^\dagger(\mathbf{r}) + \psi_s(\mathbf{r})\psi_s^\dagger(\mathbf{r}). \tag{71}$$

This is exactly the equation derived for the hologram arising from the interference of an "on-axis" reference beam and a scattered wave ψ_s (Goodman, 1968). We can see that the determination of ψ_s from j now becomes the problem of separating ψ_s and $\psi_s^\dagger$ in Eqn (71); in holography ψ_s and $\psi_s^\dagger$ are referred to as conjugate (twin) images. A Fourier transform of Eqn (71) shows that we are unable to separate the contributions of ψ_s and $\psi_s^\dagger$ to j:

$$J(\mathbf{v}) = \delta(\mathbf{v}) + S(\mathbf{v}) + S^\dagger(-\mathbf{v}) + S(\mathbf{v}) * S^\dagger(-\mathbf{v}). \tag{72}$$

Figure 16 gives the spatial frequency distribution of $J(\mathbf{v})$, where, since we

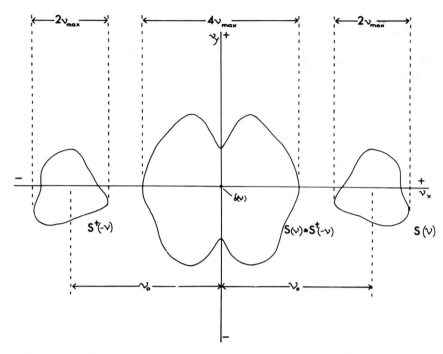

Fig. 16. The separation of conjugate images in on-axis and off-axis holography. The Fourier transform of the image intensity, j, shows the spatial separation of the transforms, S and $S^\dagger$ of the conjugate images ψ_s and $\psi_s^\dagger$, with an off-axis reference wave (tilt angle determined by v_0); in normal bright-field microscopy, the reference wave is on-axis ($v_0 = 0$). For clarity the transforms S and $S^\dagger$ are mapped as if they did not overlap the auto-correlation term $S*S^\dagger$.

are using axial illumination, $v_0 = 0$. The reference wave contributes as a sharply peaked function $\delta(\mathbf{v})$ at $\mathbf{v} = 0$, whilst the transforms $S(\mathbf{v})$ and $S^\dagger(-\mathbf{v})$ of ψ_s and $\psi_s^\dagger$ respectively are superimposed with a common centre at $\mathbf{v} = 0$, and the squared term in Eqn (72) gives the auto-correlation term $S(\mathbf{v}) * S^\dagger(-\mathbf{v})$ of frequency width $4v_{max}$, also centred on $\mathbf{v} = 0$. Thus in frequency space the three structural terms are inseparable. Even if $|\psi_s|^2$ is negligible, it is not generally possible to separate $S(\mathbf{v})$ and $S^\dagger(-\mathbf{v})$ using the Fourier transform of an on-axis hologram. In one specific case, namely, the image of a weak phase object, this superposition of the images does not prevent the determination of ψ_s: for a weak phase object the transform of the image intensity is

$$J(\mathbf{v}) \simeq \delta(\mathbf{v}) - i\Phi(\mathbf{v}) \exp\left[-i\gamma(\mathbf{v})\right] + i\Phi^\dagger(-\mathbf{v}) \exp\left[i\gamma(-\mathbf{v})\right] \quad (73)$$

with $S(\mathbf{v}) = -i\Phi \exp(-i\gamma)$.

Now since $\phi(\mathbf{r})$ is a real function, its transform Φ is complex conjugate symmetric, that is, $\Phi(\mathbf{v}) = \Phi^\dagger(-\mathbf{v})$; also since $\gamma(\mathbf{v})$ is an even function of v, $\gamma(\mathbf{v}) = \gamma(-\mathbf{v})$. Hence the last two terms in Eqn (73) become very similar, $-i\Phi \exp(-i\gamma)$ and $+i\Phi \exp(i\gamma)$, and the addition of the conjugate images gives $-2\Phi \sin \gamma$, as in Eqn (25).

Bartell and Ritz (1974) also show that on-axis holography can be used to determine the wavefunction for elastic scattering by a spherically symmetric potential distribution, for example, single atoms in a gas electron diffraction experiment; in this case the transform $S(\mathbf{v})$ is real and symmetric so that $S(\mathbf{v}) = S^\dagger(-\mathbf{v})$ in Eqn (72) and the reconstruction of ψ_s for the object is not a problem provided that the auto-correlation term is negligible. Bartell and Ritz (1974) use the large-angle nuclear scattering from the atom as a reference beam for the elastic scattering from the orbital electrons, and the optical reconstruction for ψ_s shows the radial dependence of the three-dimensional atomic potential at a resolution near to the wavelength of the incident electron beam (6 pm). However, this is an exceptional case where the conjugate image problem is non-existent, and, in general, the idea would not work for molecules.

We conclude that normal bright-field microscopy cannot be used to separate ψ_s and $\psi_s^\dagger$, unless we can use the weak phase approximation or the specimen has exceptional symmetry properties.

B. *Bright-Field Microscopy with Tilted Illumination*

One way of separating the conjugate images of ψ_s is to use an off-axis (inclined) reference wave (Leith and Upatnieks, 1962) to interfere with the scattered wave ψ_s. Of course, in this case the on-axis reference wave arising from the unscattered electron wave must be intercepted, otherwise we shall obtain a mixture of on-axis and off-axis holograms. If the reference wave is inclined to the z-axis at an angle $\beta = \lambda v_0$, then the wavefunction ψ arising from the interference of the off-axis reference wave $\exp(2\pi i v_0 x)$ and ψ_s is (Goodman, 1968):

$$\psi(\mathbf{r}) = \exp(2\pi i v_0 x) + \psi_s(\mathbf{r}) \tag{74}$$

and the image intensity is given by:

$$j(\mathbf{r}) = |\psi(\mathbf{r})|^2$$
$$= 1 + \psi_s(\mathbf{r}) \exp(-2\pi i v_0 x) + \psi_s^\dagger(\mathbf{r}) \exp(2\pi i v_0 x) + \psi_s(\mathbf{r}) \psi_s^\dagger(\mathbf{r}). \tag{75}$$

A Fourier transform of this image, either by optical or computer methods, can be used to effect the separation of ψ_s and $\psi_s^\dagger$ (Goodman, 1968):

$$J(\mathbf{v}) = \delta(\mathbf{v}) + S(v_x - v_0, v_y) + S^\dagger(-v_x - v_0, v_y) + S(\mathbf{v}) * S^\dagger(-\mathbf{v}). \tag{76}$$

Thus in the transform $J(\mathbf{v})(\mathbf{v} = (v_x, v_y))$ there is the contribution of $\delta(\mathbf{v})$

at $\mathbf{v} \simeq 0$, and an auto-correlation term $S(\mathbf{v}) * S^{\dagger}(-\mathbf{v})$ centred at $\mathbf{v} = 0$ and of frequency width $4v_{\max}$. The transforms of $\psi_s(\mathbf{r})$ and $\psi_s^{\dagger}(\mathbf{r})$, $S(\mathbf{v})$ and $S^{\dagger}(-\mathbf{v})$, are displaced from zero frequency by v_0 either side of the v_x axis as shown in Fig. 16. If the maximum spatial frequency transmitted by the objective aperture is $v_{\max}$, then $v_0 \geqslant 3v_{\max}$ will effect a complete spatial separation of the auto-correlation term. Hence the tilt angle of the reference beam β should be larger than $3v_{\max}^{\lambda}$; for $v_{\mathbf{max}} = 2 \text{ nm}^{-1}$ (0·5 nm resolution), $\beta = 0{\cdot}022$ rad. However, if the contribution to the image from the squared term $|\psi_s|^2$ is small compared to ψ_s, then we can neglect the contribution of the auto-correlation term, and in this case the tilt angle β need be only $v_{\max}\lambda$ in order to separate $S(\mathbf{v})$ and $S^{\dagger}(-\mathbf{v})$. Thus, assuming that it is practical to record an off-axis hologram in the electron microscope, the transforms $S(\mathbf{v})$ and $S^{\dagger}(-\mathbf{v})$ can be determined by excluding from the transform $J(v_x, v_y)$ either $v_x < 0$ or $v_x > 0$. Even if the auto-correlation term is not negligible, it may be still possible to find $S(\mathbf{v})$ using a smaller tilt angle than $3v_{\max}\lambda$: although $J(\mathbf{v})$ may contain contributions from both $S(\mathbf{v}) * S^{\dagger}(-\mathbf{v})$ and $S(\mathbf{v})$ for $v_x > 0$, we can calculate an approximation to $S(\mathbf{v})$ from $J(\mathbf{v})$ assuming that the auto-correlation term is negligible, and, using this approximation to $S(\mathbf{v})$, we can now calculate a value for $S(\mathbf{v}) * S^{\dagger}(-\mathbf{v})$ and apply a correction to $J(\mathbf{v})$ for the effect of the auto-correlation term. Hence we can improve the approximation to $S(\mathbf{v})$ by using the transform $J(\mathbf{v})$ for $v_x > 0$.

$\psi_s(\mathbf{r})$ can be then reconstructed from an inverse transform of $S(\mathbf{v})$; in an optical reconstruction this corresponds to a spatial filtering that allows only the transform component $S(\mathbf{v})$ transmitted at an angle β to the optic-axis to be recorded. Equations (75) and (76) are still valid if the image is affected by lens aberrations, but then the image transform $S_i(\mathbf{v})$ is determined, and this must be divided by the appropriate transfer function $\exp[-i\gamma(\mathbf{v})]$ in order to evaluate the transform of $\psi_s(\mathbf{r})$, $S(\mathbf{v})$; again the deconvolution to give ψ_s is made under ideal conditions because the modulus of the transfer function $\exp(-i\gamma)$ is unity for all $|\mathbf{v}| \leqslant v_{\max}$.

Whereas off-axis holography is possible in optics with a coherent light source, the limited coherence of electron sources may limit the practical achievement of high resolution off-axis holography in the electron microscope. There are two requirements for recording an off-axis image hologram in the electron microscope. Firstly the reference wave must be derived from the same electron wavefront as is incident on the specimen; this requires some form of electrostatic or magnetic biprism to divide the electron wave (Weingärtner et al., 1969, 1971). Secondly the unscattered (on-axis) electron beam from the specimen must be intercepted so as to avoid the formation of superimposed on-axis (Eqn (71)) and off-axis (Eqn (75)) image holograms.

Results for off-axis holography (Wahl, 1974), particularly with a field emission electron source (Munch, 1975), are encouraging. The incentive for solving the electron-optical problems involved in off-axis holography is the unique determination of the complex wavefunction ψ_s using only a single image (Wahl, 1974), unlike single-sideband holography (Section VC) which, in general, requires two complementary half-plane images.

C. Bright-Field Microscopy with Complementary Half-Plane Objective Apertures

An image hologram formed by using only one half of the Fourier spectrum of ψ_s is called a single-sideband hologram (Lohmann, 1956). In these terms normal bright-field microscopy is referred to as double-sideband holography because both Fourier "bands" of $S(\mathbf{v})$ for $v_x > 0$ and $v_x < 0$ contribute to the image. Single-sideband holography with an on-axis reference beam enables the conjugate images ψ_s and $\psi_s^\dagger$ to be separated by taking the Fourier transform of the hologram (Misell, 1974). The image intensity of the positive half-plane image ($v_x < 0$ excluded) is:

$$j_+(\mathbf{r}) = 1 + \psi_+(\mathbf{r}) + \psi_+^\dagger(\mathbf{r}) + |\psi_+(\mathbf{r})|^2. \tag{77}$$

The Fourier transform of j_+ shows how we can effect the separation of the conjugate images:

$$J_+(\mathbf{v}) = \delta(\mathbf{v}) + S(\mathbf{v}) + S^\dagger(-\mathbf{v}) + S(\mathbf{v}) * S^\dagger(-\mathbf{v}). \tag{78}$$

Since this is the transform of a positive half-plane image $S(\mathbf{v}) = S^\dagger(\mathbf{v}) = 0$ for $v_x < 0$ and hence $S^\dagger(-\mathbf{v}) = 0$ for $v_x > 0$. In the transform plane we see that the contribution to $J_+(\mathbf{v})$ from $S(\mathbf{v})$ is confined to the positive half-plane ($v_x > 0$), while $S^\dagger(-\mathbf{v})$ is confined to the negative half-plane. The auto-correlation term $S(\mathbf{v}) * S^\dagger(-\mathbf{v})$ covers both halves of the frequency plane. The Fourier transform is illustrated in Fig. 17 where all the functions in Eqn (78) have been mapped. For clarity the functions $S(\mathbf{v})$ and $S^\dagger(-\mathbf{v})$ are displaced although they overlap the auto-correlation function in their respective half-planes; so in practice both negative and positive half-planes contain contributions from $S(\mathbf{v}) * S^\dagger(-\mathbf{v})$. The important result is that, neglecting the auto-correlation term, an effective separation of $S(\mathbf{v})$ and $S^\dagger(-\mathbf{v})$ has been made by taking the transform of a single-sideband image. Ignoring the non-linear term we can evaluate $S(\mathbf{v})$ for $v_x > 0$ by masking off the negative half-plane ($v_x < 0$) in either an optical Fourier transform (Bryngdahl and Lohmann, 1968) or a computed transform (Saxton, 1974). Similarly by using the complementary half-plane aperture we can determine $S(\mathbf{v})$ for $v_x < 0$. An inverse transform of the complete $S(\mathbf{v})$ then gives $\psi_s(\mathbf{r})$. Computationally, but not optically, we can improve

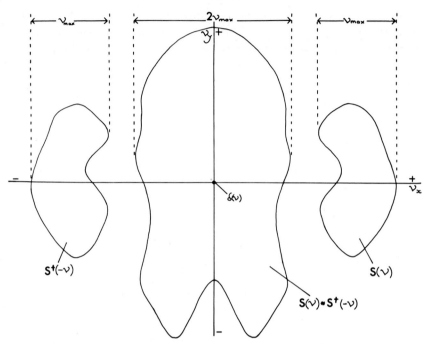

Fig. 17. The separation of conjugate images in single-sideband holography. The Fourier transform of the image intensity, j_+, shows the spatial separation of the transforms S and $S^\dagger$, of the conjugate images, ψ_+ and $\psi_+^\dagger$, obtained using a half-plane aperture (excluding $v_x < 0$). For clarity the Fourier transforms S and $S^\dagger$ are mapped as if they did not overlap the auto-correlation term $S*S^\dagger$.

on this determination of $S(\mathbf{v})$ by making corrections to $S(\mathbf{v})$ for the auto-correlation terms:

$$S(\mathbf{v}) \simeq J_+(\mathbf{v}) - S(\mathbf{v}) * S^\dagger(-\mathbf{v}) \qquad (79)$$

where $\delta(\mathbf{v})$ at $\mathbf{v} \simeq 0$ has been eliminated from the transform.

The main advantage in using this holographic analysis of half-plane images is the increased computational speed in determining $S(\mathbf{v})$ and ψ_s using the Fast Fourier transform, as opposed to the use of the Hilbert transform relation, Eqn (62). From Eqn (78) we also see why only one half-plane image is required for a weak phase object. From a single half-plane image is required for a weak phase object. From a single half-plane image we can determine $S(\mathbf{v}) = \Phi(\mathbf{v})$ for $v_x > 0$; since $\phi(\mathbf{r})$ is real $\Phi(\mathbf{v}) = \Phi^\dagger(-\mathbf{v})$, so that we can use $\Phi(\mathbf{v})$ for $v_x > 0$ to calculate $\Phi^\dagger(\mathbf{v})$ for $v_x < 0$ (see also Section IIID).

The Fourier transform analysis is applicable for an image subject to lens aberrations, when we determine $S_i(\mathbf{v})$ instead of $S(\mathbf{v})$; as before $S_i(\mathbf{v})$ may be divided by the transfer function $\exp[-i\gamma(\mathbf{v})]$ to give $S(\mathbf{v})$.

D. *Optical Reconstruction of Electron Micrographs*

Here we are interested only in the optical reconstruction methods that are related to phase determination from intensity measurements. An optical reconstruction of a normal bright-field micrograph can only be performed for a weak phase object. The optical system for holographic reconstruction is shown in Fig. 18 (Hahn, 1972; Baumeister and Hahn, 1973; Stroke and

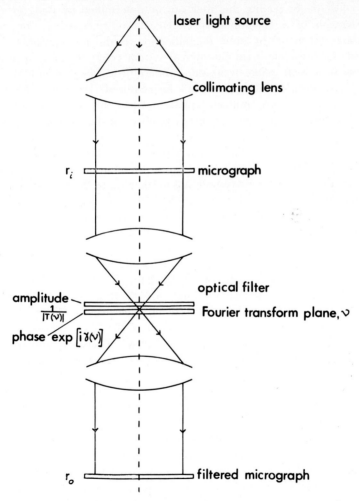

FIG. 18. Optical system for on-axis holographic Fourier transform correction of electron micrographs for lens aberrations and defocusing. In the case of an off-axis electron reference wave, the reconstruction of ψ_s would be recorded at an angle $\beta_l = \beta\lambda_l/M\lambda$ to the axis of the optical system.

Halioua, 1973a, b). A collimated laser beam is incident on the micrograph area of interest. In the Fourier transform plane an inverse filter is made from two separate filters, an amplitude and a phase filter. For the image of a weak phase object the amplitude filter is essentially $1/|\sin \gamma|$ while the phase filter produces a phase shift of $\pm \pi$ depending on the sign of $\sin \gamma$ (Stroke et al., 1974). Of course, the size of the spatial filter depends on the magnification of the electron micrograph and the optical system; in practice this constant for scaling the filter can be determined by using an electron micrograph of a crystalline specimen of known spacing (for example, catalase) taken at the same magnification as the micrograph to be processed. In principle a similar optical system could be used to process the images of a weak phase–weak amplitude object, when at least two micrographs at different defocus would be required. However, the practical problems of designing multiple filters to effect this separation of $\epsilon(\mathbf{r})$ and $\phi(\mathbf{r})$ would seem to eliminate this possibility. In the case of the image of a weak phase object the optical system shown in Fig. 18 can also be used to determine $\phi(\mathbf{r})$ for partially coherent electron illumination (Stroke and Halioua, 1972b) and incoherent electron illumination (Stroke and Halioua, 1972a), the latter case corresponding to imaging in the STEM with a large annular detector.

With a slight modification it is also possible to use this system for the reconstruction of an off-axis electron image hologram. In the Fourier plane the image transforms $S_i(\mathbf{v})$ and $S_i^\dagger(-\mathbf{v})$ are transmitted at angles β_l to the optic-axis (Goodman, 1968), so that a phase filter $1/T(\mathbf{v}) = \exp[i\gamma(\mathbf{v})]$ centred at an angle β_l will correct $S_i(\mathbf{v})$ for the effects of the microscope transfer function. Note that the angle β_l will, in general, not be the same as the original tilt angle β used for the electron reference beam, but $\beta_i = \beta \lambda_l / M\lambda$, where $\lambda_l =$ the wavelength of the laser light and $M =$ the electron-optical magnification of the image. There is now a practical problem in recording the reconstructed wavefunction ψ_s since a photographic plate will only register $|\psi_s|$, and the phase information will be lost. Thus while optical reconstruction has many advantages, particularly in processing large image areas, computer processing has the advantage of enabling both the amplitude and phase of ψ_s to be retained.

Single-sideband image holograms can also be reconstructed using an optical system to eliminate the contribution from $S^\dagger(-\mathbf{v})$ to the image transform. If the contribution to the image from the non-linear terms $|\psi_s|^2$ can be neglected, then the optical system shown in Fig. 19, with an aperture blocking off the $v_x < 0$ half-plane, will give $\psi_+(\mathbf{r})$ (Bryngdahl and Lohmann, 1968). In practice, for the complete reconstruction of ψ_s two parallel optical systems such as shown in Fig. 19 will be required, one system eliminating $v_x < 0$ from $j_+(\mathbf{r})$ and the second eliminating $v_x > 0$ from $j_-(\mathbf{r})$; the two wavefunctions $\psi_+(\mathbf{r})$ and $\psi_-(\mathbf{r})$ must then be superimposed in register (Bryngdahl and Lohmann, 1968). In this optical reconstruction two inverse filters will also be required to correct the image wavefunctions for lens defects. In the weak phase–weak amplitude approximation an optical simulation of the determination of $\phi(\mathbf{r})$ and $\epsilon(\mathbf{r})$ from two single-sideband

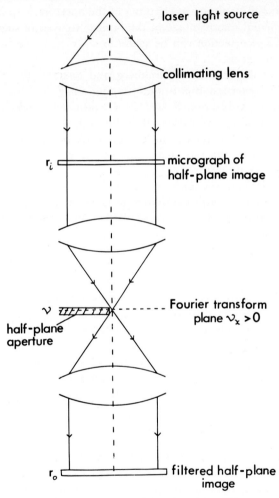

FIG. 19. Optical system for single-sideband holographic reconstruction. The conjugate images are separated by excluding one half of the transform plane $(v_x < 0)$. Two parallel optical systems are required for complementary half-plane images with a prism to refract one reconstruction onto the optic-axis of the system. Filters in the Fourier plane to correct for lens defects and other image distortions are omitted for simplicity.

holograms has been given by Downing and Siegel (1975). In order to find the transfer function for the single-sideband images Downing and Siegel (1973, 1975) superimpose a normal bright-field (double-sideband) and a single-sideband image on an optical diffractometer to give a set of interference fringes; the curvature of these interference fringes can be used to determine $\gamma(\mathbf{v})$ for the single-sideband image including the additional phase aberrations caused by electrical charging of the aperture.

The fundamental disadvantage of the optical analysis of single-sideband images is that no correction can be made to $\psi_+(\mathbf{r})$ or $\psi_-(\mathbf{r})$ for the effect of the non-linear terms.

An optical analogue of the Gerchberg and Saxton algorithm method (1972) for phase determination from diffraction-image plane measurements has been given by Gibbs and Rowe (1973); although random phases can be generated optically, it is unlikely that this optical analogue will compete with the iterative method given in Section IIIA because of the practical difficulties in making the repeated spatial filtering operations required to refine the phase solution.

All the optical reconstruction methods outlined here can be implemented, with some advantages, on a computer, provided that a scanning densitometer and a good image display are available. Optical methods have many practical problems: the production of spatial filters with a large dynamic range (Stroke and Halioua, 1972a), addition of lens defects from the optical system which cannot be compensated for, as is possible in optical holography (Goodman, 1968), alignment and vibration problems. Non-linear effects in the image cannot easily be corrected in an optical reconstruction. However, optical methods can be used on large image areas, and we do not risk degrading the original image by digitizing the micrograph. Optical methods should be viewed as a rapid way of assessing a large number of images (Burge and Scott, 1975), and the best images can be chosen for computer analysis; evidently we shall need a set of amplitude and phase spatial filters prepared for varying electron-optical conditions (Burge and Scott, 1976).

VI. Practical Problems in Phase Determination

Interpreting phase information in terms of specimen structure depends principally on the state of specimen preservation in the electron microscope; this is particularly relevant for biological specimens. Evidently phase information extending to 0·5 nm resolution cannot be relevant to structure if the specimen is severely damaged, either by radiation or by the use of negative stain. Radiation damage may limit the information on the native biological material to 1–2 nm, whereas negative stain may not reflect the true structure even at 2 nm resolution (Unwin, 1975). Using a thick substrate may also limit the accuracy with which the phase distribution for the object can be determined (Section VIA).

Many of the problems associated with radiation damage, staining and image noise (due to substrate, inelastic electron scattering) may be solved by using periodic specimens. However, regular structures suitable for electron microscopy are not easy to prepare and there is always some doubt as to the structural relationship between the isolated molecule and the crystalline structure (Section VIB).

Instrumental problems, such as that of determining defocus accurately, the limited coherence of the electron source, electrical charging of half-plane apertures, will reduce the accuracy with which the phase can be determined from intensity measurements (Section VIC).

Finally there is the contribution of the inelastic scattering to the image as a low resolution background. In all the phase determination methods given, inelastic scattering is neglected except for the indirect effect of reducing the amplitude of the elastic wave (Section VID).

A. *Radiation Damage and Specimen Preparation*

In order to obtain an adequate signal-to-noise ratio in the image of an isolated molecule the optical density of the photographic plate should be $0\cdot5$–1. In the case of normal electron microscope emulsions this requires an electron dose to the specimen of at least 1000 electrons per nm^2 area of specimen at an electron-optical magnification of about 50,000 (Beer *et al.*, 1975), which exceeds the maximum dose consistent with the structural integrity of the specimen to 1 nm resolution (Unwin and Henderson, 1975 and review by Glaeser, 1975). The noise in the image depends upon the square root of the number of electrons detected in the image. In bright-field microscopy the noise depends on the square root of the incident electron intensity n_0, because most of the incident electrons are imaged, so that the signal-to-noise ratio, S/N, in the bright-field image of a weak phase object is approximately $2\phi n_0/n_0^{\frac{1}{2}}$. Clearly for a given n_0 the S/N for an unstained specimen is significantly lower than for a stained or heavy atom labelled specimen (see Table I). S/N is further reduced by the use of a carbon substrate to support the specimen; at the very least the carbon substrate should be significantly thinner than the specimen, so that the phase contrast image of the carbon does not completely obscure the contrast due to the specimen.

The S/N is even less favourable in dark-field microscopy because the signal in the image depends on ϕ^2, with a large background in the image from the inelastic scattering, particularly for an unstained specimen (Misell and Burge, 1975); the radiation dose may have to be increased by a factor of 30 in order to obtain a S/N comparable with the corresponding bright-field image. For unstained specimens there is no obvious way of improving the signal to noise of an image recorded with a low radiation dose; aligning N_0 molecules accurately to improve S/N by $N_0^{\frac{1}{2}}$ is clearly very difficult with isolated molecules.

If the specimen is negatively stained the signal-to-noise ratio in the image will improve in proportion to 2ϕ but there is no evidence that the negative stain reflects the native structure even at 2 nm resolution. The results of Unwin (1975) on negatively stained catalase indicate that the structure of the protein is quite different from the structure determined from unstained specimens, although the periodicity of the crystal seems unaltered. There is evidence that the damage to the protein occurs mainly in the staining process, and negatively stained specimens are less sensitive to radiation damage than unstained specimens (Unwin, 1975).

Positive staining of the specimen with heavy metal atoms is potentially a high resolution technique, but for determining the positions of the heavy atoms, rather than the structure of the biological material. In this case we recommend the use of the STEM with incoherent imaging, where the S/N is substantially better than in the CTEM (see Section VII) and the STEM image is free from interference artefacts (Engel *et al.*, 1974).

One way in which the radiation damage and S/N problems can be improved is by the use of periodic specimens, where the averaging of the image over a large number of unit cells (1000–2000) can be used to increase S/N by a factor of 30–40 (Beer *et al.*, 1975). In practice this averaging is performed by taking the Fourier transform of the image, where the periodic information will give regularly spaced diffraction spots, whilst the non-periodic noise and low resolution inelastic scattering are uniformly distributed over the transform. In this case it is possible to isolate the signal from a substantial fraction of the noise (Unwin and Henderson, 1975). There are, however, severe thickness limitations of such crystalline specimens if the structure is to be determined to high resolution (Section VII).

B. *Use of Specimens with Repeating Units*

Although most of the specimen preservation problems are solved by the use of regular structures, this is clearly of limited application in biology. Few biological materials occur naturally in regular arrays, and some of these may not be organized to the high resolution required for accurate image averaging. The preparation of crystalline specimens from isolated molecules requires the active collaboration of biochemists. In the case of the protein haemagglutinin (from influenza virus), the hydrophobic part of the protein had to be removed in order to prevent aggregation of the protein; so in this example high resolution information on the crystal structure may not be directly relevant to the intact protein. There is also a restriction on the thickness of such crystals if the phase information is to be interpreted directly as a two-dimensional projection of the potential distribution in the structure; for 0·5 nm resolution in the potential map the thickness of the specimen should be less than 10 nm (see Section VII). Artificially prepared crystals thinner than 10 nm may not be very stable because they may be only one or two molecules thick. Membrane structures (protein/lipid complexes) seem to be the most promising type of specimen, but often the lipid content of membrane has to be reduced in order to encourage the membrane protein to aggregate into regular structures. Whereas the protein in a membrane may be well organized there is little evidence to suggest that the surrounding lipid is highly structured (Unwin and Henderson, 1975); thus the resolution achieved in a membrane system may be limited by the amount of lipid in the structure. Generally the removal of this lipid, in an attempt to crystallize the protein, will cause the protein structure to change from its biologically active form.

Ultimately we wish to determine the three-dimensional structure of the specimen, but a large number of tilted views will be required unless the structure has some symmetry properties. With periodic specimens only one molecule thick it is very difficult to obtain good tilted images because of the lack of flatness of the specimen.

C. Instrumental Problems

The limited coherence of the electron source causes essentially an attenuation of the high resolution (high spatial frequency) information from the specimen. Spatial incoherence arises from the beam divergence of the incident electrons from a finite source, whilst chromatic incoherence is due to the energy spread of the electrons emitted from a thermionic source; in the case of a field emission source this energy spread is only about 0·2 eV and does not sensibly affect the image. The reason that source incoherence is a serious problem is because it invalidates the basic imaging equations derived in Section II as a basis for phase determination. In simple terms the relationship between the image wavefunction $\psi_i(\mathbf{r})$ and the object wavefunction $\psi_o(\mathbf{r})$ is no longer linear, as in Eqn (15). Thus, in general, it is impossible to include the effects of limited coherence in the determination of $\psi_o(\mathbf{r})$. Only when the image intensity is linearly related to the object structure is it possible to correct for the effects of partial coherence. In the case of the weak phase object or weak phase–weak amplitude object, the effect of limited source coherence can be described by an attenuation of the higher spatial frequencies in the image transform $J(\mathbf{v})$. Thus for a weak phase object we can derive the following relationship between the image intensity and $\phi(\mathbf{r})$ (Lenz, 1971a):

$$j(\mathbf{r}) = 1 - 2\phi(\mathbf{r}) * \Gamma(\mathbf{r}) \qquad (80)$$

where $\Gamma(\mathbf{r})$ now includes not only the effects of lens defects but also the spatial (angular) or energy distribution of the incident electron beam. Unfortunately $\Gamma(\mathbf{r})$ cannot, in general, be separated into a lens aberration term and a coherence term (Frank, 1973b), so $\Gamma(\mathbf{r})$ cannot be easily determined experimentally. Although it may look as though Eqn (80) can still be solved for $\phi(\mathbf{r})$ using Fourier transforms, we shall see that high resolution information cannot be reconstructed in a partially coherent situation.

Experimentally it is clear that image contrast in bright-field microscopy is reduced by the use of partially coherent illumination (Hibi and Takahashi, 1971), although this loss in contrast is mainly relevant to high resolution information. If we assume that the angular profile of the incident electron beam is Gaussian, then the transform of Eqn (80) can be written as:

$$J(\mathbf{v}) = \delta(\mathbf{v}) - 2\Phi(\mathbf{v}) \sin[\gamma(\mathbf{v})]H(\mathbf{v}_0, \mathbf{v}), \qquad (81)$$

where the spatial coherence function $H(\mathbf{v}_0, \mathbf{v})$ depends on the angular width, $v_0(=\beta/\lambda)$, of the incident electron beam in addition to the lens parameters C_s and Δf (Frank, 1973b). Since H decreases rapidly at high spatial frequencies, the transform $J(\mathbf{v})$ contains only a small contribution from high resolution information unless v_0 is small. Thus in the optical transform of a thin phase object, the transform intensity $|J|^2 \propto H^2 \sin^2\gamma$, will still show a ring structure due to the oscillations of $\sin \gamma$, but now the diffraction rings will fall off in intensity at high spatial frequencies. The extent of the loss of this high frequency information will depend on the beam divergence β (Frank, 1975); the attenuation will be negligible for $\beta = 5 \times 10^{-4}$ rad and sufficiently serious for $\beta = 1\cdot5 \times 10^{-3}$ rad to halve the effective frequency spectrum of the object (Beorchia and Bonhomme, 1974). Thus if information of the object structure is required to a resolution of 0·3 nm the beam divergence should be less than 5×10^{-4} rad corresponding to the use of a smaller condenser aperture (50 μm) than normally used (200 μm). A similar result applies to partial chromatic coherence where H now depends on the chromatic aberration constant of the objective lens, C_c, and the energy spread of the incident electron beam E_f; $H \simeq \exp(-bv^4)$ for a Gaussian energy distribution, where $b \propto C_c^2 E_f^2$ (Hanszen and Trepte, 1971). Figure 20 shows the effect of partial chromatic coherence on the optical transform intensity $|J|^2$ for increasing E_f. Evidently for a resolution of 0·5 nm ($v = 2$ nm^{-1}), the energy spread can be as large as 2 eV, but if the thermionic filament is run at a very high emission current, spatial frequencies as low as 1 nm^{-1} (1 nm resolution) can be severely attenuated. Hence to minimize the effect of chromatic incoherence the thermionic source should be used at a relatively low filament current. The combined effect of spatial and chromatic coherence leads to an overall reduction in high resolution information; although the functional form of H in Eqn (81)

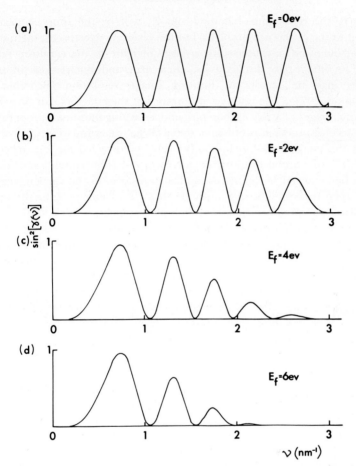

FIG. 20. Theoretical curves showing the effect of beam incoherence on the intensity $\sin^2[\gamma(\mathbf{v})]$ of the optical transform of a weak phase object for a defocus $\Delta f = 250$ nm with a value for E_f of (a) 0 eV, (b) 2 eV, (c) 4 eV and (d) 6 eV. Microscope parameters: $C_s = 1\cdot9$ mm, $C_c = 1\cdot6$ mm and $E_0 = 100$ keV.

may be known, it is not possible to reconstruct high resolution information in the image. The division of the rapidly decreasing transform $J(\mathbf{v})$ in Eqn (81) by small values of $H \sin \gamma$ at high frequencies will lead only to an amplification of noise. Note also that Eqn (81) shows that the image contrast will be reduced because $\Phi(\mathbf{v})$ is reduced by a factor H; thus the integration of $J(\mathbf{v})$ over $\mathbf{v}$ will give a smaller value for $\phi(\mathbf{r}) * \Gamma(\mathbf{r})$ than in the case of coherent illumination ($H{=}1$). This reduction in image contrast mainly arises from the loss of high resolution information, whereas low resolution information is not similarly affected by source incoherence.

Clearly the reduction of both β and E_f will be the simplest practical solution to the coherence problem, but the resulting decrease in the incident electron intensity may necessitate a large increase in the exposure time to record an image; in this case specimen drift and fluctuations in power supplies may be factors in limiting image resolution (Beorchia and Bonhomme, 1974). The relative importance of these factors can be assessed by taking images of a *thin* carbon film under varying illumination conditions.

The second practical problem is the accurate determination of C_s and Δf so that the image wavefunction $\psi_i(\mathbf{r})$ can be corrected for lens defects to give $\psi_o(\mathbf{r})$. In normal bright-field microscopy the determination of C_s and Δf can be achieved by taking an optical transform of the carbon substrate image. The carbon substrate must be thin (5–10 nm) so that the optical transform corresponds to that of a weak phase object; a thick substrate may give significant amplitude contributions depending on $\cos \gamma$ and the positions of the minima in $|J|^2$ will be displaced. Secondly, the defocus cannot be determined to an accuracy better than the thickness of the specimen, t, because the image transform will include a focus difference t between the top and bottom of the specimen (see Section VII). Because of the dependence of $\gamma(\mathbf{v})$ on $C_s v^4$ and $\Delta f v^2$, the accuracy of C_s and Δf must be very good at high spatial frequencies; thus although a defocus error of 10 nm will give an error of only 0·12 rad in $\gamma(\mathbf{v})$ at 1 nm^{-1} (1 nm resolution), this error will be 0·46 rad at 2·0 nm^{-1} (0·5 nm resolution), and 1·86 rad at 4·0 nm^{-1} (0·25 nm resolution). Such large phase errors in $\exp[-i\gamma(\mathbf{v})]$ will give correspondingly large errors in the phase of the object transform $S(\mathbf{v})$ calculated from $S_i(\mathbf{v})/\exp[-i\gamma(\mathbf{v})]$. For a phase error of less than 0·2 rad in $\gamma(\mathbf{v})$, Δf should be determined to within ± 4 nm at 0·5 nm resolution and to within ± 1 nm at 0·25 nm resolution. The effect of the defocus error on the interpretation of $S(\mathbf{v})$ and the object wavefunction $\psi_o(\mathbf{r})$ will be discussed in Section VII.

It is not possible to determine Δf from the optical transform of a dark-field image of the carbon substrate, because this transform has an almost uniform appearance nearly independent of defocus (Thon, 1971). The accuracy of focusing obtained by tilting the electron illumination from bright-field to dark-field microscopy is not good enough because the change in electron optics can give focus changes of 100–200 nm (Cowley et al., 1974). The changes in focus and astigmatism can be even larger when an objective aperture with a dark-field stop is used. Cowley et al. (1974) suggest that optimum defocus can be determined in dark-field to within ± 20 nm by observing maximum contrast for a hole in a carbon film.

In the case of half-plane aperture images, not only is the optical transform independent of defocus, but additional phase shifts are introduced into $\gamma(\mathbf{v})$ by the electrical charging of the edge of the aperture (Thon, 1971;

Downing and Siegel, 1973). Experimentally it is very difficult to eliminate the cause of this electrical charging since the half-plane aperture edge intercepts a relatively intense electron beam near to the unscattered beam. Downing and Siegel (1973) suggest that the phase shift $\gamma(\mathbf{v})$, including the effects of electrical charging, can be determined by recording the optical diffraction pattern of a superimposed half-plane image and a normal bright-field micrograph taken nominally at the same defocus. The curvature of the interference fringes in the diffractogram represents the differences in $\gamma(\mathbf{v})$, $\Delta\gamma(\mathbf{v})$, for the two micrographs; since $\gamma_{BF}(\mathbf{v})$ for the normal bright-field image can be determined independently by optical diffractometry, the phase shift $\gamma(\mathbf{v})$ for the half-plane image can be calculated from $\gamma_{BF}(\mathbf{v}) + \Delta\gamma(\mathbf{v})$ (Downing and Siegel, 1975).

D. *Inelastic Electron Scattering*

Inelastic electron scattering is the main cause of radiation damage in biological specimens. Inelastic scattering is almost independent of atomic number Z, whereas elastic scattering cross-section is dependent on $Z^{\frac{3}{2}}$; thus the contribution of inelastic scattering to the image is relatively more important for unstained biological materials $(Z \simeq 6)$ than for stained specimens $(Z \simeq 70\text{--}90)$. Essentially inelastic scattering contributes to the image as a low resolution background, as a result of its non-local nature (Isaacson *et al.*, 1974); the inelastic image is further degraded in resolution as a result of chromatic aberration in the CTEM objective lens (Misell, 1975). Since the principal energy loss E of biological materials is about 25 eV, the inelastic image is out of focus by $\Delta f \simeq C_c E/E_o = 500$ nm, and displays a resolution of about 5 nm. The inelastic image can be optimally focused by an underfocus of $\Delta f_I \simeq 500$ nm, when the elastic image will be far from its optimum defocus of about 100 nm underfocus.

The contrast of the elastic bright-field image is determined by interference effects, whereas the inelastic image corresponds to incoherent imaging with a low contrast, and it is essential to take images of biological materials well away from Δf_I. In this case the inelastic scattering will contribute only as a low resolution background to the high resolution elastic image (Misell and Burge, 1975). In dark-field microscopy the contribution to the image from inelastic scattering is much more serious because the dark-field elastic image depends on ϕ^2 without any significant phase contrast effects (Misell, 1975).

Since inelastic scattering corresponds to low order Fourier coefficients in the image transform $J(\mathbf{v})$, it will affect image reconstruction most at low resolution (2 nm); in particular, inelastic scattering may be a serious source of error in the determination of the object wavefunction of negatively stained specimens in the frequency region 0–0.5 nm^{-1} where the phase contrast term $\overset{\ast}{\underset{\sim}{\Phi}} \sin \gamma$ is small. In the case of the image of a periodic structure, stained or unstained, the effects of inelastic scattering may be largely eliminated by sampling the image transform only at the diffraction spots. This reduction in the inelastic scattering is even possible at the large under-focus values 500–1000 nm required to make $\Phi \sin \gamma$ significantly large at low spatial frequencies because the transform peaks, corresponding to the periodic structure, can still be isolated from the diffuse inelastic background (Erickson and Klug, 1971). Other than the use of crystalline specimens, there is another way of reducing the contribution of inelastic scattering to the image, namely, image subtraction using two electron micrographs taken near optimum elastic defocus, Δf_E (Misell and Burge, 1975); although the character of the elastic image will change for a defocus difference of 50–100 nm, the inelastic image will be virtually unchanged. Thus subtraction of images taken at defocus Δf_E and $\Delta f_E \pm 50$ nm will eliminate 60–70% of the inelastic scattering. There are several practical problems in implementing this type of image subtraction particularly in dark-field microscopy (Krakow *et al.*, 1976).

It will be evident that nearly all the phase determination methods of Sections II and III ignore inelastic scattering.

In the case of non-crystalline specimens, both the two defocus and the half-plane aperture methods give incorrect phase solutions under conditions which correspond to inelastic scattering from an unstained specimen (Misell, 1973b; Misell and Greenaway, 1974a). The phase solutions can be improved by excluding the low order Fourier coefficients in the image transforms, but this procedure also leads to incorrect low resolution information because of the discontinuities in the image transform. The Gerchberg and Saxton (1972) diffraction-image plane method requires crystalline specimens (see Section IIIA) and the method does not suffer seriously from the effects of inelastic scattering. The dark-field/bright-field image method (Frank, 1973c) does effect a partial subtraction of the inelastic scattering because the object wavefunction is determined from $j_{\mathrm{BF}} - j_{\mathrm{DF}} = 1 + 2|\psi_s| \cos \eta$. Both j_{BF} and j_{DF} include contributions from the inelastic scattering; however, the amplitude $|\psi_s| = j_{\mathrm{DF}}^{\frac{1}{2}}$ may be subject to a large error as a result of large inelastic contributions to j_{DF}.

In summary it seems that all phase determination methods examined in this review will produce accurate phase solutions only if the specimen has a regular structure. Then both radiation damage and inelastic scattering effects can be reduced to minor significance. In addition, for crystalline specimens the non-uniqueness problems for the phase solution can be minimized for both the two defocus and the dark-field/bright-field methods.

VII. Interpretation and Use of Phase Information

It is essential to relate the phase information determined by either direct or indirect methods to the structure of the specimen. The amplitude and phase of the object wave-function $\psi_o(\mathbf{r})$ may be determined to high accuracy but in the case of a thick specimen the high resolution information cannot be simply related to the two-dimensional projection of the potential distribution in the object (Lipson and Lipson, 1972). This thickness effect preventing the structural interpretation of high resolution information can be considered in several ways: in the phase object approximation there are phase differences between electrons scattered in different elemental slices of the specimen (Cowley and Moodie, 1957; Hanszen, 1971); alternatively these phase differences can be considered to arise from the variation in defocus through the specimen thickness, t; finally Lipson and Lipson (1972) use an optical analogue to describe multiple diffraction effects in the specimen. All these reasons for the difference between $\psi_o(\mathbf{r})$ and the projected object potential, $V(\mathbf{r})$, give the same dependence of the phase difference on object thickness and resolution. Unfortunately this thickness effect cannot be corrected, although its effect on the validity of the projected potential model can be assessed (see Section VIIA, B, C).

Finally in this section we examine the problems in interpreting phase information obtained from images of single atoms or of heavy atom labelled molecules; in these cases the phase information is not essential and the use of the STEM with incoherent imaging is recommended (Section VIID).

A. *Weak Phase Object*

The derivation given in Section II of the phase grating approximation for the object wavefunction $\psi_o(\mathbf{r}) = \exp[-i\phi(\mathbf{r})]\exp[-\epsilon(\mathbf{r})]$ neglected interference effects between electrons scattered in different elemental slices of the specimen, z_n (Cowley and Moodie, 1957). In this case a direct relationship between $\psi_o(\mathbf{r})$ and the projection of the object potential $V(\mathbf{r}, z)$, Eqns (7), (8) and (9), is obtained. However, for a thick specimen the phase difference between electrons scattered at the top and the bottom of the specimen may be comparable to the phase shift caused by the object potential (Hanszen, 1971). Thus in the original phase object approximation (Cowley and Moodie, 1957) $\psi_o(\mathbf{r})$ depends on the specimen thickness; unfortunately this thickness dependence is so complex that it is, in general, not possible to assess its effect. An attempt will be made to simplify the analysis so that the conditions for interpreting $\psi_o(\mathbf{r})$ in terms of $V(\mathbf{r})$ can be assessed.

In the weak phase approximation $\psi_o(\mathbf{r}) \simeq 1 - i\phi'(\mathbf{r}, t)$, where ϕ' now depends on specimen thickness; we wish to determine the conditions under which this thickness dependence can be neglected. The image intensity for a weak phase object will now be:

$$j(\mathbf{r}) = 1 - 2 \text{ Re } [i\phi'(\mathbf{r}, t) * G(\mathbf{r})] \qquad (82)$$

where Re denotes the real part of the bracketed expression; in the case where the specimen is thin so that $\phi'(\mathbf{r}, t) \equiv \phi(\mathbf{r})$, Eqn (82) reduces to the weak phase approximation $j = 1 - 2\phi * q$, Eqn (24). The Fourier transform of the image intensity will be

$$J(\mathbf{v}) = \delta(\mathbf{v}) - 2\text{Re } [i\Phi'(\mathbf{v}, t) \exp (-i\gamma(\mathbf{v}))]. \qquad (83)$$

Again if the specimen is thin so that $\Phi'(\mathbf{v}, t) = \Phi(\mathbf{r})$ Eqn (83) reduces to the normal weak phase approximation, Eqn (25). However, from Eqn (83) we do not now determine the Fourier transform, $\Phi(\mathbf{v})$, of the projection of the potential, but

$$\Phi'(\mathbf{v}, t) \simeq \Phi(\mathbf{v}) \exp [i\pi t\lambda v^2]. \qquad (84)$$

The phase term $\exp [i\pi t\lambda v^2]$ measures the phase difference between electrons scattered at the top $(z = 0)$ and bottom $(z = t)$ of the specimen; it is exactly the same phase difference as would occur with a defocus difference $\Delta f = t$ for imaging the top and bottom of the specimen. Although Eqn (84) can be used to assess the effect of specimen thickness on Φ', the relationship *cannot* be used to correct Φ' to give Φ; this is because the exact form for Eqn (84) should contain an integration through the specimen thickness. In order to interpret Φ' as Φ, the phase shift $\pi t\lambda v^2$ must be significantly less than the phase of Φ. It can be seen that the deviation of the phase of Φ' from Φ depends linearly on specimen thickness and on the square of v; thus as the resolution obtained in the image improves the deviations will increase rapidly.

Table III shows the dependence of the phase difference $\Delta\Phi(\mathbf{v}, t) = \pi t\lambda v^2$ (rad) on specimen thickness t (nm), and resolution, r (nm) $(=1/v)$ for $E_o = 100$ keV $(\lambda = 3 \cdot 7$ pm). Note that these are maximum phase errors, $\Delta\Phi$, because the mean phase error will correspond to the phase difference $\pm \pi t\lambda v^2/2$ between the centre of the specimen and the top or bottom face of the specimen.

The weak phase approximation for the expansion of $\exp (-i\phi)$ as $1 - i\phi$ is valid for $t < 15$ nm for unstained specimens and $t < 5$ nm for stained specimens (see Table I). However, depending on the resolution of the image, the validity of this expansion may not be the limiting factor in the interpretation of ϕ' or its transform Φ'. The phase of Φ varies between 0 and 2π, so that a phase error, $\Delta\Phi$, of $0 \cdot 2$ rad is acceptable. Now, Table III shows that at 2 nm resolution $(v = 0 \cdot 5$ nm$^{-1})$ the specimen thickness may be in excess of 50 nm, but at $0 \cdot 5$ nm resolution $(v = 2$ nm$^{-1})$ t must be less than 5 nm; in the case of the specimen structure giving image and diffraction data to $0 \cdot 25$ nm resolution $(v = 4$ nm$^{-1})$ the specimen should

TABLE III

The phase error in Φ, $\Delta\Phi$ (rad), as a function of specimen
thickness, t (nm), and resolution, r (nm)

t (nm)	Resolution (nm)			
	2	1	0·5	0·25
5	0·01	0·06	0·23	0·93
10	0·03	0·12	0·47	1·86
15	0·04	0·17	0·70	2·79
20	0·06	0·23	0·93	3·72
25	0·07	0·29	1·16	4·65
30	0·09	0·35	1·40	5·58
40	0·12	0·47	1·86	7·44
50	0·15	0·58	2·33	9·30

be less than 2 nm thick. Even allowing for a factor of 2 reduction in $\Delta\Phi$, the specimen thickness limits at high resolution will be difficult to satisfy experimentally.

Also note that an error in determining the defocus Δf will cause exactly the same phase errors in Φ (Lynch *et al.*, 1975), so that an error in the determination of $\gamma(\mathbf{v})$ from a bright-field micrograph may lead to serious errors in Φ. Thus a micrograph recorded with defocus of 110 nm, but corrected for a defocus value of 100 nm, will have a phase error of 0·47 rad at a spatial frequency of 2 nm^{-1} (0·5 nm resolution). This is why it is important to use thin substrates for determining Δf so that the defocus measured by optical diffractometry is near to the actual focus level of the specimen. At low resolution (2 nm) an accurate determination of Δf is not so important.

In the case of an unstained biological specimen the interpretation of the phase information at high resolution is limited, not by the validity of the weak phase approximation, but by the thickness effect. The reverse is true for stained specimens; however, this is not relevant because images of negatively stained specimens do not usually show a resolution better than 2 nm.

Recently there have been several publications on the charge density, $\rho(\mathbf{r})$, interpretation of electron microscope images (for example, Lynch *et al.*, 1975); for the weak phase approximation it will be shown that this interpretation of $\phi'(\mathbf{r}, t)$ is not valid. A relationship between ϕ and ϕ' will be derived using Eqns (83) and (84): substituting for Φ' from Eqn (84), Eqn (83) becomes

$$J(\mathbf{v}) = \delta(\mathbf{v}) - 2\mathrm{Re}\left[i\Phi(\mathbf{v}) \exp\left(i\pi t\lambda v^2\right) \exp\left(-i\gamma(\mathbf{v})\right)\right]. \qquad (85)$$

In practice Eqn (85) is divided by $2 \sin \gamma$ in order to correct for the effects of the transfer function, so that

$$\Phi'(\mathbf{v}, t) \simeq \Phi(\mathbf{v}) \cos (\pi t \lambda v^2) - \Phi(v) \cot [\gamma(\mathbf{v})] \sin (\pi t \lambda v^2) \qquad (86)$$

is determined in contrast to the determination of $\Phi(\mathbf{v})$ from Eqn (25). Evidently if $\Delta\Phi = \pi t \lambda v^2 \ll 1$, $\cos (\Delta\Phi) \simeq 1$ and $\sin (\Delta\Phi) \simeq \Delta\Phi$, and the expression for $\Phi'(\mathbf{v}, t)$

$$\Phi'(\mathbf{v}, t) \simeq \Phi(\mathbf{v}) - \pi t \lambda v^2 \Phi(v) \cot [\gamma(\mathbf{v})] \qquad (87)$$

includes a leading term $\Phi(\mathbf{v})$ and a correction term depending not only on $\pi t \lambda v^2$ but also on $\cot \gamma$. Thus the difference between ϕ and ϕ' can be calculated from the inverse Fourier transform of Eqn (87)

$$\phi'(\mathbf{r}, t) \simeq \phi(\mathbf{r}) - F^{-1}[\pi t \lambda v^2 \Phi(\mathbf{v}) \cot (\gamma(\mathbf{v}))]. \qquad (88)$$

The inverse transform of $v^2\Phi(\mathbf{v})$ is essentially the second derivative of $\phi(\mathbf{r})$, $\nabla^2\phi(\mathbf{r})$ (Lynch *et al.*, 1975), provided that $\cot \gamma \simeq 1$ in the resolution range of interest; in this case Eqn (88) becomes

$$\phi'(\mathbf{r}, t) \simeq \phi(\mathbf{r}) - \frac{t\lambda}{4\pi} \nabla^2\phi(\mathbf{r}). \qquad (89)$$

The projected potential $V(\mathbf{r}) = \phi(\mathbf{r})/\sigma$ (Eqn (9)) is related to the charge density distribution $\rho(\mathbf{r})$ by Poisson's equation $\nabla^2 V(\mathbf{r}) = - \rho(\mathbf{r})/\epsilon_0$, and Eqn (89) becomes

$$\phi'(\mathbf{r}, t) \simeq \sigma[V(\mathbf{r}) + t\lambda\rho(\mathbf{r})/4\pi\epsilon_0]. \qquad (90)$$

Hence the final Fourier map obtained by an inverse transform of Φ' is a superposition of two-dimensional potential and density distributions. It is difficult to say how the interpretation of the Fourier map will be affected by this superposition of $V(\mathbf{r})$ and $\rho(\mathbf{r})$. Clearly if t is small, the contribution to ϕ' from $\rho(\mathbf{r})$ will be unimportant. However, in no circumstances can the Fourier map be interpreted in terms of the charge density alone; the condition for $t\lambda\rho(\mathbf{r})/4\pi\epsilon_0 \gg V(\mathbf{r})$ will correspond to a thick specimen and in this case the approximations $\cos (\Delta\Phi) \simeq 1$, $\sin (\Delta\Phi) \simeq \Delta\Phi$ will not be valid because terms in $(\Delta\Phi)^2$ will be significant. Also in order to arrive at the simple result in Eqn (89) the transfer function was assumed to be constant over the resolution range of interest; clearly this is not possible even at optimum defocus. Finally the derivation of Eqn (90) assumes a large objective aperture (effectively infinite) so that the transform of $v^2\Phi(\mathbf{v})$ can be evaluated analytically to give $\nabla^2\phi(\mathbf{r})$.

Since the high density peaks in $V(\mathbf{r})$ and $\rho(\mathbf{r})$ will not coincide, the Fourier map will effectively show a loss in resolution as compared to the projection $V(\mathbf{r})$ alone.

The contribution to the image from inelastic scattering, which is neglected in the weak phase approximation, will also affect the interpretation of the

Fourier map; the inelastic contribution will probably cause a broadening of peaks in the map and limit the ultimate resolution, particularly for the smaller peaks, which may no longer be resolved. This detrimental effect of inelastic scattering will be reduced by the use of crystalline specimens.

B. *Weak Phase–Weak Amplitude Object*

In the weak phase–weak amplitude approximation it was pointed out that the validity of the expansion $\exp\left[-i\phi(\mathbf{r}) - \epsilon(\mathbf{r})\right] \simeq 1 - i\phi(\mathbf{r}) - \epsilon(\mathbf{r})$ could be extended by including the $\phi^2(\mathbf{r})/2$ term with $\epsilon(\mathbf{r})$. This extends the thickness limit for the expansion in terms of $\phi(\mathbf{r})$ to about 10 nm for stained specimens and 25 nm for unstained specimens (see Section IIB). Under these conditions it is no longer possible to interpret $\epsilon(\mathbf{r})$ in terms of the attenuation of the elastic scattering; the $\epsilon(\mathbf{r})$ term should be considered as an additional parameter used to describe the image. However, the validity of the weak phase–weak amplitude approximation for an increased thickness range does not mean that the result for $\phi'(\mathbf{r}, t)$ can be interpreted in terms of specimen structure. From Table III it can be seen that for the thickness limit of 25 nm in unstained specimens, $\phi'(\mathbf{r}, t)$ can only be interpreted as $V(\mathbf{r})$ for a resolution lower than 1 nm; for stained specimens, thickness limit 10 nm, $\phi'(\mathbf{r}, t)$ will give a correct structure for 0·7 nm resolution. Again this resolution limit may be irrelevant for negatively stained specimens where the resolution is limited by specimen preservation to 2 nm (Erickson and Klug, 1971; Unwin, 1975). So in the case of negatively stained specimens up to a thickness limit of about 10 nm, $\phi'(\mathbf{r}, t)$ can be interpreted structurally to a resolution normally limited by the stain. The use of negatively stained specimens much thicker than 10 nm will invalidate the weak phase–weak amplitude approximation. The amplitude term $\epsilon(\mathbf{r})$ cannot, in general, be interpreted because it is a combination of other amplitude terms such as $\phi^2(\mathbf{r})/2$. Under no circumstances can $\epsilon(\mathbf{r})$ be interpreted in terms of electron scattering outside the objective aperture although its effect is numerically similar in reducing the amplitude of the elastically scattered wave (Erickson, 1973).

C. *A Thick (Stained) Specimen*

It will be evident that although the direct methods for phase determination can be used to determine the complex wavefunction $\psi_o(\mathbf{r}) = \exp\left[-i\phi(\mathbf{r}) - \epsilon(\mathbf{r})\right]$ without assuming that ϕ and ϵ are small, there will be a serious problem in interpreting $\phi(\mathbf{r})$ in terms of specimen structure. In fact Table III sets the thickness and resolution limits for interpreting $\psi_o(\mathbf{r})$ in terms of genuine structure. So although the amplitude and phase of ψ_o may be known to 0·5 nm resolution for a thick unstained specimen, the information cannot be used in practice. It has been suggested (Lynch *et al.*, 1975) that the images of thick specimens can be interpreted in terms of electron density $\rho(\mathbf{r})$, but this is only an approximation.

For a pure phase object, exp $[-i\phi(\mathbf{r})]$, a relation between $\psi_o(\mathbf{r})$ and $\phi(\mathbf{r})$ can be derived in a similar way to that used in Section VIIA. The object wavefunction, determined after correcting the transform of the image wavefunction for the effects of the transfer function exp $(-i\gamma)$, is

$$\psi_o(\mathbf{r}, t) \simeq \exp\left[-i\phi(\mathbf{r})\right]\left[1 + \frac{t\lambda\sigma\rho(\mathbf{r})}{4\pi\,\epsilon_0}\right] \tag{91}$$

assuming that exp $(i\pi t\lambda v^2) \simeq 1 + i\pi t\lambda v^2$. If $|\psi_o|^2$ is calculated from Eqn (91) then:

$$|\psi_o(\mathbf{r}, t)|^2 \simeq 1 + t\lambda\sigma\rho(\mathbf{r})/2\pi\,\epsilon_0. \tag{92}$$

Equation (92) implies that the determination of $|\psi_o|^2$, rather than ψ_o, gives a Fourier map depending on the charge distribution $\rho(\mathbf{r})$ only. However, this result is misleading for two reasons. Firstly the expansion of exp $(i\pi t\lambda v^2)$ is valid only for $\pi t\lambda v^2 \ll 1$ (Lynch *et al.*, 1975); for example, if $\pi t\lambda v^2 = 0.4$ (a 20% error in the expansion), $t/r^2 \leqslant 34.4$ for a resolution r (nm) $(=1/v)$; in the case of a thick specimen (that is, outside the validity of the weak phase–weak amplitude approximation), $t = 25$–100 nm, the resolution limits ($\propto t^{\frac{1}{2}}$) are 0.9–1.7 nm. The second reason for Eqn (92) being approximate is the assumption of a large objective aperture so that the Fourier spectrum of the wavefunction exp $(-i\phi(\mathbf{r}))$ is unaffected by the aperture function; in this way the exp $(-i\phi)$ term in Eqn (91) cancels with its complex conjugate exp $(i\phi)$ on calculating $|\psi_o|^2$. In practice the wavefunction determined will be the band-limited version of exp $(-i\phi)$ which will not be self-cancelling. The conclusion here is that the specimen thickness should be limited so that the interpretation of $\phi'(\mathbf{r}, t)$ as the projection of the object potential $V(\mathbf{r})$ is a reasonable approximation, namely, that thickness determined from Table III for a given image resolution. Evidently if the image corresponds to fairly low resolution, such as negatively stained specimens (2 nm) or magnetic structures (5–10 nm; see Chapman, 1975b), the thickness limits are quite large, 50 nm–1 μm, although the approximate (indirect) methods are no longer valid. For high resolution applications (0·5–1·0 nm) thin specimens must be used ($t = 10$–30 nm), where approximate methods may give adequate results. However, approximate methods used near to the limit of their validity, may give misleading results; in such cases direct methods for phase determination should be used.

D. *Resolving Single Heavy Atoms*

Whereas it is clear that phase information adds to the structural information determined for molecules, unstained and stained crystalline specimens, there is one class of specimen where the phase information may not be particularly useful, namely, a specimen comprising isolated atoms. Often heavy atoms in organometallic compounds are used specifically to label biological macromolecules such as DNA; in this case the positions of the atoms along the molecule are of interest and no attempt is made to determine the structure of the macromolecule.

If the heavy atoms are separated by distances much larger than the resolution of the microscope, then interference or phase contrast effects between the atoms will not occur in the CTEM used in the bright-field mode. However, if the atoms are only separated by about 0·5 nm, the CTEM image will be complicated by interference effects and it will be very difficult to determine the correct pattern of heavy atoms without image processing (Engel *et al.*, 1974). The STEM, when used under incoherent imaging conditions, gives an image which cannot be misinterpreted (Engel., *et al* 1974). In addition, if calculations are made for the signal-to-noise ratio for the image of a single atom, the STEM is to be preferred to the CTEM for a given radiation dose.

Firstly, in the STEM the size of the annular detector can now be increased considerably in order to collect the large-angle elastic scattering from the atom, whereas in the CTEM the objective aperture size will be limited by the spherical aberration of the objective lens. Secondly, the inelastic scattering, particularly from the substrate (usually comparable to the specimen in thickness), can be separated from the signal in the STEM using an annular detector aperture, whereas in the CTEM the inelastic scattering will contribute to noise in the image. Lastly, CTEM bright-field images of the carbon substrate will show significant granularity due to phase contrast effects and contribute only to the noise in the image; in the STEM the phase contrast from the substrate is negligible. So although the bright-field CTEM signal depends on 2ϕ while the STEM signal depends on ϕ^2, the S/N in the CTEM will be only 1·1 for a substrate thickness of 2 nm ($a = 0·01$ rad), while the S/N in the STEM (a large) will be about 2·2 for an electron dose of $n_0 = 100$ electrons per nm^2 of specimen. The dark-field CTEM image has an even lower S/N of about 0·8, although the use of hollow cone illumination (Hoch, 1973) does give atomic images comparable with those of the STEM.

In incoherent imaging the discrimination between different atoms depends on the square of the atomic amplitude for electron scattering $|f(\boldsymbol{\theta})|^2$. It has been suggested that since the scattering factor is complex $f(\boldsymbol{\theta}) = |f(\boldsymbol{\theta})| \exp [i\eta(\boldsymbol{\theta})]$ (Raith, 1968), improved discrimination between different types of atoms would be obtained by determining both $|f|$ and η (Frank, 1972, 1973a). In this case it would be essential to use coherent imaging in the CTEM or STEM so as not to lose the phase of $f(\boldsymbol{\theta})$; although in principle the STEM can be used to form phase contrast images by the use of a complicated annular detector system (Rose, 1974), the calculation of the phase of $f(\boldsymbol{\theta})$ is not easy. In the CTEM the imaging of an atom with a complex scattering factor is described by the same equations as used in the weak phase–weak amplitude approximation (Frank, 1972) giving an image transform $J(\mathbf{v})$ which depends on $|f| \cos \eta$ and $|f| \sin \eta$:

$$J(\mathbf{v}) = \delta(\mathbf{v}) - 2|f(\mathbf{v})| \cos [\eta(\mathbf{v})] \sin [\gamma(\mathbf{v})]$$

$$+ 2|f(\mathbf{v})| \sin [\eta(\mathbf{v})] \cos [\gamma(\mathbf{v})] \qquad (93)$$

assuming $|f(\mathbf{v})|^2 \ll 1$. Thus at least two micrographs are required to determine both $|f(\mathbf{v})|$ and $\eta(\mathbf{v})$.

However, the case for determining both $|f|$ and η is not convincing. Figure 21 shows the dependence of $|f|$ and η on atomic number Z (Raith, 1968) for an angle of scattering of 0·0074 rad ($v = 2\cdot0$ nm^{-1}). The values

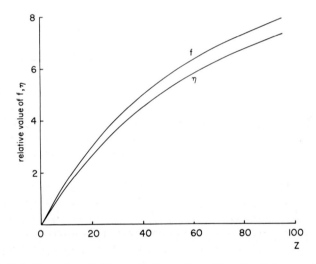

FIG. 21. Relative values (with respect to carbon, Z = 6) of the amplitude $|f(\theta)|$ and phase $\eta(\theta)$ of the electron scattering factor for a single atom as Z increases. $\theta = 0\cdot0074$ rad (resolution $\simeq 0\cdot5$ nm at 100 keV).

for both $|f|$ and η are calculated relative to $|f|$ and η for carbon (Z = 6) and, although there are some fluctuations in the values of $|f|$ and η with Z continuous curves are shown. Figure 21 shows that the dependence of both $|f|$ and η on Z are virtually identical for $\theta = 0\cdot0074$ rad. There seems to be no advantage in determining $|f| \exp(i\eta)$ rather than $|f|$ for discrimination between light and heavy atoms.

VIII. Discussion on Phase Determination and Refinement Techniques

The object of this review has been a critical evaluation of methods for determining the phase of the object wavefunction from intensity measurements alone. We have been mainly interested in phase information that can be related to the structure of the specimen; evidently it is possible by image processing to determine the object wavefunction to the ultimate resolution of the microscope (0·3 nm), but this high resolution information may be structurally irrelevant. The fundamental limitations on the use of phase information at high resolution arise from: (i) radiation damage, (ii) the specimen preparation including staining effects and (iii) specimen thickness. Clearly with crystalline specimens the effects of (i) and (ii) can be reduced by using subminimal radiation doses and unstained specimens (Unwin and Henderson, 1975). The thickness effect (iii) sets clear limits for the valid interpretation of the object wavefunction in terms of the structure (potential distribution) (Lipson and Lipson, 1972): at 2 nm resolution t may be greater than 100 nm but at 0·5 nm resolution t must be less than 10 nm reducing to 2 nm for a resolution of 0·25 nm. At the same time we note that the use of approximate methods limits the specimen thickness to 5 nm and 15 nm in the weak phase approximation (Unwin and Henderson, 1975), and to 10 nm and 25 nm in the weak phase–weak amplitude approximation for stained and unstained specimens respectively (Erickson and Klug, 1971; Frank, 1973a). Thus it seems that only in low resolution (> 1 nm) applications should the use of direct methods of phase determination be necessary, because at high resolution the maximum thickness of the specimen is determined not by the weak phase or the weak phase–weak amplitude approximation, but by the phase difference between electrons imaged from the top and the bottom of the specimen.

Outside the thickness limits for these approximations it is essential to use one of the direct methods for phase determination: the diffraction-image plane method (Gerchberg and Saxton, 1972), the two defocus method (Misell, 1973a), the dark-field/bright-field method (Frank, 1973c) or the complementary half-plane aperture method (Hoppe et al., 1970). Of these methods only the half-plane image method gives a unique solution for the object wavefunction in bright-field microscopy (Misell and Greenaway, 1974a); so the remaining three methods must all be used in conjunction with approximate methods or other information such as the band-limited nature of the image (see below). All methods including indirect methods require at least two sets of information; even the weak phase approximation requires at least a second image to avoid frequency gaps in the object wavefunction.

At high resolution, with the thin specimens required for structural interpretation, the indirect methods are valid; the principal reason for choosing direct methods in these cases is the ideal nature of the image deconvolution. In both approximate methods the correction of the image wavefunction to give the object wavefunction is made by dividing the image transforms by a function, sin γ, which has zero or small values at certain spatial frequencies. In the direct methods the deconvolution to give the object wavefunction is made by dividing the image transforms by a function, $\exp(-i\gamma)$, whose modulus is unity, and so noise in the image is not amplified. This advantage is not so important for images of crystalline specimens, because the noise can, in any case, be reduced by sampling the image transform only at reciprocal lattice points.

Dark-field microscopy cannot be recommended for phase determination because of the absence of any direct or indirect method that will give unique phase solutions. In addition, dark-field images suffer not only from interpretative problems but also from increased specimen radiation damage if we wish to obtain the same signal-to-noise ratio as in the corresponding bright-field images; inelastic electron scattering also contributes more significantly to the dark-field image intensity, because of the dependence of the intensity on ϕ^2 rather than on 2ϕ as in bright-field microscopy (Misell, 1975).

When it is clear that the amplitude and phase terms are too large for the approximate methods to be used, direct methods must be employed. The main hope of deriving accurate phase solutions will depend on the use of approximate solutions together with other information on the object structure.

Both the band-limited (finite transform) nature (Bates, 1969) and the finite size of the object (specimen) wavefunction (Barrett et al., 1971) can be used to test the veracity of wavefunctions determined by the direct methods listed above. In the case of crystalline specimens there are numerous phase refinement methods that could be used; most of these, that have been used with success in X-ray crystallography, lead to mathematical relationships between the Fourier coefficients of the object wavefunction $S(\mathbf{v})$. Unfortunately most of these relationships comprise infinite sums to high resolution, for example, the positivity of $\rho(\mathbf{r})$ (Karle and Hauptman, 1964), the squaring of $\rho(\mathbf{r})$ setting $\rho(\mathbf{r}) = \rho^2(\mathbf{r})$ (Sayre, 1952; Barrett and Zwick, 1971; Allegra and Colombo, 1974). It is not clear that these mathematical relations can be used in the resolution range $0\cdot5–1\cdot0$ nm, when the number of Fourier coefficients determined by electron microscopy is significantly less than in X-ray crystallography (about $0\cdot3$ nm resolution by isomorphous replacement methods); physically, both the positivity and squaring methods depend on having a Fourier map near atomic resolution.

In the cases where direct methods lead to 2^n solutions for n image points (for example, the dark-field/bright-field method), these refinement techniques may be useful in at least reducing the number of phase solutions. In the case of a centrosymmetric structure the unitarity relation applied to electron scattering by a crystal leads to a relation between the imaginary part of $S(\mathbf{v})$ and a summation involving $S(\mathbf{v})$ (Boyce and Roberts, 1974); again this relation cannot be used to derive a unique solution for $S(\mathbf{v})$, but it can be used to distinguish between a large number of solutions for $S(\mathbf{v})$. Mention should also be made of "deconvolution" methods in X-ray diffraction that determine $\rho(\mathbf{r})$ from the Patterson function, $\rho(\mathbf{r}) * \rho(-\mathbf{r})$, derived from the transform of $|S(\mathbf{v})|^2$ for a centrosymmetric structure (Hosemann and Bagchi, 1962); similarly there are "deconvolution" methods based on the sharpening of the Patterson map (Raman and Katz, 1967) for equal atoms, or atoms whose atomic scattering factors can be expressed as $f_j(\mathbf{\theta}) = Z_j \hat{f}(\mathbf{\theta})$ with a single atomic shape factor $\hat{f}(\mathbf{\theta})$.

While discussing phase refinement techniques we should also mention the possibility of analytic continuation. In the general case where the amplitude and phase information is known only to a certain resolution $v(\text{nm}^{-1})$, it will not be possible reliably to extend the resolution of the object wave-function by using the concept of analytic continuation; noise in the image will be the fundamental limitation. However, in several cases, such as the purple membrane, amplitude information has been obtained to a resolution of about $2v$ from electron diffraction data, while the phase information obtained from the image of a weak phase object extends only to about v (Unwin and Henderson, 1975). Thus in the Fourier transform $S(\mathbf{v}) = |S(\mathbf{v})|$ $\exp[i\omega(\mathbf{v})]$, $|S(\mathbf{v})|$ is known to $v \simeq 3$ nm^{-1} and $\omega(\mathbf{v})$ is determined to $v \simeq 1 \cdot 5$ nm^{-1}. The analytic continuation of $S(\mathbf{v})$ to $v = 3$ nm^{-1} is then possible with the restriction on $S(\mathbf{v})$ that its amplitude $|S(\mathbf{v})|$ must be the same as determined from the electron diffraction measurements. This is relevant to more than this one example of the purple membrane because it seems that high resolution electron diffraction data are easier to obtain than correspondingly high resolution images of crystalline biological specimens.

Phase information will lead to additional structural information in the cases of crystalline specimens and low contrast objects such as unstained biological macromolecules. Thus for these types of specimen it is essential to use a CTEM with coherent illumination in order to preserve the phase information in the image. The use of the STEM with an annular detector and incoherent imaging is not recommended for low contrast (unstained) specimens because of the irretrievable loss of phase information (except for a weak phase object) and the inferior signal-to-noise ratio in the image for a given radiation dose to the specimen as compared to the CTEM. However, the phase information does not seem to be relevant for the effective resolution of single atoms of high atomic number ($Z \geqslant 30$) used to label biological macromolecules; in this case phase contrast effects in the CTEM lead to images which are very difficult to interpret in terms of individual atoms (Engel *et al.*, 1974). Solving the phase problem in the CTEM in order to determine the complex electron scattering factor $f(\mathbf{\theta}) = |f(\mathbf{\theta})| \exp [i\eta(\mathbf{\theta})]$, has no clear advantage over the determination of $|f(\mathbf{\theta})|$ in the STEM because the Z dependence of $|f(\mathbf{\theta})|$ and $\eta(\mathbf{\theta})$ are similar. In addition the signal-to-noise ratio for the detection of single heavy atoms is significantly greater in the case of the STEM used with a large annular detector.

ACKNOWLEDGEMENTS

I am grateful to Professor R. H. T. Bates for pointing out the relationship between the phase problem in electron microscopy and in optics. I should like to thank the authors who kindly allowed me to use their results to illustrate this review. To Janet Misell and Elaine Brown I am grateful for their patience in typing the paper and preparing the diagrams.

REFERENCES

Allegra, G. and Colombo, A. (1974). *Acta Crystallogr.* **A30,** 727–729.
Ansley, D. A. (1973). *Optics Commun.* **8,** 140–141.
Badde, H. G. and Reimer, L. (1970). *Z. Naturf.* **25a,** 760–765.
Barrett, A. N. and Zwick, M. (1971). *Acta Crystallogr.* **A27,** 6–11.
Barrett, A. N., Barrington Leigh, J., Holmes, K. C., Leberman, R., Mandelkow, E., Sengbusch, P. von and Klug, A. (1971). *Cold Spring Harb. Symp. Quant. Biol.* **36,** 433–448.
Bartell, L. S. and Ritz, C. L. (1974). *Science* **185,** 1163–1165.
Bates, R. H. T. (1969). *Mon. Not. R. astr. Soc.* **142,** 413–428.
Bates, R. H. T. and Napier, P. J. (1972). *Mon. Not. R. astr. Soc.* **158,** 405–424.
Bates, R. H. T., Napier, P. J., McKinnon, A. E. and McDonnell, M. J. (1976). *Optik* **44,** 183–201 and 253–272.
Baumeister, W. and Hahn, M. H. (1973). *Nature* **241,** 445–7.
Beer, M., Frank, J., Hanszen, K.-J., Kellenberger, E. and Williams, R. C. (1975). *Q. Rev. Biophys.* **7,** 211–238.
Belvaux, Y. and Vareille, J. C. (1971). *Nouv. Rev. d'Optique appliquée* **2,** 149–162.
Beorchia, A. and Bonhomme, P. (1974). *Optik* **39,** 437–442.
Boyce, J. F. and Roberts, S. A. (1974). *Acta Crystallogr.* **A30,** 543–548.
Bryngdahl, O. and Lohmann, A. (1968). *J. opt. Soc. Am.* **58,** 620–624.
Burge, R. E. (1973). *J. Microscopy* **98,** 251–285.
Burge, R. E. and Scott, R. F. (1975). *Optik* **43,** 53–64.
Burge, R. E. and Scott, R. F. (1976). *Optik* **44,** 159–172.
Burge, R. E., Fiddy, M. A., Greenaway, A. H. and Ross, G. (1974). *J. Phys. D: Appl. Phys.* **7,** L65–68.
Chapman, J. N. (1975a). *Phil. Mag.* **32,** 527–540.

Chapman, J. N. (1975b). *Phil. Mag.* **32,** 541–552.
Cowley, J. M. (1973). *Acta Crystallogr.* **A29,** 529–536.
Cowley, J. M. (1975). *J. Phys. D: Appl. Phys.* **8,** L77–79.
Cowley, J. M. and Moodie, A. F. (1957). *Acta Crystallogr.* **10,** 609–619.
Cowley, J. M. and Rees, A. L. G. (1958). *Rep. Prog. Phys.* **21,** 165–225.
Cowley, J. M., Massover, W. H. and Jap, B. K. (1974). *Optik* **40,** 42–54.
Crewe, A. V. (1971). *Phil. Trans. R. Soc. Ser. B* **261,** 61–70.
Cullis, A. G. and Maher, D. M. (1975). *Ultramicroscopy* **1,** 97–112.
Downing, K. H. and Siegel, B. M. (1973). *Optik* **38,** 21–28.
Downing, K. H. and Siegel, B. M. (1975). *Optik* **42,** 155–175.
Drenth, A. J. J., Huiser, A. M. J. and Ferwerda, H. A. (1975). *Optica Acta* **22,** 615–628.
Engel, A., Wiggins, J. W. and Woodruff, D. C. (1974). *J. appl. Phys.* **45,** 2739–2747.
Erickson, H. P. (1973). *In* "Advances in Optical and Electron Microscopy" (R. Barer and V. E. Cosslett, eds), Vol. 5, pp. 163–199. Academic Press, London and New York.
Erickson, H. P. and Klug, A. (1971). *Phil. Trans. R. Soc. Ser. B* **261,** 105–118.
Ferwerda, H. A. and Hoenders, B. J. (1975). *Optica Acta* **22,** 25–34.
Frank, J. (1972). *Biophys. J.* **12,** 484–511.
Frank, J. (1973a). *In* "Advanced Techniques in Biological Electron Microscopy" (J. K. Koehler, ed.), pp. 215–274. Springer Verlag, Berlin.
Frank, J. (1973b). *Optik* **38,** 519–536.
Frank, J. (1973c). *Optik* **38,** 582–584.
Frank, J. (1974). *Optik* **41,** 90–91.
Frank, J. (1975). *Optik* **43,** 103–109.
Gabor, D. (1949). *Proc. R. Soc. Ser. A* **197,** 454–487.
Gabor, D. (1951). *Proc. phys. Soc.* **64,** 449–469.
Gerchberg, R. W. (1972). *Nature* **240,** 404–406.
Gerchberg, R. W. (1974). *Optica Acta* **21,** 709–720.
Gerchberg, R. W. and Saxton, W. O. (1971). *Optik* **34,** 275–284.
Gerchberg, R. W. and Saxton, W. O. (1972). *Optik* **35,** 237–246.
Gibbs, A. J. and Rowe, A. J. (1973). *Nature* **246,** 509–511.
Glaeser, R. M. (1975). *In* "Electron Microscopy and Microbeam Analysis" (B. M. Siegel and D. R. Beaman, eds), pp. 205–229. John Wiley and Sons, New York.
Goodman, J. W. (1968). "Introduction to Fourier Optics". McGraw-Hill, New York.
Grinton, G. R. and Cowley, J. M. (1971). *Optik* **34,** 221–233.
Hahn, M. H. (1972). *Optik* **35,** 326–337.
Haine, M. E. and Mulvey, T. (1952). *J. opt. Soc. Am.* **42,** 763–773.
Hanszen, K.-J. (1969). *Z. Naturf.* **24a,** 1849.
Hanszen, K.-J. (1971). *In* "Advances in Optical and Electron Microscopy" (R. Barer and V. E. Cosslett, eds), Vol. 4, pp. 1–84. Academic Press, London and New York.
Hanszen, K.-J. (1973). *In* "Image Processing and Computer Aided Design in Electron Microscopy" (P. W. Hawkes, ed.), pp. 16–53. Academic Press, London and New York.
Hanszen, K.-J. and Trepte, L. (1971). *Optik* **32,** 519–538.
Haydon, G. B. and Lemons, R. A. (1972). *J. Microscopy* **95,** 483–491.
Hibi, T. and Takahashi, S. (1971). *J. Electron Microsc.* **20,** 17–22.
Hoch, H. (1973). *Optik* **38,** 220–222.

Hoppe, W. (1970). *Acta Crystallogr.* **A26,** 414–426.
Hoppe, W. (1971). *Z. Naturf.* **26a,** 1155–1168.
Hoppe, W., Langer, R. and Thon, F. (1970). *Optik* **30,** 538–545.
Hosemann, R. and Bagchi, S. N. (1962). "Direct Analysis of Diffraction by Matter", Chapter 4. North-Holland Press, Amsterdam.
Isaacson, M., Langmore, J. P. and Rose, H. (1974). *Optik* **41,** 92–96.
Johnson, D. J. and Crawford, D. (1973). *J. Microscopy* **98,** 313–324.
Karle, J. and Hauptman, H. (1964). *Acta Crystallogr.* **17,** 392–396.
Krakow, W., Welles, K. B. and Siegel, B. M. (1976). *J. Phys. D: Appl. Phys.* **9,** 175–181.
Leith, E. N. and Upatnieks, J. (1962). *J. opt. Soc. Am.* **52,** 1123–1130.
Lenz, F. (1971a). *In* "Electron Microscopy in Material Science" (U. Valdrè, ed.), pp. 541–569. Academic Press, New York and London.
Lenz, F. (1971b). *In* "Proceedings 25th Anniversary Meeting of EMAG". Institute of Physics, London, pp. 224–229.
Lipson, H. and Lipson, S. G. (1972). *J. appl. Crystallogr.* **5,** 239–240.
Lohmann, A. (1956). *Optica Acta* **3,** 97–99.
Lohmann, A. (1974). *Optik* **41,** 1–9.
Lynch, D. F., Moodie, A. F. and O'Keefe, M. A. (1975). *Acta Crystallogr.* **A31,** 300–307.
Misell, D. L. (1973a). *J. Phys. D: Appl. Phys.* **6,** 2200–2216.
Misell, D. L. (1973b). *J. Phys. D: Appl. Phys.* **6,** 2217–2225.
Misell, D. L. (1974). *J. Phys. D: Appl. Phys.* **7,** L69–71.
Misell, D. L. (1975). *In* "Physical Aspects of Electron Microscopy and Microbeam Analysis" (B. M. Siegel and D. R. Beaman, eds), pp. 63–79. Wiley, New York.
Misell, D. L. and Burge, R. E. (1975). *J. Microscopy* **103,** 195–202.
Misell, D. L. and Greenaway, A. H. (1974a). *J. Phys. D: Appl. Phys.* **7,** 832–855.
Misell, D. L. and Greenaway, A. H. (1974b). *J. Phys. D: Appl. Phys.* **7,** 1660–1669.
Misell, D. L., Burge, R. E. and Greenaway, A. H. (1974). *Nature* **247,** 401–402.
Misell, D. L., Stroke, G. W. and Halioua, M. (1974). *J. Phys. D: Appl. Phys.* **7,** L113–117.
Molière, G. (1947). *Z. Naturf.* **2a,** 133–145.
Munch, J. (1975). *Optik* **43,** 79–99.
Napier, P. J. and Bates, R. H. T. (1974). *Astron. Astrophys. Suppl.* **15,** 427–430.
Nussenzveig, H. M. (1967). *J. Math. Phys.* **8,** 561–572.
O'Neill, E. L. and Walther, A. (1963). *Optica Acta* **10,** 33–40.
Peřina, J. (1972). "Coherence of Light", Chapter 4, pp. 55–62. Van Nostrand Reinhold, London.
Raith, H. (1968). *Acta Crystallogr.* **A24,** 85–93.
Ramachandran, G. N. and Srinivasan, R. (1961). *Nature* **190,** 159–161.
Raman, S. and Katz, J. L. (1967). *Z. Kristallogr.* **124,** 43–63.
Roman, P. and Marathay, A. S. (1963). *Nuovo Cimento* **30,** 1452–1463.
Rose, H. (1974). *Optik* **39,** 416–436.
Santis, P. de and Gori, F. (1975). *Optica Acta* **22,** 691–695.
Saxton, W. O. (1974). *J. Phys. D: Appl. Phys.* **7,** L63–64.
Sayre, D. (1952). *Acta Crystallogr.* **5,** 60–65.
Sayre, D. (1972). *Acta Crystallogr.* **A28,** 210–212.
Sayre, D. (1974). *Acta Crystallogr.* **A30,** 180–184.
Scales, D. J. (1974). *J. Microscopy* **102,** 49–58.
Scherzer, O. (1949). *J. appl. Phys.* **20,** 20–29.

Schiske, P. (1968). *In* "Electron Microscopy" (D. S. Bocciarelli, ed.), Vol. I, pp. 145–146. Tipografia Poliglotta Vaticana, Rome.

Schiske, P. (1974). *Optik* **40,** 261–275.

Schiske, P. (1975). *J. Phys. D: Appl. Phys.* **8,** 1372–1386.

Spence, J. C. H. (1974). *Optica Acta* **21,** 835–837.

Srinivasan, R. (1961). *Proc. Indian Acad. Sci.* **53A,** 252–261.

Stroke, G. W. and Halioua, M. (1972a). *Optik* **35,** 50–65.

Stroke, G. W. and Halioua, M. (1972b). *Optik* **35,** 489–508.

Stroke, G. W. and Halioua, M. (1973a). *Optik* **37,** 192–203.

Stroke, G. W. and Halioua, M. (1973b). *Optik* **37,** 249–264.

Stroke, G. W., Halioua, M., Thon, F. and Willasch, D. (1974). *Optik* **41,** 319–343.

Thon, F. (1971). *In* "Electron Microscopy in Material Science" (U. Valdrè, ed.), pp. 570–625. Academic Press, New York and London.

Unwin, P. N. T. (1975). *J. molec. Biol.* **98,** 235–242.

Unwin, P. N. T. and Henderson, R. (1975). *J. molec. Biol.* **94,** 425–440.

Wahl, H. (1974). *Optik* **39,** 585–588.

Walther, A. (1963). *Optica Acta* **10,** 41–49.

Weingärtner, I., Mirandé, W. and Menzel, E. (1969). *Optik* **30,** 318–322.

Weingärtner, I., Mirandé, W. and Menzel, E. (1971). *Ann. Phys. (Leipzig)* **26,** 289–301.

Wolf, E. (1962). *Proc. phys. Soc.* **80,** 1269–1272.

Zernike, F. (1942). *Physica* **9,** 686–698 and 974–986.

Electron Microscopical Analysis of the Three-Dimensional Structure of Biological Macromolecules

B. K. VAINSHTEIN

Institute of Crystallography, Academy of Sciences, Moscow

I. Introduction

THE development of the theoretical, instrumental and preparative techniques, as well as the methods for image processing, have raised modern electron microscopy to a new level. This allows one to proceed from qualitative conclusions about the structure of the observed objects to the exact mathematical description of their structure. In this sense electron microscopy has now become a method for the structural analysis of matter (i.e. establishment of its spatial structure) analogous to such methods as X-ray, neutron and electron diffraction.

In recent years many valuable results have been obtained, using electron microscopy, in the investigation of the structure of biological macromolecules and their associations; this topic will be the specific subject of our discussion.

Within this field of research belong the establishment of the external shape of molecules of globular proteins, the packing and shape of subunits in complex molecules and the investigation of mutual packing of molecules in associations (i.e. in layers, tubes and crystals), in virus particles and other biological microsystems. Studies of the conformation and mutual packing of chain and elongated molecules—nucleic acids, fibrous proteins of some nucleoproteides, etc.—also refer to this sphere of investigation.

Electron microscopy is one of the most effective physical methods for the study of large molecules and other biological structures—it produces a direct image of the object. However, it is subject to some inherent restrictions. First of all, we get a two-dimensional image of the object which is its enlarged "shadow", or projection. The most important characteristics of an image are resolution and contrast. However, the simultaneous improvement of these is not always possible. Bearing in mind the problem raised, investigators are in search of the optimal combination of possibilities defined by the character of the object, the method of its preparation, the potentialities of the electron microscope itself and, finally, the methods of image processing.

Let us consider the main principles of electron microscopy as they apply to its use as a method of analysis of the three-dimensional structure of matter.

As is well known, when radiation is transmitted through matter, one can observe the phenomenon of scattering (coherent or incoherent) and absorption. The electrostatic potential due to the charges on the nuclei and on the electron shells of atoms appears to be the "scattering matter" for electrons. Therefore, in electron microscopy (as well as in electron diffraction) structure analysis, one obtains, as a result of structural investigations, a picture of the potential of the object (Vainshtein, 1964). The potential distribution has the same character as the electron density distribution of the object, as recorded by the X-ray diffraction method. In both cases the scattering density value will be larger the higher the atomic number of the object-forming atoms and the greater the number of atoms per unit volume.

Bearing in mind that the electrostatic potential of an object is the scattering matter for electrons, we shall denote this scattering matter—its density—by the value

$$\rho(\mathbf{r}) = \rho(x, y, z). \tag{1}$$

It is known that owing to the small aperture ($\sim 10^{-2}$ radians) the depth of focus of the electron microscope amounts to about 2000 Å, which approximately matches (or slightly exceeds) the thickness of the studied objects. Thus, for a three-dimensional object $\rho_3(\mathbf{r})$, examined by transmission, we can observe a projection. (Fig. 1)

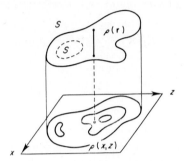

FIG. 1. Three-dimensional object ρ_3 and its two-dimensional projection ρ_2.

$$\rho_2(x, y) = \int \rho_3(x, y, z)dz \tag{2a}$$

Here the projection is taken along z, and indices 3 or 2 indicate the number of spatial dimensions. In the general case, for projection along an arbitrary vector τ, we can write

$$\rho_2(\mathbf{x}_\tau) = \int \rho(\mathbf{r}) \, d\mathbf{r}, \tag{2b}$$

where $\mathbf{x} = \mathbf{x}_\tau(\perp \tau)$ is the two-dimensional vector of the projection plane.

The image $D_2(\mathbf{x}')$ of function $\rho_2(\mathbf{x})$ is defined in electron microscopic experiments, as a two-dimensional distribution of intensity of incident electrons in the image plane with a vector $\mathbf{x}'$ (and coordinates x', y'). $D_2(\mathbf{x}')$ is specified by the projection ρ_2 and thereby by the three-dimensional structure ρ_3. When the electron beam is transmitted through the object there arise the phenomena of coherent and incoherent scattering, absorption, etc. The structure of an object may be imperfect. The scattering may be kinematic or may possess a more complicated character—the dynamic one; secondary scattering effects may also arise. Furthermore, the observed picture of the intensity of an image depends on the optics of the instrument, i.e. on instrumental effects, as well as on various kinds of "noise". The image may be measured either photographically—taking account of some law of blackening—or by some other method whose characteristics must also be known. It follows that the enlarged picture of the projection $\rho_2(\mathbf{x})$ observed in the detector is the result of modification of ρ_2 by a transfer function of the microscope, f, transforming ρ_2 into D_2 and, furthermore, by modification of the image D_2 by the detector function F, transforming D_2 into D_2^r:

$$\rho_2(\mathbf{x}) \to f[\rho_2] = D_2(\mathbf{x}') \to F[D_2] = D_2^r(\mathbf{x}'). \tag{3a}$$

If we know the transfer function f and the detector function F (for instance, the blackening law of the plate), we can perform the required inverse transformation

$$D_2^r(\mathbf{x}') \to D_2(\mathbf{x}') \to \rho_2(\mathbf{x}). \tag{3b}$$

Later we shall assume the transformation $D_2^r \to D_2$ to be always accomplished and we shall concentrate our attention on the transformation $D_2 \to \rho_2$. Qualitative electron microscopy is based on the fact that all three functions are roughly equal: $D^r \simeq D \simeq \rho_2$; in other words, the electron micrographs may be considered as enlarged projections ρ_2.

For many years, electron microscopists had been satisfied with these two-dimensional data and only from time to time proposed, on this basis, approximate qualitative spatial models for some object or other.

However, a few years ago, there appeared works in which the authors showed how to solve the naturally-arising question of deriving the spatial structure of an object from its projections:

$$\text{set } \rho_2(\mathbf{x}_{\tau i}) \to \rho_3(\mathbf{r}). \tag{4}$$

Intuition prompts the suggestion that one projection may not suffice for this process and that several or many projections are needed. How many and in what cases, we shall see later. If the transformation indicated by Eqn (4) is practically possible, then electron microscopy actually becomes an analogue of the methods for crystal structure analysis, giving the three-dimensional spatial structure. It should be noted here that the mathematical apparatus of three-dimensional structure analysis is, in essence, the same in all methods. This is associated with the fact that image formation in the optical or electron microscope has, as its intermediate stage, the scattering or diffraction of radiation by an object ρ, while Fourier transform theory serves as a mathematical description of the phenomenon. Actually, the information on the structure of the object $\rho(\mathbf{r})$ [Eqn (1)] is contained, as is known already from the Abbe microscope theory, not only in its image $D_2(\mathbf{x}')$ [Eqn (3)] (Fig. 2), but also in a set of amplitudes $\Phi(\mathbf{X})$ of scattered radiation in the diffraction plane. In the general case, the value $\Phi(\mathbf{X})$

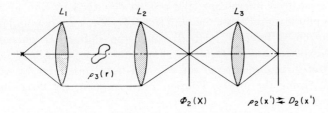

FIG. 2. Diagram: object ρ_3, diffraction plane Φ_2, image D. L_1 = condensor, L_2 = objective and L_3 = projection lens.

distributed continuously in this plane is the (two-dimensional) Fourier transform of the projection [Eqn (2)] of the three-dimensional object ρ_3.

$$\Phi_2(\mathbf{X}) = \Phi(X, Y)$$
$$= \int \rho_2(x, y) \exp\{2\pi i(xX + yY)\}\, dx\, dy = \mathscr{F}\,[\rho_2(x, y)], \qquad (5)$$

where $\mathscr{F}$ is the Fourier operator. If we know the moduli $|\Phi(X, Y)|$ (the square of these defines the diffraction pattern intensity) and the phases $\phi(x, y)$ of the complex value Φ,

$$\Phi = |\Phi| \exp\{i\phi\}, \qquad (6)$$

then this is equivalent to knowing the image $\rho_2(x, y)$. In fact, the physical process of collecting the diffracted beams to form an image with the lens L_2 (Fig. 2) is equivalent to the inverse Fourier transformation

$$\mathscr{F}^{-1}[\Phi_2(\mathbf{X})] = \mathscr{F}^{-1}[\mathscr{F}[\rho_2(\mathbf{x})]] = \rho_2(\mathbf{x}). \qquad (7)$$

It should be noted that the information on the structure of an object contained in the moduli and phases of the scattered waves need not be found only in the diffraction plane of the object (Φ_2 in Fig. 2). According to Huygens principle, any intermediate plane or curvilinear surface behind the object also carries this information. However, it is in the diffraction plane that such information has the form most convenient for recording and processing, and Eqn (7) holds true only for this plane.

In the general case of the Fourier transformation of the three-dimensional function

$$\mathscr{F}[\rho_3(\mathbf{r})] = \Phi(\mathbf{S}) \qquad (8a)$$

the transform Φ is distributed continuously in three-dimensional reciprocal space with vector $\mathbf{S}(X, Y, Z)$. But in diffraction from periodic structures— e.g. crystals—one can obtain only discrete diffracted beams corresponding to the reciprocal lattice points at $\mathbf{S} = \mathbf{H}_{hkl}$, i.e. in two- and three-dimensional cases, respectively:

$$\Phi_2(\mathbf{X}) = \text{set } \Phi_{hk}, \quad \Phi_3(\mathbf{S}) = \text{set } \Phi_{hkl}, \qquad (8b, c)$$

where hkl are the indices of diffraction spots.

In the electron microscope, the process described by Eqn (7) is carried out by a physical procedure, i.e. with lenses. In X-ray analysis and in electron and neutron diffraction methods, only the diffraction phenomenon is realized experimentally (Eqns (8)). From the two-dimensional sets Φ_2, we obtain the three-dimensional set Φ_3, and from this latter we get mathematically, using the inverse Fourier transformation, the three-dimensional structure:

$$\text{set } \Phi_2^i \to \Phi_3 \to \mathcal{F}[\Phi_3] = \rho_3(\mathbf{r}). \tag{9}$$

From diffraction intensities of reflections $I_{hkl} \sim |\Phi_{hkl}|^2$, we can obtain only the moduli, whereas to perform the transformation given in Eqn (9) we must know the phases ϕ [Eqn (6)]. Here lies the main difficulty: the so-called phase problem inherent in structural diffraction methods. In electron microscopy (both in the experimental aspect and from the viewpoint of mathematical procedures) one can reconstruct the investigated structure ρ_3 directly from its image ρ_2 [Eqn (4)] or from experimental diffraction data Φ_2 [Eqns (5) and (6)], with further mathematical reconstruction by reference to Eqn (9). In the second method, the solution of the phase problem using Fourier transformation appears to be very simple due to the presence of the image $\rho_2(\mathbf{x})$. It should be noted that in electron microscopy there also exist experimental methods of phase determination based on the ideas of coherent optics and holography.

Let us dwell on the problem of resolution of structure details of an object $\rho(\mathbf{r})$. The resolution is defined by the highest harmonics with the values $|\mathbf{S}_{\max}|$ of its Fourier expansion:

$$\mathcal{F}[\rho] = \Phi(\mathbf{S}); \; \Phi(\mathbf{S}) \begin{cases} \neq 0 \text{ for } |\mathbf{S}| < S_{\max}, \\ = 0 \text{ for } |\mathbf{S}| > S_{\max}. \end{cases} \tag{10a}$$

If the scattering angle is equal to $\alpha = 2\theta$ and the wavelength is λ, then, as is known, the following relationships exist:

$$2 \sin \theta/\lambda = d^{-1} = |\mathbf{S}| \simeq \alpha/\lambda; \quad S_{\max} = d_{\min}^{-1}, \tag{10b}$$

where $d_{\min}$ is the value which is connected with the smallest dimension δ of the physical inhomogeneities in the object (Fig. 3). In the inverse Fourier transformation $\rho = \mathcal{F}^{-1}[\Phi]$, the limiting values $d_{\min}$ (natural or restricted artificially) determine the periodicity of the highest harmonics (highest space frequencies) of the expansion and, thereby, the resolution δ. The resolution is usually defined as the minimal distance between the narrowest peaks of the distribution δ, at which they do not as yet merge into a common peak (δ is also approximately equal to the half-width of the narrowest peaks). According to the classical theory of diffraction, in one-, two- and three-

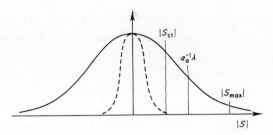

FIG. 3. Curves of average values $|\overline{\Phi}|$. Solid line is the natural fall with limit $|\mathbf{S}_{\max}|$; dashed line is the fall for stained object with limit $|\mathbf{S}_{st}|$. $\lambda\alpha_a^{-1}$ is the aperture limit.

dimensional cases $\delta_{(1)} = 0\cdot5d_{\min}$, $\delta_{(2)} = 0\cdot61d_{\min}$, $\delta_{(3)} = 0\cdot72d_{\min}$, respectively. Sometimes, the value $d_{\min}$ is taken as the measure of resolution which, as is seen, is not equivalent to the value $\delta_{\min}$.

In diffraction from crystals [Eqns (8b, c)] $|\mathbf{H}_{\max}| = d_{\min}$ corresponds to the minimal interplanar spacings in the lattice.

In the scattering of electrons by crystals or other objects the natural diffraction field may reach very small d, of the order of $1\cdot0$ Å and less. However, there exist a number of reasons that impede the realization of such a resolution in electron microscopy. One such reason is aberrations of the lens and, in particular, spherical aberration (Cosslett, 1972). Spherical aberration diminishes as the aperture of the objective lens becomes smaller. This means that the cut-off of the scattered beams occurs at $a > a_a$. Consequently, the instrumental resolution,

$$d_{\text{instr}} = |\mathbf{S}_{(\text{instr})}^{-1}| \approx \lambda\alpha_a^{-1}, \tag{11}$$

is inversely proportional to a_a. Therefore, one has to choose the optimal value a_a (Fig. 3). However, in studying biological objects it is not this particular circumstance that is found to be the resolution-limiting factor. The point is that *in vivo* such objects scatter electrons very weakly and give very poor contrast. In addition, they are not stable in the evacuated conditions in the electron microscope and are extremely sensitive to radiation damage.

One may overcome these difficulties by using the staining technique which, however, brings the natural resolution down to $|\mathbf{S}_{st}| \approx 20$ to 30 Å, or to 10 Å at best [Eqns (10a), (10b)].

If unstained specimens are under investigation, one can increase the resolution up to several Ångstrom units, but the problem of image reconstruction then becomes particularly difficult due to the weak contrast and other reasons.

II. Biological Macromolecules and Negative Staining

The main objects of the use of electron microscopy in the structural investigation of biomolecules are globular and fibrillar proteins, nucleic acids, spherical and rodlike viruses, bacteriophages, cellular particles like ribosomes, chromatin, etc.

What do these studies provide, and what level of organization of biomolecules is accessible to electron microscopy? We recall that almost all biological molecules are polymeric. The chemical formula of the sequence of links in a biopolymer is called the primary structure. This is the topological invariant of the multitude of possible spatial configurations. Some particular stable conformation of certain regions of the chain, e.g. the α-helix or the extended β structure in proteins, or the double helix in DNA, is called the secondary structure. The tertiary structure is the particular conformation of a given biopolymer, e.g. the spatial structure of a polypeptide chain as packed in the compact globule of some protein. The information on these secondary and tertiary structures, which requires atomic resolution, comes from X-ray diffraction analysis. The molecules of many proteins consist of several (two, four or a larger number) so-called "subunits" each one being an individual coiled polypeptide chain. The subunits of the protein molecule may be identical, or of two or more sorts. The spatial combinations of subunits into the complex molecule is called the quaternary structure. This latter, i.e. the mutual packing of subunits, is, as a rule, symmetrical.

Currently, electron microscopy of biomolecules is engaged mainly in studying quaternary structures and, in individual cases, in getting certain crude data on tertiary and secondary structures. At the same time, studies are being undertaken on the combination of molecules of proteins, nucleic acids and nucleoproteins into aggregates: native ones, such as viruses, ribosomes, chromosomes, or membranes, and synthetic ones, such as planar monomolecular films, tubes or crystals. We can call this level of organization the fifth-order level, or "quinary" structure. The number of atoms combined into a quaternary or quinary structure is of the order of 10^5–10^7. Of course they cannot, at present, be observed individually. However, we can get direct information on the dimensions, shape and mutual arrangement of the molecules made up of these atoms, and on conformational changes in the quaternary structure when such occur.

Thus, both in the attainable resolution and in the level of organization of biosystems, electron microscopy extends the "atomic" level of X-ray diffraction analysis towards larger objects of study.

Biological molecules are made up mainly of the light atoms C, N, O, H which scatter electrons weakly. *In vivo*, when their structure is conserved, they appear to be wet, i.e. surrounded by the mother liquor (water). The contrast of these objects is very weak. In addition, such wet objects are particularly unstable in vacuum in the electron microscope and are very sensitive to radiation damage.

One may overcome these difficulties by staining biological preparations with substances containing heavy atoms which enhance the contrast and stabilize the object.

Let $\rho_{M}(\mathbf{r})$ be the distribution of scattering density in a biological macromolecule, say, a globular protein. The inhomogeneities in this distribution, i.e. atoms, have dimensions of the order of $1 \cdot 5$–3 Å. At lower resolution they are invisible; therefore, at a low resolution we can describe the protein molecule as a "clump" of polypeptide substance with the approximately constant density $\rho_{M}(\mathbf{r}) = 1$, having some definite shape and boundary $G(\mathbf{r})$.

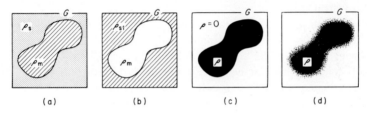

FIG. 4. (a) A biological macromolecule with the boundary G surrounded by the mother liquor; (b) the molecule in negative stain; (c) "1–0" description of a stained object; (d) smearing-out of an edge of the molecule in a stained object.

The density ρ_{S} of the mother liquor surrounding the molecule is constant and differs very slightly from ρ_{M}. Therefore, the contrast of the overall distribution $\rho_{M} + \rho_{S}$ proves to be insufficient [Fig. 4(a)]. Hence, one introduces into the specimen substances that strongly scatter electrons, e.g. uranyl acetate, phosphotungstic acid, etc. In positive staining, one covers or wraps the surfaces of the biomolecules or some of their aggregates with a thin layer of such a material. The method of negative staining is more customary. Here the specimen is immersed in a mass of stain. The latter forms a "mould" of the object. The stain also penetrates into the cavities of the studied object, e.g. in studying protein crystals it replaces the crystallization liquid that lies between the biomolecules or their subunits in such a crystal [Fig. 4(b)]. Since the contrasting substance with larger (constant) scattering density replaces the solvent, the density of the object can now be described by the function $\rho_{st} + \rho_{M}$, with $\rho_{st} \gg \rho_{M}$. In this case, ρ_{M} may be neglected, the object being described by the density $\rho = \rho_{st}$. This function is, practically, equal to zero within the surface G_{M}, and is constant outside it. However, for the sake of clarity and simplicity (the result remaining unchanged) one can describe the structure of the stained object in an opposite way—as being constant (and equal to unity) within G and zero outside* [Fig. 4(c)]:

$$\rho(\mathbf{r}) = \begin{cases} 1 \text{ inside } G(\mathbf{r}), \\ 0 \text{ outside } G(\mathbf{r}). \end{cases} \tag{12}$$

It is assumed that the stain into which the molecule is immersed forms a layer of equal thickness [Fig. 4(c)]; otherwise, an account of the thickness of the layer of the stain would be needed.

It should be noted that, according to the Babinet principle, the reversed contrast produces no influence on the diffraction pattern, and at a low resolution the electron diffraction pattern from a stained (or unstained) object, the X-ray diffraction from the same object and the optical diffraction from an electron micrograph of that object will all be, in the first approximation, identical.

The function $\rho(\mathbf{r})$ has a "sharp" edge G $(0,1)$ [see Eqn (12)]; however, in real staining and three-dimensional reconstruction the molecular boundaries appear to be smeared out.

Let us consider this case using a protein crystal as an example.

In the absence of contrasting material in a wet preparation, all molecules are packed in the same manner to an accuracy of a factor

$$(\sqrt{(2\pi \overline{u_T^2})})^{-1} \exp (-x^2/2\overline{u_T^2}), \tag{13}$$

which describes the thermal and other displacements of atoms in the molecule as well as the shifts of the molecules as a whole with the root-mean-square shift $\sqrt{(\overline{u_T^2})}$.

In the X-ray diffraction pattern, this factor [Eqn (13)] manifests itself as a temperature factor

$$\exp [-B (\sin \theta/\lambda)^2] = \exp (-2\pi^2 \overline{u_T^2} S^2) \tag{14}$$

defining the decrease in intensity and the boundary S_{max} of the diffraction field. For proteins $\sqrt{(\overline{u_T^2})} \approx 1$ Å; this corresponds to $B \approx 50$–100 Å^2.

In negative staining, the structure of the stain and its influence on the shape and arrangement of the molecules become the resolution-limiting factor. Granularity of the stain, i.e. the dimensions of the inhomogeneities in it, σ_1, does not allow us to determine the boundary contours of the molecule with an accuracy greater than σ_1. Besides, the coarse particles of the staining material may distort the surface of the molecule by a certain mean value σ_2. The non-uniform penetration of the stain into the gaps

* The theory of three-dimensional reconstruction considered below does not impose any restrictions on the form $\rho(\mathbf{r})$, and, of course, may also be applicable in the particular case of Eqn (12).

between the molecules may shift the molecules from their equilibrium positions. In three-dimensional reconstruction (as in X-ray experiments) the restoration is performed not from a pattern of one molecule but from a symmetrical set of many molecules. In other words, here the shifts from equilibrium positions which may be described by the value σ_3 also play a part. All these factors acting together yield the value

$$\sqrt{(\sigma_1^2 + \sigma_2^2 + \sigma_3^2)} = \sigma = \sqrt{(\overline{u_e^2})}, \qquad (15)$$

where $\sqrt{(\overline{u_e^2})}$ plays exactly the same role as $\sqrt{(\overline{u_T^2})}$ does in Eqn (14). The factor given in Eqn (13) smudges the "boundary" of the molecule $S(r)$ [Fig. 4(d)] and defines, according to Eqn (14), the decrease in intensities in electron diffraction from a stained specimen or in optical diffraction from an electron micrograph.

Taking the normal (Gaussian) law for the disordering action of the stain [as in Eqn (13)], we write it in the form

$$\phi(x) = (\sqrt{(2\pi)}\sigma)^{-1} \exp{(-x^2/2\sigma^2)}. \qquad (16)$$

The Fourier transform, defining the decrease in intensities, ("quasi-temperature" factor) has, in reciprocal space, the form

$$\exp{\{-[B_e(\sin\theta/\lambda)^2]\}} = \exp{\{-2\pi^2\sigma^2 X^2\}} = \exp{\{-[\tfrac{1}{2}X^2/\Delta^2]\}}, \qquad (17)$$

where $\Delta = 1/2\pi\sigma$ is the dispersion of the Gaussian distribution in reciprocal space. Equation (17) is shown in Fig. 5(a). One usually assumes the Gaussian function to be damped at $X = 3\Delta$, i.e. $3\Delta = d_{min}^{-1} = |X_{max}|$ is the boundary of reflections observed in a diffraction pattern; this boundary defines the minimal interplanar spacing; the value $\sigma = 0.5\ d_{min}$. In negative staining, the observed values d_{min} are of the order of 10–30 Å (Fig. 3). Such boundaries of the diffraction field are characterized by values $\sigma = \sqrt{(\overline{u_e^2})}$ and B_e; they are considerably larger than in X-ray diffraction. This can be seen from the following figures:

d_{min} (Å)	0·5	1	2·5	5	10	20	30	40	50
$\sigma = \sqrt{(\overline{u^2})}$ (Å)	0·24	0·48	1·2	2·4	4·8	9·6	14·4	18·4	24
B (Å²)	4·5	18	114	450	1800	7300	16 000	27 000	45 000

In order to describe the averaged stained molecule, we have to form the convolution

$$\rho(\mathbf{r}) = \int \rho_m(\mathbf{r})\phi(\mathbf{r} - \mathbf{r}')\ \mathrm{d}v_{\mathbf{r}'} = \widehat{\rho_m\phi}. \qquad (18)$$

For the one-dimensional case, Fig. 5(b) shows both $\rho_{st}(x)$ and $\phi(x)$. Convolution [Eqn (18)] is expressed via the probability integral

$$\frac{1}{\sqrt{\pi}} \int\limits_0^1 \exp{[-t^2/2]}\ \mathrm{d}t = \Phi(t). \qquad (19)$$

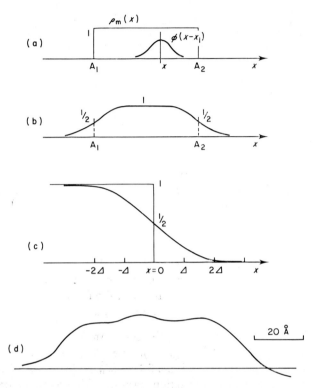

Fig. 5. (a) Molecule $\rho_m(x)$ and the Gaussian function ϕ (one-dimensional case); (b) their convolution; (c) result of smearing-out of the edge [cf. Fig. 4(d)]; (d) profile of cross-section of the catalase molecule, ($\sigma = 12$ Å).

Here the edge of function ρ_m, i.e. function G, is not the sharp break $(0,1)$ [Eqn (12)], but is shown to be described in the direction x, perpendicular to the surface of the molecule, by expression

$$G(x) = \begin{cases} \frac{1}{2} - \Phi(x), & x > 0, \\ \frac{1}{2} + \Phi(x), & x < 0. \end{cases} \tag{20}$$

This function is shown in Fig. 5(c); it is equal to 1 at $x < -2\sigma$ and reduces to zero near $x > 2\sigma$; in other words, it appears to be somewhat smoother than the Gaussian function [Eqn (6)], giving rise to "smearing-out" effects. The width of the "edge" is about 3–4 Å. Figure 5(d) shows the profile of a cross-section of the catalase molecule for which $d_{min} = 25$ Å, i.e. $\sigma = 12$ Å.

In a number of works it has been pointed out that on irradiation negative-stained objects change their structure to some extent. In an investigation of tobacco mosaic virus stained with uranyl acetate, Unwin (1974a) found qualitative differences in micrographs and, correspondingly, in models of three-dimensional reconstruction obtained at small radiation doses (0·02 C cm^{-2}) and at large ones (0·2–1·0 C cm^{-2}). On irradiation, the uranium oxide UO_3 with density 7·3 g cm^{-3} converts to uranium dioxide UO_2 with density 11·0 g cm^{-3}, i.e. the volume of the stain decreases. This fact accounts for redistribution of the stain in the regions near the external and internal surfaces of protein particles. The linear compression of the stain is estimated to be 15%. Unwin (1971, 1972, 1974b) also pointed out that, when investigating stained specimens, one may discriminate between the contributions to an image by the stain and the protein, if an electrostatic phase plate is used. It consists of an aperture in which a spanned thread is placed. Such a plate is located in the diffraction plane of the microscope. In this case the contrast, in the author's opinion, owes its origin mainly to the distribution of protein.

III. RECONSTRUCTION OF TWO-DIMENSIONAL IMAGES

The two-dimensional image $D^2(\mathbf{x}')$ [Eqns (3a, b)] is the experimental data for obtaining a picture of the projection ρ_2 of the structure ρ_3 [Eqns (2a, b)]. In a number of cases, we simply assume that $D_2(\mathbf{x}) \approx \rho_2(\mathbf{x})$; however, when quantitative data are needed, the strict transformation $D_2(x', y') \to \rho_2(x, y)$ must be performed. In this strict transformation lies the meaning of the term "reconstruction of two-dimensional image". It should be noted that in those cases in which the structure under investigation ρ_3 has a small thickness in the direction of projection, as, for example, in the case of monomolecular layers, membranes, etc., its two-dimensional projection already contains a wealth of information.

The operation in reciprocal space with the two-dimensional transform $\Phi_2(\mathbf{X}) = \mathscr{F}[\rho_2]$ is the most effective method of reconstruction of ρ_2.* These possibilities manifest themselves most distinctly when we deal with an object ρ possessing some definite symmetry and a periodic structure. Then, in reciprocal space, the periodic [Eqn (8b)] and aperiodic (noise) components of the Fourier transform are separated automatically.

This approach is physically realized in the method of optical filtering of electron micrographs. In this case, the electron micrograph itself, $D_2(X, Y)$, serves as object, and in the optical diffractometer (in the larger beam) we can observe its optical diffraction pattern [Figs 2, 6(a)], corresponding to the transformation in Eqn (5) (Klug and Berger, 1964).

In the general case, the values $\Phi^D = \mathscr{F}(D)$ are distributed continuously in the diffraction plane. The optical density of a micrograph is a super-

* See, for instance, the review by Birch (1972).

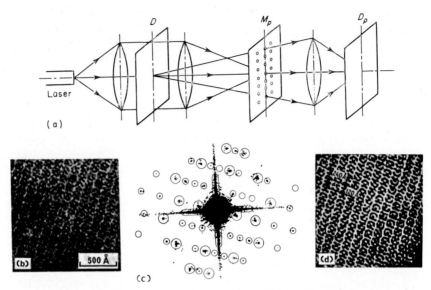

FIG. 6. (a) Diagram of an optical diffractometer. D is the object (an electron micrograph), M_p is the diffraction plane and a mask that transmits only Φ_{hk}, D_p is the plane of the (filtered) image; (b) an electron micrograph of a crystalline layer of the protein phosphorylase b; (c) its optical diffraction pattern (the circles correspond to the holes in the mask that transmits only the Φ_{hk} diffracted beams from the periodic component of the image); (d) the filtered image.

position of the image D_p of the periodic structure and the background ("noise") D_b:

$$D = D_p + D_b. \tag{21}$$

The background includes the image of the support and deviations from periodicity in the object itself. The diffraction from the periodic component

$$\mathscr{F}[D_p] = \int D_p(X, Y) \exp [2\pi i(hX + kY)] \, dX \, dY = \Phi_{hk}^D$$
$$= |\Phi_{hk}^D| \exp \{i\phi_{hk}^D\} \tag{22}$$

is concentrated at the reciprocal lattice points hk with the coordinates $X = h/a$ and $Y = k/b$ (where a and b are the periods). Figure 6(b) gives as an example an electron micrograph of a monomolecular layer of a "two-dimensional crystal" of the protein phosphorylase b. Figure 6(c) shows the optical diffraction pattern of this layer. If we collect the diffracted beams of Fig. 6(c) with a lens, which corresponds to the inverse Fourier transform [Eqn (5)], then we get again an image [Fig. 6(d)] from the micrograph. However, if we can use the fact that the diffracted beams Φ_{hk}^D from the periodic component are spatially isolated in the diffraction plane, according to the scheme in Fig. 6(a), we can place a screen in the diffraction plane with apertures (a "mask") having coordinates corresponding to the reciprocal lattice points; i.e. we can perform optical filtering [Fig. 6(d)] (Klug and De Rosier, 1966). The mask is prepared to fit the diffraction pattern. Then, only certain components will make contributions to image formation and, as in any optical instrument, the transmitted Φ_{hk}^{D} will keep their own phases—which would have been lost if a photograph had been taken in the diffraction plane, since a photographic plate records $I \sim |\Phi^{D}|^{2}$. However, the diffracted beams $\mathscr{F}[D_{b}^{D}]$ will be stopped. Thus we get a cleaned-up ("filtered") picture of the periodic structure alone:

$$\mathscr{F}^{-1}[\Phi_{hk}^{D}] = D_{p}(x', y'). \tag{23}$$

In addition to the problem of refining the image, optical diffractometry permits one to determine the periods of the two-dimensional crystal lattice, as well as the crystal symmetry and the symmetry of helical structures.

An elegant application of this method, which reveals the structure of the object in the third dimension, is diffraction from helical (cylindrical) structures like viruses, phage tails and tubes with monomolecular walls. Here, the analogue of the reciprocal crystal lattice is the so-called cylindrical reciprocal lattice, which also possesses a discrete system of maxima. Figure 7(a) shows the optical micrograph of a tubular crystal of phosphorylase b, with the coordinate grid of a plane section of the cylindrical reciprocal lattice drawn on it. It is important to note that this plane section actually breaks down into two nets (which are provisionally denoted in Fig. 7(c) with one in solid lines and the other in dotted lines). One of them corresponds to diffraction from the "front" wall, and the other from the "back" wall of the tube made up of helically packed molecules.

This circumstance allows us to use the idea of optical filtering by preparing a mask with holes corresponding to one of the nets [Fig. 7(c)]. The slits in the mask are made to fit the profile of the diffraction maxima. The zero-order peak is attenuated with a filter to half-intensity. The image obtained [Fig. 7(d)] is thus of one side of the tube; the background has also been filtered out of it. The mirror equivalent mask [see Fig. 7(c)] transmits the diffracted beams from the other side of the tube, and correspondingly gives its image [Fig. 7(e)]. We can distinctly see the helical packing in these images, and the structure of the individual protein molecules that form the packing can be recognized. Their appearance in different angular orientation in the tube made it possible to build a model of the molecule. It is made of four bent subunits arranged at the vertices of a tetrahedron [Fig. 7(f)].

We have described the method of optical filtering with the laser beam. It should be noted that, in principle, the filtering of electron beams could

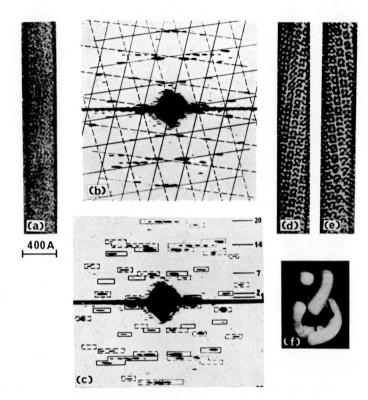

FIG. 7. Electron micrograph of a tubular crystal of phosphorylase b (a). Its optical diffraction with two families of diffraction spots corresponding to the front and back sides of the tube (b); the same pattern with the slits of the two corresponding masks (c); the filtered image of the front and back sides of the tube (d) and (e), and a model of the molecule (f). (Kiselev *et al*, 1971).

also be performed directly in the electron microscope itself. However, a solution of this problem will, evidently, encounter experimental difficulties.

The filtering can be carried out in all its stages by computation, and not by means of a physical procedure. If we used the approximation $D_2(\mathbf{x}) = \rho_2(\mathbf{x})$, which holds true for low resolution down to 20–30 Å, then the transforms of the image D and object ρ are equal, $\Phi^D(\mathbf{X}) = \Phi(\mathbf{X})$, as well as their periodic components $\Phi_{hk}^D = \Phi_{hk}$. Thus, the calculation of $\mathscr{F}[D(\mathbf{X})]$, extraction of Φ_{hk} and calculation of the Fourier synthesis $\mathscr{F}^{-1}[\Phi_{hk}] = \rho_2$, analogously to Eqn (23), give the reconstructed image.

However, at higher resolution (and when it is necessary to get more accurate results) one must take into account the difference between $D_2(\mathbf{x}')$

and $\rho_2(\mathbf{x})$, since the bright field image D_2 is modified, according to Eqn (3), by the transfer function.

This function depends on spherical aberration (with the coefficient C_s) and defocusing of the beam Δf. A certain underfocusing is an advantage, since, in this case, the contrast of the image is enhanced. This consideration (for negligibly weak, so-called amplitude contrast, owing its existence to inelastic scattering) yields, as a result, an expression for the Fourier transform of the image $D(\mathbf{x})$:

$$\mathscr{F}[D(\mathbf{x}')] = \Phi_2^D(\mathbf{X}') = - A(a)\Phi_2(\mathbf{X}) \sin f(a). \tag{24}$$

Here $\sin f(a)$ is the phase contrast transfer function—PCF (Scherzer, 1949; Hoppe, 1969, 1970, 1971; Hoppe et al., 1970). The phase shift f is given by

$$f(a) = (2\pi/\lambda)[\Delta f a^2/2 - C_s\, a^4/4]. \tag{25}$$

The periodic components $\Phi_2(\mathbf{X})$ at the lattice points h, k of the reciprocal lattice will describe, after the inverse Fourier transform, the reconstructed image ρ_2.

The appearance of the transfer function for optimal underfocusing is shown in Fig. 8 (Erickson and Klug, 1970). This real function changes the magnitudes of values $|\Phi'|$. However, at optimal underfocusing, there are no changes of the phases in a large region of reciprocal space up to a certain limiting value of $\mathbf{X}$, but for remote ring areas the phase (sign) begins to change periodically. This means that in the image $D(\mathbf{x}')$ the details corresponding to high resolution are distorted.

Thus, if we perform the inverse Fourier transformation $\mathscr{F}[D_2(\mathbf{x}')] = \Phi_2^D(\mathbf{X}')$, and pass on to $\Phi_2(\mathbf{X})$ according to Eqn (24), and carry out the inverse Fourier transformation again, $\mathscr{F}^{-1}[\Phi_2(\mathbf{X})] = \rho(\mathbf{x})$, we get the reconstruction of ρ_2. It is important that the PCF can be found directly from the electron micrograph itself. As was indicated by Thon (1966), it manifests itself as a ring modulation of a diffraction pattern from the "noise" component of the image. This modulation can be observed in an optical diffraction pattern from overexposed micrographs of the support film [Fig. 8(b)]. Thus, using the transfer function, we can find from the image itself the true $|\Phi|$ and ϕ of the object. However, we have to emphasize the following: the true $|\Phi_{\text{exp}}|$ can be obtained and measured directly from diffraction experiments on a given object—it is known that they do not get distorted in diffraction. The phasing $|\Phi_{\text{exp}}|$ will be carried out by means of the indicated calculation procedure. Then

$$\rho(\mathbf{x}) = \sum_{h,k} |\Phi_{\text{exp}}| \exp\{i\phi_{calc}\} \exp\{2\pi i[\mathbf{x}\mathbf{H}_{hk}]\}. \tag{26}$$

In principle, such a calculation is possible in the three-dimensional case as well. Moreover, here possibilities are opened up of combining various

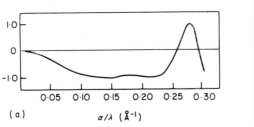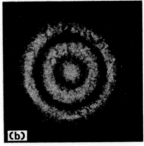

FIG. 8. (a) The transfer function of the phase contrast PCF for underfocusing $\Delta f = 900$ Å; (b) a visualization of PCF by means of optical diffraction.

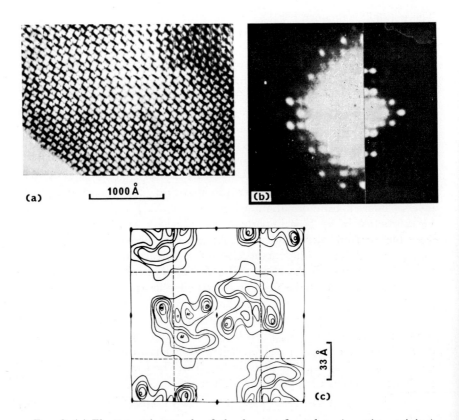

FIG. 9. (a) Electron micrograph of the layers of catalase (negative staining); (b) electron diffraction: right, low angle reflections; left, wide angle reflections; (c) the reconstructed image.

methods, e.g. of obtaining $|\Phi_{exp}|$ from X-ray diffraction, and the phases from electron microscopy, etc.

Let us consider some examples of using the PCF. Figure 9 shows the image of a stained specimen of one of the modifications of catalase and its electron diffraction pattern (Vainshtein *et al.*, 1976a). The periods are: $a = 150$ Å, $b = 168$ Å, $d_{min} = 18$ Å. Figure 9 is the result of mathematical reconstruction of this image carried out from Eqn (26) with phase calculations performed by means of the described procedure. The four peaks observed in the projection of the catalase molecule correspond to its four subunits (the structure of various modifications of this protein is discussed in more detail on p. 332).

The investigations of unstained specimens are very promising indeed. In this case one has to apply a special method for their stabilization. One of the possibilities is the use of the so-called wet chamber, which preserves

FIG. 10. Electron diffraction pattern from native crystals of catalase obtained in a wet specimen chamber.

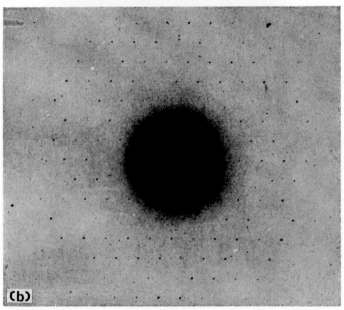

Fig. 11.

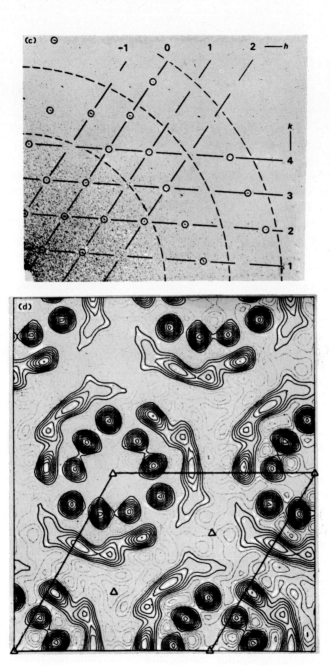

FIG. 11. Investigation of purple membranes. (a) An electron micrograph; (b) a low angle electron diffraction pattern; (c) an optical diffraction pattern; (d) reconstruction of a two-dimensional image.

protein specimens against drying. Using such a chamber, Dorset and Parsons (1975) obtained electron diffraction patterns from native specimens of catalase (Fig. 10) with extremely high orders of reflections—up to ~ 3.2 Å (this modification of protein differs from that given in Fig. 9).

Unwin and Henderson (1975) managed to obtain the reconstruction of images from unstained specimens by taking account of the PCF. They investigated specimens of layers of catalase, stabilized by 1% glucose, and obtained diffraction patterns and a reconstructed image with $d_{\min}$ reaching 9 Å. The other objects investigated were platelets of membranes of purple bacteria. These platelets are protein–lipid systems, which are stable in the electron microscope in the native state. In the investigations of these objects the image contrast was extremely low, and it was impossible to reveal visually the structure on the micrograph. Nevertheless, electron diffraction, as well as optical diffraction from micrographs [Fig. 11(b), (c)] shows reflections which point to the presence of the periodic regular component in the image. One can get such micrographs only at very low exposures, while the usual doses give rise to radiation damage which can be accounted for by the loss of structure regularity. The calculation of the Fourier transform of an image was carried out over a discrete set of 2048×2048 grid points; it yielded the $\Phi^D(\mathbf{X}')$ amplitudes. Evaluation of the PCF obtained from optical diffraction patterns enables one to perform the transition to Φ_{hk} and to find phases ϕ_{hk}. The Fourier synthesis [Eqn (26)] was constructed from the experimental $|\Phi_{hk\ \exp}|$ and ϕ_{calc}.

Figure 11(d) shows the reconstructed image ρ_2 of a purple membrane (this structure is discussed in more detail below—on p. 335).

There also exist direct experimental methods of phase determination based on the ideas of coherent optics and holography. Here one uses sources of electrons with improved characteristics (for instance, a field emission cathode) and changes the conditions of scattering by an object at the expense of interference of mutually scattered beams using the methods of holography with the basic beam or the single sideband method. We shall not dwell on these methods since, to date, they have been of little use in structural electron microscopy (see, for instance, Gabor, 1949, 1951; Zaitzev et al., 1968, 1969; Hanszen, 1969; Stroke, 1971; Stoyanova and Anaskin, 1972).

Finally, let us consider a method for improving two-dimensional images with rotational symmetry. The presence of an N-fold axis means that the structure is brought into coincidence with itself on rotation through $\alpha = 2\pi/N$. However, imperfections of the real image give rise to distortion of symmetry and impede its evaluation. If, following Markham et al. (1963), we rotate the image through arbitrary angles and bring it into coincidence with the initial image, then the best coincidence of densities will take place on rotation at an angle $a = 2\pi/N$ which defines N. The averaging of the picture over all such rotations will give an improved image of the structure.

Another way, analogous to finding the translational periodic component [Eqn (22)] is based on the Fourier expansion of the image in polar coordinates, over the angles (Crowther and Amos, 1971a).

$$\rho_2(r, \phi) = \sum_{n=-\infty}^{+\infty} g_n(r) \exp (in\phi). \tag{27}$$

Integration over the radius from azimuthal components g_n gives their "power":

$$p_n \sim \int_0^a |g_n|^2 r \, dr. \tag{28}$$

The set of p_n forms a spectrum, the least common multiple n of strong peaks defining the N-fold symmetry. After performing the double Fourier transformation in polar coordinates [see Eqns (39b, c) below], we get the two-dimensional reconstructed image of the particle with rotational symmetry. Figure 12 shows such an example.

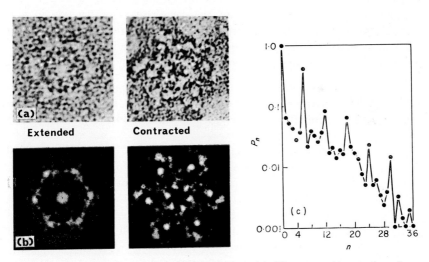

FIG. 12. The rotational filtering of an image. (a) Electron micrographs of two forms of the base plates of bacteriophage T_4; (b) the image reconstructed using harmonics with $n = kN$; (c) rotational power spectrum p_n.

IV. The Mathematical Apparatus of Three-dimensional Reconstruction

The problem consists in reconstruction of the three-dimensional structure from a set of its projections:

$$\text{set } \rho_{2,i}(\mathbf{x}_\tau) \to \rho_3(\mathbf{r}); \; \rho_2(x_i) = \int \rho_3(\mathbf{r})\, d\tau \tag{29}$$

or, in a more general form, of a function ρ_n from its projections in subspace ρ_{n-1}.

Radon (1917), the German mathematician, was the first to consider this problem. Somewhat later, independently of this work, a number of investigators, working in various branches of science concerned with reconstruction, proposed a number of methods for solving this problem. In electron microscopy three-dimensional reconstruction was first applied in the works of De Rosier and Klug (1968) and Vainshtein et al. (1968, 1969).

These methods have been intensively applied not only in electron microscopy, but also in medical radiography, radioastronomy, in methods of image analysis and, in general, of any zero-dimensional signals. Many reviews on this subject have been published (Birch, 1972; Vainshtein, 1973a, b; Smith et al., 1973; Marr, 1974; Merserau and Oppenheim, 1974; Finch, 1975; Crowther and Klug, 1975).

In this chapter we shall consider the main mathematical principles and algorithms of various methods of three-dimensional reconstruction. These methods are divided into two main classes: direct reconstruction in real space (DR) and reconstruction with the use of Fourier space (FSR). In addition to analytical methods, there also exist the algebraic methods (AR). We shall use the following main notations:

$\rho_3(\mathbf{r})$ three-dimensional function describing the object in real space of a three-dimensional vector $\mathbf{r}$. In Cartesian coordinates $\mathbf{r} = \mathbf{r}(x, y, z)$, in cylindrical coordinates $\mathbf{r} = \mathbf{r}(r, \psi, z)$;

$\rho_2(\mathbf{x})$ two-dimensional function in the space of a two-dimensional vector $\mathbf{x}$, $\mathbf{x} = \mathbf{x}(x, y)$, $\mathbf{x} = (r, \psi)$;

$\rho_2(\mathbf{x}_\tau)$ projection of function ρ_3 along the unitary vector $\tau(|\tau| = 1)$ onto the plane $\mathbf{x} \perp \tau$;

$\rho_1(x)$ one-dimensional function;

$\rho_1(\mathbf{x}_\psi) = L(\mathbf{x}_\psi)$, one-dimensional projection of function $\rho_2(x)$ at an angle ψ to the x-axis;

$\mathscr{F}$ Fourier transform operator;

$\Phi_3(\mathbf{S}) = \mathscr{F}[\rho_3]$ three-dimensional transform of the object, $\mathbf{S} = \mathbf{S}(X, Y, Z) = \mathbf{S}(R, \Psi, Z)$;

$\Phi_2(\mathbf{X}) = \mathcal{F}[\rho_2]$ two-dimensional transform, $\mathbf{X} = \mathbf{X}(X, Y) = \mathbf{X}(R, \Psi)$,
$$\mathbf{X} \perp \tau, \mathbf{X}_\tau \parallel \mathbf{x}_\tau; \angle \tau, \mathbf{x} = \psi$$
$\Phi_1(X) = \mathcal{F}[\rho_1]$ one-dimensional transform; $X_\psi \parallel x_\psi$

We shall omit the lower index of dimensionality of ρ or Φ in cases where this does not give rise to misunderstanding.

In the general case, the projection of a three-dimensional object ρ_3, vector τ may be oriented arbitrarily in space [Fig. 13(a)]; it may also occupy on the unit sphere either some one or two-dimensional, continuous point sets or discrete point sets.

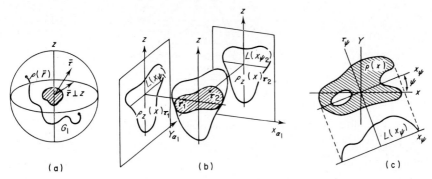

FIG. 13. The object ρ_3 and its two-dimensional projections ρ_2. (a) The image of a set of projection vectors τ on the sphere of directions; (b) coaxial projections; (c) a one-dimensional projection $L(x_\psi)$ of a two-dimensional object $\rho_2(x)$.

A. *Coaxial Projection. Discretization*

Important for practical work is the case where the projection directions τ are always perpendicular to a certain straight line: $\tau \perp z$ [Fig. 13(b)]. Here, the rotation axis of an object is perpendicular to the electron beam. Then the three-dimensional problem reduces to the two-dimensional one, since each cross-section $\rho_2, z = $ constant is represented by its one-dimensional projections [Fig. 13(c)]:

$$\rho_1(x_\psi) = \int \rho_2(\mathbf{x}) \, d\tau_\psi. \tag{30a}$$

The continuous (depending on ψ) set of projections $L(x_\psi)$ of the object $\rho_2(\mathbf{x})$ can be called its projection transform. Figure 14 shows a two-dimensional asymmetric object—a wrench—and its projection transform as represented as a set of "cross-sections" having $\Delta\psi = \pi/8$.

The following normalization condition holds for the function and any of its projections

$$\Omega = \int \rho(\mathbf{r}) \, dv_\mathbf{r} = \int \rho_2(\mathbf{x}) \, d\mathbf{x}. \tag{31}$$

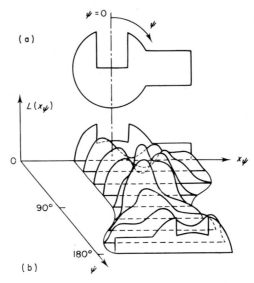

FIG. 14. A wrench (a) and its projection transform (b).

In the approximation ρ = constant = 1 within the object, Ω is simply the volume of the object (or its area in the two-dimensional case). The volume of the object, e.g. molecules, viruses, etc., is usually known from data on the density or molecular weight.

In practice, one reconstructs ρ within a certain volume (within an area in the two-dimensional case). If the cross-section of the function $|\rho| > 0$ is D, then one can perform the reconstruction in an area having side $a \geqslant D$, so that

$$\bar{\rho} = \Omega/a^2 \tag{32}$$

where $\bar{\rho}$ is the averaged value.

The experimentally obtained projections L^i are either measured directly as a set of discrete values $L^i(x_{\psi i})$ at a certain spacing in x_ψ, or they are transformed into the latter for input into a computer. On the other hand, $\rho(\mathbf{r})$ is reconstructed over a certain discrete point set. In this case, if we consider the two-dimensional case, and bear Eqn (32) in mind, we shall dissect the square region of side $a \geqslant D$ into m^2 points having weights $\rho_{jl} = \rho(ja/m_i, la/m)$ (Fig. 15). Let us choose the same spacing a/m for the projection. Then, upon oblique projection,

$$L(x_{\psi i}) \approx L^i_k(ka/m) = \Sigma\rho_{jl}. \tag{30b}$$

Here the summation Σ is taken over the points ρ_{jl} that lie in a strip of width a/m along the axis $r_{\psi i}$ passing through the point $x_{\psi i} = ka/m$.

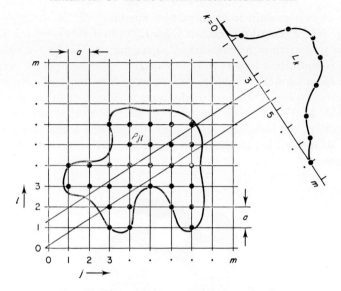

Fig. 15. Discretization and oblique projection.

B. *Symmetry Properties of Projections*

One can get information on the three-dimensional structure of asymmetric objects only when one has different projections of the object. They can be recorded if the object rests at random on a substrate in different orientations, but these orientations must be determined. One can get systematic information by photographing an asymmetric object at different inclinations to the beam.

It is always true of an asymmetric object that

$$L(\psi, x_\psi) = L(\psi + \pi, -x_\psi), \qquad (33a)$$

i.e. projections rotated by an angle π are alike, but run in opposite directions [see Fig. 14(b)]. If the object has an N-fold rotation axis, then

$$L(\psi, x_\psi) = L(\psi + i(2\pi/N), x_{\psi + i(2\pi/N)}) \quad (i = 1, 2, \ldots, N), \qquad (33b)$$

while Eqn (33a) is simultaneously obeyed. Figure 16 gives an example of an object with $N = 6$. The projections along its directions differing by $2\pi/6 = 60^0$ are identical. We must also bear in mind a property of projections of objects having a twofold axis $N = 2$ (and in general for symmetry axes of even order $N = 2k$). Since here $\rho(x, y) = \rho(-x, -y)$, then

$$L(\psi, x_\psi) = L(\psi, -x_\psi), \qquad (33c)$$

while again Eqn (33a) holds simultaneously. In other words, the projections of such objects contain independent information only in the region $0, x_\psi$ (see Fig. 16). Taking into account Eqns (33b) and (33c), we can now say that one projection of a symmetrical object may suffice for reconstruction, since it is equivalent to $\rho = N$ (for N odd) or $\rho = N/2$ (for N even) projections of an asymmetric object. In fact, in such an object the independent asymmetric region occurs in ρ orientations with respect to the direction of projection. If $N \rightarrow \infty$, then the function has spherical symmetry, and all its projections are identical. This means that in such a case one projection ρ_1 fully defines ρ_2, i.e. its exact reconstruction can be performed from one projection.

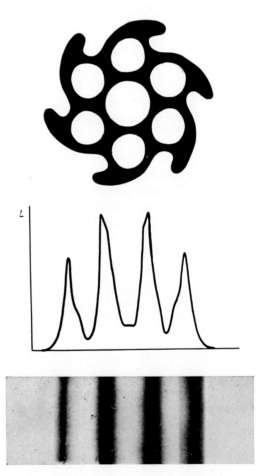

FIG. 16. A figure having the symmetry $N = 6$ and its projection.

Many biological objects possess helical symmetry (Fig. 17); in other words, they are brought into coincidence with themselves by operation $s_{p/q}$ of a screw displacement, where p is the integer number of packing units in the helical structure per q turns of the continuous helix. Operation $s_{p/q}$ consists of rotation through an angle of $\psi = 2\pi q/p$ and simultaneous displacement along the axis z by c/p. In addition, the helical structures may also have an ordinary rotation symmetry axis N, defining the "strandedness" of the helix.

$$s_{7/2}$$

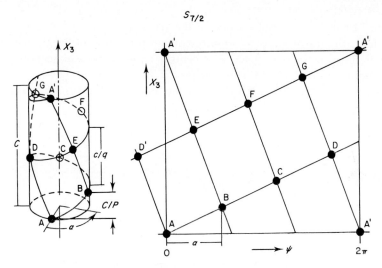

FIG. 17. (a) An object with helical symmetry and parameters of the screw translation $s_{p/q}$ $(p/q = 7/2)$; (b) the corresponding radial projection.

For helical structures (in projection perpendicular to z) conditions hold that are analogous to Eqns (33b) and (33c), but the projections are displaced to different levels z according to

$$L(\psi, x_{\psi,z}) = L(\psi + i(2\pi/p), x_{\psi + i(2\pi/p)}, z + i\,(c/p))\ \ (i = 1, 2, \ldots, p). \quad (33d)$$

If the symmetry group is $s_{p/q}N$, then the order of the group is $N = pN$, and one projection is equivalent to N or $N/2$ (for even N) projections. Thus the symmetry group is $s_{7/2}6$ for many phages (see Table III) and one micrograph [see below, Fig. 53(a), (b)] is equivalent to 21 projections.

Objects like the spherical viruses or individual molecules are described by point groups of symmetry. Spherical viruses have the icosahedral symmetry 532 (see below Fig. 63), i.e. they possess symmetry axes 5, 3 and 2. The symmetry order of this group is 60. The projection of such viruses along the symmetry axes has the corresponding symmetry. Such a projection is, consequently, equivalent to $p = 60/5 = 12$, or $p = 60/3 = 20$, or $p = 60/2 = 30$ projections. To take a projection along an asymmetric direction is to most advantage ($p = 60$), but such an orientation is difficult to be determined. In this case, the matrix for transformation of the icosahedral group 532 yields the relation between the projection vectors τ.

C. *Reconstruction with the Use of Fourier Space (FSR)*

This method, as applied to the problems of radioastronomy, was proposed by Bracewell (1956) and in electron microscopy by De Rosier and Klug (1968). It is based on one of the principal theorems of the Fourier method: the transform of a two-dimensional projection of the three-dimensional function in real space is a central two-dimensional section of the three-dimensional transform in reciprocal space. The function ρ_3 and its Fourier transform $\Phi_3 = \mathscr{F}(\rho_3)$ (the same as ρ_2 and Φ_2) are oriented, each

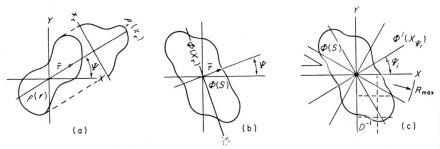

FIG. 18. The theorem about projections of ρ and cross-sections of Φ. (a) An object ρ and its projection; (b) reciprocal space Φ and cross-section $\Phi(X_i)$ in it; (c) a set of cross-sections $\Phi(X_{\tau_i})$.

in its space, strictly and definitely with respect to each other [Fig. 18(a), (b)]. The three-dimensional transform is

$$\Phi_3(\mathbf{S}) = \Phi(X, Y, Z) = \int \rho(x, y, z) \exp \{2\pi i\} (xX + yY + zZ)\, dx\, dy\, dz. \quad (34)$$

Let us consider a two-dimensional "slice" of the transform, for instance, section $Y = 0$:

$$\Phi_3(\mathbf{S})_{Y=0} = \Phi_3(X, 0, Z) = \Phi_2(X, Z) = \int \rho_3(x, y, z) \exp \{2\pi i\}(xX + y0 + zZ) \cdot$$

$$\cdot dx\, dy\, dz = \int \rho_3(x, y, z) \exp \{2\pi i\} (xX + zZ)\, dx\, dy\, dz =$$

$$= \int \rho_2(x, z) \exp 2\pi i(xX + zZ)\, dx\, dz = \mathscr{F}[\rho_2(\mathbf{x})] = \Phi_2(\mathbf{X}). \quad (35)$$

Transition from ρ_3 to ρ_2 in the integral ensues from Eqn (2) and, as a result, it turns out that the central section of a three-dimensional transform on the plane X, perpendicular to the projection vector τ, is a two-dimensional transform of Φ_2 of the corresponding projection ρ_2. To different projections $\rho_2(\mathbf{x}_{\bar{\tau}})$ of function ρ_3, obtained on changing the projection vectors τ, there correspond different (and again oriented perpendicular to τ) central sections $\Phi_2(\mathbf{X}_r)$ of the three-dimensional function $\Phi(\mathbf{S})$. It goes without saying that this also holds true for one-dimensional projections $L(x_\psi)$ of two-dimensional functions ρ_2 and corresponding sections $\Phi_1(X_\psi)$ of the two-dimensional transform Φ_2 (Fig. 18).

If we know several projections, then we can calculate the corresponding sections in reciprocal space

$$\mathcal{F}_i\left[\rho_2(\mathbf{x}_{\tau i})\right] = \Phi_i(\mathbf{X}_{\tau i}) \tag{36}$$

and, if there are many of these cross-sections, then interpolation between them gives a representation of the structure of the transform $\Phi(\mathbf{S})$, from which we can transform, by Eqn (9), to $\rho(\mathbf{r})$ [Fig. 18(c)].

Thus, the scheme of reconstruction here is

$$\text{set } L^i \to \text{set } \mathcal{F}^i(X_{\Psi_i}) \to \Phi_2(\mathbf{X}) \to \rho_2(\mathbf{x}). \tag{37a}$$

Such a calculation is carried out for all cross-sections ρ_{2j} of the three-dimensional function ρ_3, which is thus reconstructed as

$$\text{set } \rho_{2j}(\mathbf{x}_j) = \rho_3(\mathbf{r}). \tag{37b}$$

The Fourier transform can be calculated in Cartesian co-ordinates. If the object has helical symmetry (which is frequently encountered in the electron microscopy of macromolecules), then cylindrical co-ordinates appear to be most suitable. Diffraction from such structures having the period c and scattering density $\rho(r, \psi, z)$ is determined by the Fourier–Bessel transform

$$\Phi(R, \Psi, Z) = \sum_{n=-\infty}^{+\infty} \exp\left[in\left(\Psi + \frac{\pi}{2}\right)\right] \int_0^\infty \int_0^{2\pi} \int_0^c \rho(r, \psi, z) \times$$
$$g_n(2\pi rR) \exp\left[-i(n\Psi + 2\pi zZ)\right] r\,\mathrm{d}r\,\mathrm{d}\psi\,\mathrm{d}z =$$
$$= \sum_n G_n(R, Z) \exp\left[in(\Psi + \pi/2)\right] \tag{38}$$

(Cochran *et al.*, 1952; Klug *et al.*, 1958).
The inverse transformation has the form

$$\rho(r, \psi, z) = \sum_n \int g_n(r, Z) \exp(in\,\psi) \exp(2\pi izZ)\mathrm{d}Z, \tag{39a}$$

so that g_n and G_n are mutually reciprocal Bessel transforms

$$G_n(R, Z) = \int_0^\infty g_n(r, Z)J_n(2\pi rR)2\pi r\,\mathrm{d}r, \tag{39b}$$

$$g_n(r, Z) = \int_0^\infty G_n(R, Z)J_n(2\pi rR)2\pi R\,\mathrm{d}R. \tag{39c}$$

In view of the periodicity along the z-axis with period c, the transform G_n exists in reciprocal space only at $Z = lc^* = l/c$, i.e. on layer lines with index l.

Owing to helical symmetry, only those of the Bessel functions enter into Eqn (39) which can be defined by the selection rule

$$l = mp + (nq/N), \qquad (40)$$

where N, q and p are symmetry parameters of the helix, $m = 0, \pm 1, \pm 2$, etc. The selection rule [Eqn (40)] accounts for the fact that each layer line is, in practice, determined by one function J_n with the lowest n, the contribution of other functions being neglected.

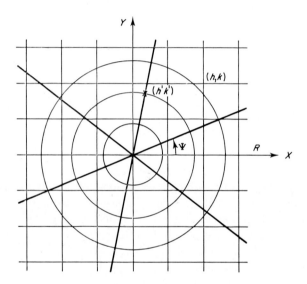

FIG. 19. Discretization of reciprocal space.

As has been noted already, the symmetry of helical structures leads to the fact that one projection is equivalent to the pN projections which practically suffice for reconstruction. It should be noted that, if a function may be represented in Fourier expansion by a finite number of harmonics, then its exact reconstruction can be performed from the finite number of projections, and, in a special case, from one projection.

After densitometering, the electron microscope image is represented as a discrete set of points, i.e. in numerical form. The Fourier transformation also reduces to the calculation, according to the discrete system, of points h, k in reciprocal space [Fig. 19] (Crowther et al., 1970a, b; De Rosier and Moore, 1970). In the general case, however, this system does not coincide with points h', k', lying on the available planes of data. Transition is carried out by the least squares solution of normal Whittaker–Shannon equations. The calculation is performed for fixed values ψ^i for which G_n are transformed into g_n [Eqn 39c], and then ρ is reconstructed from Eqn (39a). Different methods of interpolation are discussed by Merserau and Oppenheim (1974).

As an illustration, in Fig. 20 the values of the modulus and phase of one of the harmonics of an image of the tail of bacteriophage T4 are given.

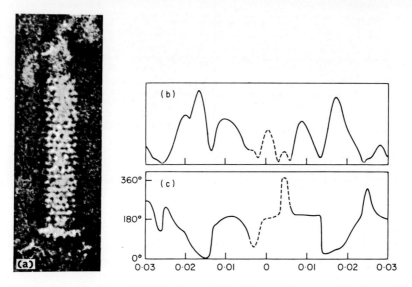

Fig. 20. The tail of phage T4 (a); the modulus (b); and the phase (c) of one of the harmonics of its cylindrical transform (De Rosier and Klug, 1968).

Figure 21 is the calculated two-dimensional distribution of $|\Phi|$ for a tobacco mosaic virus. It is a computer analogue of optical diffraction. If we take from this distribution only the values of the Bessel function maxima amplitudes and corresponding calculated phases, and perform the inverse Fourier transformation [Eqn (23)], we get the "mathematical filtering" of the helical structure.

The resolution of micrographs can be determined by calculation or from optical diffraction data. Therefore, in reconstruction, the Fourier components with $|S| > d_{\min}^{-1}$ which represent only the "noise" are ruled out.

The FSR method in cylindrical co-ordinates may be applied to spherical viruses as well, though in this case the natural symmetry of particles is not used in full.

314   B. K. VAINSHTEIN

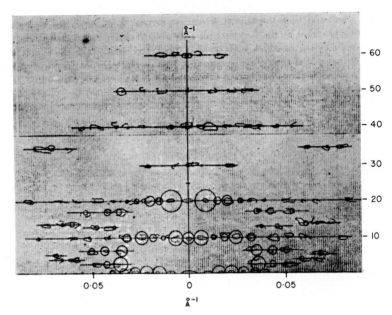

Fig. 21. The modulus of a Fourier transform of tobacco mosaic virus. The value of amplitudes is proportional to the area of the circles.

One of the variant mathematical methods for reconstructing two-dimensional functions is that due to Cormack (1963, 1964) involving expansion of $\rho_2(\mathbf{x})$ and projections $L(\psi, x_\psi)$ in sets of orthogonal functions.

D. Methods of Direct Reconstruction (DR)

These methods work directly in space $\mathbf{r}$ and require no intermediate calculations in space S. They need less computer time in comparison with FSR.

(a) Synthesis by projection functions (SPF); two-dimensional case (Vainshtein, 1970, 1971a, b, c)

If we extend each projection $L(x_{\psi_i})$ of function $\rho(\mathbf{x})$ along τ_{ψ_i} [Fig. 22(a)] by a certain length b, we shall get the projection function

$$L^i(\mathbf{x}) = \frac{1}{b} L^i(x_i)u(\tau_i), \quad u(\tau_i) = \begin{cases} 1 \text{ inside } b, \\ 0 \text{ outside } b. \end{cases} \tag{41}$$

Let us now construct the synthesis of projection functions, i.e. superpose the p functions L_i on one another [Fig. 22(b)]:

$$\sum_{i=1}^{p} L^i(\mathbf{x}) = \Sigma_p(\mathbf{x}) \tag{42}$$

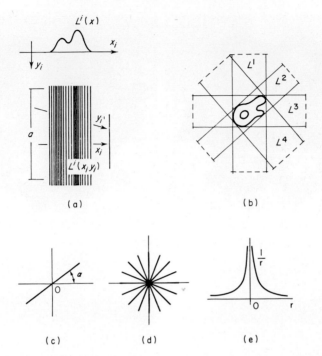

Fig. 22. (a) Formation of a projection function; (b) superposition of these functions; (c) the projection function of a point; (d) superposition of these functions; and (e) formation of the function $|r|^{-1}$.

Analogously, the continuous synthesis of a multitude of $L(\psi, x)$ gives

$$\int_0^\pi L(\psi, x) \, d\psi = \sum (\mathbf{x}) \tag{43}$$

It can readily be seen [Fig. 22(c)] that the projection function for a point will be a straight line; $\sum_p$ [Eqn (42)] for a point gives a star [Fig. 22(a)], while the image of the point, according to Eqn (43), will be a function $|\mathbf{x}|^{-1}$ [Fig. 22(e)]. Hence, an image of any two-dimensional $\rho_2(x)$ will be its convolution with $|\mathbf{x}|^{-1}$:

$$\sum_2(\mathbf{x}) = \int \rho(\mathbf{x}') \frac{1}{|\mathbf{x} - \mathbf{x}'|} \, dS_{\mathbf{x}'} = \widehat{\rho(\mathbf{x})|\mathbf{x}|^{-1}}$$

$$\approx \rho(\mathbf{x}) + B(\mathbf{x}). \tag{44}$$

Since $|\mathbf{x}|^{-1}$ becomes infinite at $x = 0$, convolution with it reproduces the original function $\rho(\mathbf{x})$ well. However, a background arises around each point of $\rho(\mathbf{x})$ that is proportional to $\rho(\mathbf{x})$ at that point, and which declines

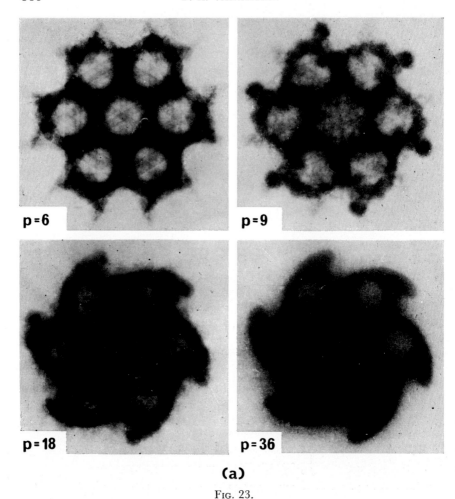

(a)

FIG. 23.

like r^{-1}. This will give a certain overall background B. Nevertheless Σ_2 gives a good reproduction of ρ_2, which is especially true of the contrast functions. This is explained by the fact that the background can easily be distinguished, if we use, for instance, the normalization condition [Eqn (31)]. Examples of restoration are given in Fig. 23. The three-dimensional function $\rho_3(\mathbf{r})$ is restored in coaxial projection as a set of cross-sections $\rho_2(\mathbf{x}, z_j)$. The restoration is performed over the discrete square grid with interpolation of discretized values of L_i projected onto the grid nodes [Fig. 15].

The method of projection functions is very simple, but it gives a back-

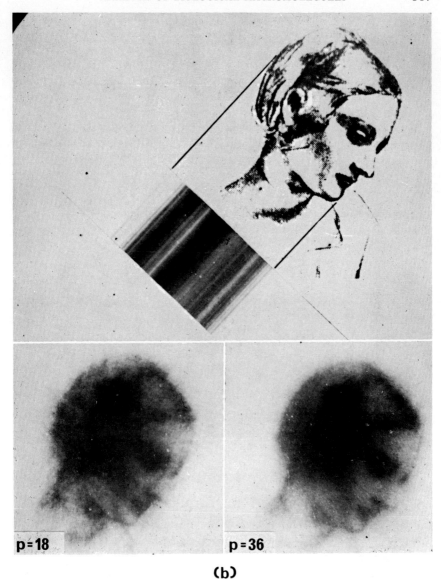

p=18   p=36

(b)

FIG. 23. Examples of reconstruction by the SPF method (the number p of projections is indicated).

ground. One can get an exact reconstruction of ρ in real space. Here two methods are possible. The first one is the reconstruction from the obtained distribution Σ [Eqn (43)], the second is the modification of projections L^i

such that their synthesis, analogous to Eqn (43), could give the accurate function ρ. Let us consider the first method.

(b) Reconstruction of ρ_2 from Σ_2

In the two-dimensional case, functions $|\mathbf{x}|^{-1}$ and $|\mathbf{X}|^{-1}$ are mutually reciprocal transforms: $|\mathbf{x}|^{-1} = \mathscr{F}|\mathbf{X}|^{-1}$. Now, by forming the self-convolution $\overbrace{|\mathbf{x}|^{-1}}^{2}$ and applying the Laplace operator Δ, we find that

$$\Delta \overbrace{|\mathbf{x}|^{-1}}^{2} = \Delta \int \frac{\mathrm{d}S\mathbf{r}'}{|\mathbf{x}'| \,|\mathbf{x} - \mathbf{x}'|} = \Delta \int |\mathbf{x}|^{-2} \exp{(2\pi i\mathbf{x}\mathbf{X})}\,\mathrm{d}S_{\mathbf{x}'} =$$
$$= -(2\pi)^2 \delta(\mathbf{x}). \qquad (45)$$

In the synthesis of $\Sigma(\mathbf{x})$ [Eqn (43)], the point δ is imaged as $|\mathbf{x}|^{-1}$, and the analytical expression of this imaging is Eqn (45). Hence, the integral equation in Eqn (44) can be solved by the expression

$$\rho(\mathbf{x}) = -\frac{1}{(2\pi)^2}\,\Delta \int \frac{\Sigma(\mathbf{x})}{|\mathbf{x} - \mathbf{x}'|}\,\mathrm{d}S_{r'} = \frac{1}{(2\pi)^2}\int \frac{\Sigma(\mathbf{x}) - \Sigma(\mathbf{x}')}{|\mathbf{x} - \mathbf{x}'|^3}\,\mathrm{d}S_{\mathbf{x}'} \quad (46)$$

(Vainshtein and Orlov, 1972a, b). Equation (46) gives the exact reconstruction, but requires the calculation of a two-dimensional integral [Eqn (46)] from $\Sigma(\mathbf{x})$. However, one can reduce this problem to calculating the one-dimensional functions $\tilde{L}$ from L and then construct the synthesis analogous to Eqns (42) and (43). This can be achieved in the following way.

(c) Synthesis of modified projection functions (SMPF)

This method produces the exact, direct two-dimensional reconstruction D_2R. Let us write the two-dimensional Fourier transform of the object $\Phi(\mathbf{X})$ in terms of its radial cross-sections $\Phi(\mathbf{X}_\Psi)$:

$$\Phi(\mathbf{X}) = \int_0^\pi \Phi(X_\Psi)2\pi R\,\mathrm{d}\Psi, \qquad (47)$$

where
$$R = |X_\Psi| = |\mathbf{X}|.$$

The transform of $\Phi(\mathbf{X})$ is $\rho_2(\mathbf{x})$. The transform of the product in the integral of Eqn (47) corresponds to the convolution of the transform of $\Phi(X_\Psi)$ and R:

$$\mathscr{F}[\Phi(X_\Psi)]\,\mathscr{F}\,[R] = \overbrace{L(x_\psi)K(x)} = \tilde{L}(x_\psi). \qquad (48)$$

Here the first function being convoluted is the original projection $L(x_\psi)$, which we know, and

$$K(x) = \mathscr{F}\,[R] = \int_{-\infty}^{\infty} R\exp{(-2\pi iRx)}\,\mathrm{d}R. \qquad (49a)$$

This function (which is the same for all angles) diverges. However, using different mathematical methods, one may find the exact expression for $\tilde{L}$ [Eqn (48)] (Radon, 1917; Gel'fand and Shilov, 1964; Berry and Gibbs, 1970; Vainshtein and Orlov, 1972; Gilbert, 1972a; Smith *et al.*, 1973). Thus, bearing in mind that $\mathscr{F}[\partial f(x)/\partial x] = 2\pi i x \mathscr{F}[f(x)]$ and that $\mathscr{F}[x^{-1}] = i\pi \, \mathrm{sgn} X$, where $\mathrm{sgn}\, X = +1$ for $X > 0, = 0$ and $= -1$ for $X < 0$, we obtain the "modified projection"

$$\tilde{L}(x) = \frac{1}{2\pi^2} \int \frac{\partial L(x)}{\partial x} \frac{1}{x} \, \mathrm{d}x \tag{50}$$

instead of Eqn (48), or, in a form convenient for calculation,

$$\tilde{L}(x) = \frac{1}{2\pi^2} \int_0^\infty \frac{L(x'_\psi + x_\psi) + L(x'_\psi - x_\psi) - 2L(x'_\psi)}{(x'_\psi - x_\psi)^2} \, \mathrm{d}x'_\psi. \tag{51}$$

This expression may be called the Radon operator. We can now calculate

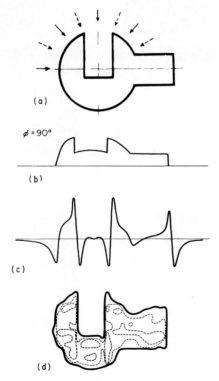

(a)

$\phi = 90°$

(b)

(c)

(d)

FIG. 24. (a) The wrench; (b) one of its projections L; (c) modified projection $\tilde{L}$; (d) reconstruction by the SMPF method from eight projections.

320   B. K. VAINSHTEIN

Fɪɢ. 25. Reconstruction by SMPF. (a), (b) The original patterns; (c), (d) reconstruction at $p = 64$; (e), (f), (g), (h) reconstruction of (a) from 16, 32, 64 and 128 projections (Merserau and Oppenheim, 1974).

$\rho_2(\mathbf{x})$ by analogy with Eqns (42) and (43), not from the observed L, but from modified projections $\tilde{L}$:

$$\rho_2(\mathbf{x}) = \int_0^\pi L(\psi, \mathbf{x}) \, d\psi \approx \sum_i \tilde{L}(\psi_i, \mathbf{x}). \qquad (52)$$

This is precisely the synthesis of modified projection functions (SMPF). Figure 24 shows an example of reconstruction from Eqns (51) and (52). We see that $\tilde{L}(x_\psi)$ acquires minima that will cut off the positive background that arises upon integration of the other $\tilde{L}(x_\psi)$ over the angles ψ. In practice, the modified projection functions $\tilde{L}(\psi_i, x)$ (Eqn 51) are calculated as discrete sums. Further, the function $\rho(x)$ is also reconstructed as the finite sum on the discrete grid of the type shown in Fig. 15. The dependence on the number of projections is exemplified in Figs 23 and 25.

On the other hand, we can calculate $\tilde{L}(x)$ in a rough way using integral [Eqn 49a] in the finite (wide) range and forming convolution [Eqn 48] (Bracewell and Riddle, 1967):

$$K(x, R_{max}) = R_{max} \frac{\sin 2\pi x R_{max}}{\pi x} - \frac{\sin^2 \pi x \, R_{max}}{(\pi x)^2}. \qquad (49b)$$

If we replace the integration by discrete summation in Eqn (49b) by $x = na$ [also in the finite (wide) range] (Ramachandran and Lakshminarayanan, 1971), we find

$$K(na) = \frac{1}{4a^2} \ (n = 0); \ K(na) = \begin{cases} \dfrac{-1}{\pi^2 n^2 a^2} \ (n_{\text{even}}), \\[2ex] 0 (n_{\text{odd}}). \end{cases} \qquad (49c)$$

Then convolution (48) is expressed as

$$\tilde{L}_\psi(na) = \frac{L(na)}{4a} - \frac{1}{\pi^2} \sum \frac{L[(n+m)a]}{m^2}. \qquad (53)$$

This expression is nothing other than the discrete approximation of Eqn (51).

(d) Three-dimensional reconstruction in the general case (D_3R)

Let us consider the general (non-coaxial) case where the projection vector may occupy any position on the projection sphere [Fig. 13(a)]. Then, in analogy with Eqn (43), we can construct a spatial synthesis. To do this, let us transform the two-dimensional projections $\rho_2(\mathbf{x}, \tau)$ [by extending them along τ, analogously to Eqn (41)], into three-dimensional functions $\rho_3(\mathbf{r}_\tau)$ and, integrating over the angle ω, we get

$$\Sigma_3(\mathbf{r}) = \int \rho_3(\mathbf{r}_\tau) \, d\omega_r. \qquad (54a)$$

Thereafter, following the D_2R method, we can obtain exact expressions for the reconstruction of the three-dimensional function $\rho_3(\mathbf{r})$ (Vainshtein and Orlov, 1974; Orlov, 1975; see also Gel'fand *et al.*, 1967).

The function $|\mathbf{r}|^{-2}$ will be an image of the three-dimensional point $\delta(\mathbf{r})$ in the synthesis of $\Sigma_3(\mathbf{r})$ [Eqn (54a)]. This can readily be seen from the analogy with the two-dimensional case [Fig. 22(e)]. Consequently, in analogy with Eqn (44)

$$\Sigma_3(\mathbf{r}) = \int \rho_3(\mathbf{r}')|\mathbf{r} - \mathbf{r}'|^{-2}\, dv_{\mathbf{r}'} = \widehat{\rho(\mathbf{r})|\mathbf{r}|^{-2}} \qquad (54b)$$

is the convolution of the sought function with $|\mathbf{r}|^{-2}$.

Hence, the expression $\rho_3(\mathbf{r})$ may be found from $\Sigma_3(\mathbf{r})$. Let us take the Fourier integral of convolution [Eqn (54b)]: it will be the product of Fourier integrals of co-factors:

$$\mathscr{F}[\Sigma_3] = (2\pi^3)\,\frac{1}{4\pi|\mathbf{S}|}\,\Phi(\mathbf{S}). \qquad (55)$$

Let us transfer the factors of $\Phi(\mathbf{S})$ to the left; then, taking the inverse transform and using again the convolution theorem, we find

$$\rho_3(\mathbf{r}) = -\frac{1}{4\pi^4}\,\varDelta\int |\mathbf{r} - \mathbf{r}'|^{-2}\,\Sigma_3(\mathbf{r}')\, dv_{\mathbf{r}'}, \qquad (56)$$

where $\varDelta$ is the Laplace operator. This is the three-dimensional analog of Eqn (46).

It is more convenient, however, not to calculate Σ_3 [Eqn (54a)] and find ρ_3 from Eqn (56), but to express ρ_3 via the projection functions. We can obtain the appropriate expression by substituting Eqn (54a) in Eqn (56) and integrating it along τ. Then we get the modified projection $\tilde{\rho}_2$ from each $\rho_2(\mathbf{x}_\tau)$, i.e.,

$$\tilde{\rho}_2(\mathbf{x}_\tau) = \int \frac{\rho_2(\mathbf{x}_\tau) - \rho_2(\mathbf{x}_\tau)}{|\mathbf{x} - \mathbf{x}'|^3}\, d\mathbf{S}_{\mathbf{x}'}. \qquad (57)$$

This is the two-dimensional analog of Eqn (50).

By extending $\tilde{\rho}_2(\mathbf{x}_i)$ along τ, we transform them into $\tilde{\rho}_3(\mathbf{r}_\tau)$. Now the synthesis over the solid angles ω within the boundary of a hemisphere will give

$$\rho_3(\mathbf{r}) = \frac{1}{4\pi^3}\int \tilde{\rho}_3(\mathbf{r}_\tau)\, d\omega_\tau \approx \sum_i \tilde{\rho}_{3i}(\mathbf{r}_{\tau_i}). \qquad (58a, b)$$

On the right is written the approximation of a discrete set of angles.

It should be noted that Eqn (58a) contains a wealth of information. To reconstruct any three-dimensional function it is not necessary to know its projections for all solid angles ω. For example, in the case of coaxial projection a trace of τ on the surface represents a semi-circumference [Fig.

13(b)]. In the general case it is sufficient that the trace τ should form on the sphere a one-dimensional curve or two-dimensional, range G [Fig. 13(a)], which connects diametrically opposite points. This can be understood, if one bears in mind that to any one projection $\rho_2(\mathbf{x})$ there corresponds a transform $\Phi_2(\mathbf{X})$, and that to a set of projections satisfying the indicated condition there corresponds a set $\Phi_2(\mathbf{X})$ which will fill the entire volume in reciprocal space, $\Phi_3(\mathbf{S})$.

For the general case of projection into any such range the reconstruction equations will have the form

$$\rho_3(\mathbf{r}) = -\frac{1}{(2\pi)^2}\, \varDelta \int_{\mathbf{S}\mathbf{x}\tau} \mathrm{d}G \int_S \frac{\rho_3(\mathbf{r}_\tau - \mathbf{r}'_\tau)}{|\mathbf{r}'|L([\tau\mathbf{r}'])}\, \mathrm{d}\mathbf{S}_{\mathbf{x}'}, \qquad (59a)$$

$$L(\mathbf{r}) = |\mathbf{r}| \int_G \delta(\tau\mathbf{r})\, \mathrm{d}G_\tau. \qquad (59b)$$

FIG. 26. Three-dimensional reconstruction of human wart virus using Eqn (60).

Here Δ is the Laplace operator, dG_τ is an element of the length (area) of the one-dimensional (two-dimensional) range G, $\mathbf{S_{x\tau}}$ is the plane $\mathbf{X} \perp \boldsymbol{\tau}$, $\delta(\mathbf{r}\boldsymbol{\tau})$ is the one-dimensional δ-function along $\boldsymbol{\tau}$. If G is a hemisphere, then $L = \pi$, and we return to Eqns (57) and (58). If G is a semi-circumference of the large circle, then $L = |\mathbf{r}|/|\mathbf{rZ}|$, and the Radon formula ensues from Eqn (59a, b).

In the general case [Eqn 59a, b)], we do not limit ourselves to the condition of coaxial projection, thereby broadening the possibilities of experiment. In particular, the symmetry of objects can fully be used, e.g. the symmetry of icosahedral viruses with the point symmetry 532. In this case, the symmetrically independent range is a spherical triangle the vertices of which are defined by the points of exit on the sphere of axes 5, 3 and 2 [see Fig. 62], and it is sufficient to know $\rho_2(\mathbf{x}_\tau)$ for any line connecting a vertex of the triangle with an opposite side or neighbouring vertex. Expression (58b), i.e. the discrete approximation for spherical viruses, takes on the form

$$\rho_3(\mathbf{r}) \approx \sum_{k=1}^{N} \widetilde{\rho_3}[\widehat{\mathscr{F}}_k, \mathbf{r}_{\tau_i}], \tag{60}$$

where one projection (or several projections) within the boundary of the symmetrically independent range is multiplied by operators $\widehat{\mathscr{F}}_k$ of transformation of group 532. Figure 26 shows the image thus obtained of regions of maximal density in the protein coat of a human wart virus.

E. *Algebraic Reconstruction (AR)*

These methods have been developed for the two-dimensional case and, consequently, are applicable to three-dimensional reconstruction in the case of coaxial projection.

Let us reconstruct $\rho_2(\mathbf{x})$ over a discrete point set ρ_{ij} with the grid m^2 drawn on it (Fig. 15). Then Eqn (31) will involve discrete sums. Along the rational directions

$$L_k^i = \sum \rho_{ij}. \tag{61}$$

For oblique directions, Eqn (61) is replaced by Eqn (30b) at the points that fall on the strips having width a/m. The number of known ρ_{jl} in each Eqn (61) is approximately equal to m.

If there are p projections $L^i(i = 1, 2, \ldots, p)$, then there are pm known L_k^i and m^2 unknown ρ_{jl}. The condition for unique solvability of Eqn (61) is

$$pm \geqslant m^2, \text{ i.e. } p \geqslant m. \tag{62a}$$

The method of linear equations [Eqn (61)] was first used in the investigation of catalase (Vainshtein *et al.*, 1968, 1969; Barynin and Vainshtein, 1971, 1972), and was also considered by Crowther *et al.*, 1970a, b).

The condition (62) may prove to be excessively rigid. Thus, evidently, when $L_3^i = 0$, all of the $\rho_{jl} = 0$. This gives directly a convex enveloping contour about the outer contour S. The solution is found by inverting the matrix of the linear Eqns (61). An example of solution is given below (Fig. 27).

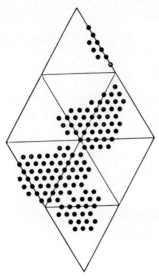

FIG. 27. One of the plane-sections of the structure of hexagonal catalase, reconstructed algebraically. The points correspond to the area where protein is present.

For binary functions, when the possible values of ρ_{ij} are 0 or 1, reconstruction algorithms have been developed that work on the principle of sorting (Chang, 1971; Chang and Shelton, 1971). Here, as estimates have shown, one can get a satisfactory reconstruction at

$$ m = (3 \div 5)p. \tag{62b} $$

The conditions (62a) and (62b) define the optimum choice of m, i.e. the cells of the partition grid a/m that give a unique solution. In a certain sense (see p. 00 below), the quantity a/m corresponds to the "resolution" of the reconstructed structure.

Gordon, Bender and Herman (1970) (see also Frieder and Herman, 1971; Gordon and Herman, 1971) have suggested the reconstruction by iterations that cause a given $\rho(x)$ initial distribution to approach one satisfying the condition that its projections will resemble the set L^i ("the algebraic reconstruction technique", ART). On a discrete grid, let us assign ρ_{jl} in a zero-order approximation to be a uniform distribution of mean values

$$\rho_{jl}^0 = \bar{\rho} = \Omega/m^2. \qquad (63)$$

The projection of the q-th approximation ρ_{jl}^q at the angle ψ_i [used to account for discreteness (Fig. 15)] is $L_k^{i,q}$.

The next approximation ρ^{q+1} for each point jl can be obtained by the "multiplication" procedure:

$$\rho_{jl}^{q+1} = (L_k^i/L_k^{i,q})\rho_{jl}^q \qquad (64a)$$

or by "addition":

$$\rho_{jl}^{q+1} = \max [\rho_{jl}^q + (L_k^i - L_k^{i,q})/N_{Lk}^i; \ 0]. \qquad (64b)$$

Here N_{Lk}^i is the number of points in the projection L_k^i. The latter procedure is less sensitive to errors in measuring the projections. We see that one iteration "adjusts" the projection L_k^q of the previous distribution ρ^q to L_k^i.

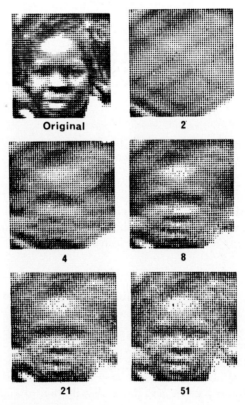

FIG. 28. Reconstruction by the ART method (the number of projections p is indicated) (Gordon *et al.*, 1970).

One cycle of iterations consists in "running" of ρ_{ij}^q around all the angles ψ_i. However, proceeding to another angle can impair the results obtained by the iterations at the previous angles. The iteration process leads at some $q = Q(Q \approx 10$–$20)$ to getting a certain distribution

$$\rho_{jl}^{Q} \approx \rho_{jl}. \tag{65}$$

Figure 28 gives an example of such a reconstruction.

The ART-method was improved and its possibilities were considered by Herman *et al.* (1973) and Herman and Rowland (1973). Gilbert (1972a, b) suggested that in the iteration one should take account of the contribution not only of the given projection, but of all other ones (simultaneous iterative reconstruction technique, SIRT) by the relation

$$\rho_{jl}^{q+1} = \max \left[\rho_{jl}^q + \left(\sum L^i / \sum l_i \right) - \left(\sum_k L_k^{iq} / \sum N_{Lk}^i \right), 0 \right] \tag{66}$$

(l_i is the length along y_{ψ_i}). By this method the convergence of the process is improved. Figure 29 is an example of reconstruction by SIRT.

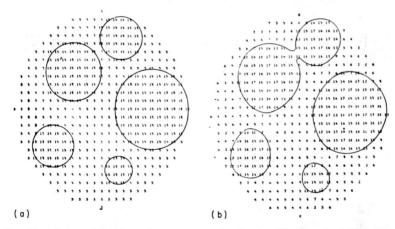

(a)   (b)

FIG. 29. (a) A model object; (b) reconstruction by the SIRT method from 25 projections (Gilbert, 1972a, b).

F. *Accuracy of Reconstruction from a Finite Number of Projections, and Resolution*

Evidently these characteristics of ρ depend on the number p of existing projections and the experimental errors. The reconstruction is performed on a discrete grid of $m \times m$ nodes with a spacing $a \geqslant D/m$, where D is the diameter of the function ρ (Figs 15 and 18). The condition of algebraic solvability has in general the form $p = m$ [Eqn (62a)]. This means that differing values of ρ_{jk} can be determined with the spacing D/p. These conditions determine the best choice of spacing of the subdivision grid. The function ρ can be characterized by the dimensions δ of its inhomogeneities, or the "half-width" of its narrowest peaks. The latter are resolved (a minimum appears between them) if the distance between them amounts to δ (see p. 287). On a discrete grid, various values of ρ_{ij} can be distinguished, if there is a minimum between them, let us say in binary representation ... 11011. ... This means that only those of the peaks are resolved which are at a distance of

$$\delta \gtrsim 2D/p \qquad (67a)$$

(Vainshtein, 1973a, b). On the other hand, it is possible to estimate the resolution in the language of reciprocal space (Crowther *et al.*, 1970a, b; Klug and Crowther, 1972). The transform $\Phi = \mathscr{F}[\rho]$ declines to $|\Phi(\mathbf{S})| \approx 0$ when $|S_{\max}^{-1}| \approx d_{\min}$ [Eqn (10)]. In order to reconstruct a ρ with a diameter of D, we must have a grid in reciprocal space with a spacing of D^{-1} [see Fig. 18(c)]. The cross-sections Φ diverge at distances greater than D^{-1} (i.e. they cease to cover the grid) when $\pi d^{-1}/p \approx D^{-1}$. Taking the value $d_{\min}$ as a measure of resolution, we get the estimate

$$\pi D/p. \qquad (67b)$$

Taking into account that in the two-dimensional case the resolution $\delta = 0\cdot61\, d_{\min}$, we get

$$\delta = 0\cdot61\, \pi D/p \approx 2D/p \qquad (67c)$$

which matches [Eqn (67a)]. The resolution in the ART method was considered by Herman and Rowland (1971).

The objects studied in the electron microscopy of biomolecules usually have dimensions $D \approx 200\text{--}400$ Å. Given the experimental $d_{\min}$ of stained specimens $\approx 20\text{--}30$ Å, the number of projections needed for reconstruction therefore amounts to $p \approx 10\text{--}20$.

If the projections L^i have a sharply inhomogeneous angular distribution, e.g. being concentrated in a certain angular range, then the resolution will be anisotropic: greater in the direction perpendicular to the "concentration" direction, and less along that direction.

We can take the correlation function of the deviation of the reconstructed ρ' from the true ρ as a measure of the accuracy of reconstruction:

$$R_1 = \Omega^{-1} \int |\rho' - \rho|\, d\mathbf{S_r}, \quad R_2 = \int |\rho' - \rho|^2\, d\mathbf{S_r}\Big/ \int \rho^2\, d\mathbf{S_r}.$$

If the mean relative error in the determination of the projection ρ is b, then

$$R_1 \approx b + (1/2p). \qquad (68)$$

G. *Overall Scheme of Three-dimensional Reconstruction*

Study of a given object encompasses a series of stages. The first is biochemical: to isolate and purify the specimen. In preparation for electron microscopy, special procedures are performed of depositing on a substrate,

staining, and sometimes crystallization. Then one obtains electron micrographs, taking them at different inclination angles if the object is asymmetric. The usual electron microscopical magnification is of the order of
50 000–100 000. It is very important to select good micrographs. The
image is corrected by the detector function and, if necessary, by the transfer
function of the instrument. Figure 30 shows an overall diagram of how a
study is conducted.

After we get the projections, we can use one of the algorithms of reconstruction—DR, FSR, etc. The possibilities of using diffraction data in
combination with electron or X-ray diffraction are indicated in the
diagram.

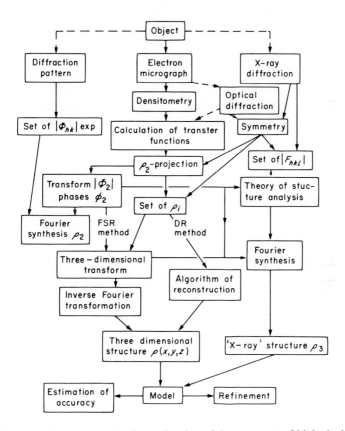

FIG. 30. Block diagram for the determination of the structure of biological objects
from electron micrographs. Centre, basic operations of three-dimensional reconstruction; left, use of electron diffraction; right, combination with X-ray diffraction.

V. Experimental Studies of Three-dimensional Structure

Biological macromolecules and their associations show different kinds of symmetry. In three-dimensional space the possible symmetry groups are G_m^3, $m = 0, 1, 2, 3$. Here the upper index indicates the number of space dimensions and the lower one gives the number of dimensions along which the periodicity occurs. The packing of subunits in individual molecules and any other spatial arrangement of molecules containing a finite number of particles, e.g. spherical viruses, is described by the point groups of symmetry G_0^3. The G_1^3 groups describe ribbon or helical structures and the G_2^3 (layer) groups are used in the description of two-dimensional "crystals". Space groups of symmetry G_3^3 are applied to ordinary three-dimensional crystals. While in the non-living world the packing of systems composed of a large number of particles is always of a kind of three-dimensional regular crystal lattice, biological systems quite often form structures with one- and two-dimensional periodicity (G_1^3 and G_2^3). The reason can be found in the directional character of the interaction between the biological macromolecules in the mother medium, which favours their crystallization in the form of structures with two- or one-dimensional periodicity. Often structures of such a kind have a close connection with biological functions and should be considered as a result of evolution (phage tails, membranes, etc.). On the other hand, some biological macromolecules can be crystallized to give a pattern of symmetry and structure that is never formed by these molecules *in vivo*. A striking example can be seen in the tubular crystals formed by the molecules of enzymes. The creation of ordered molecular associations *in vitro* broadens the possibilities for structural analysis of the molecules involved, in particular by three-dimensional electron microscopy.

A. *Studies of the Structure of Individual Protein Molecules in Crystals and Layers*

An example of a model built up in a semiquantitative manner on the basis of electron microscope data comes from the study of the enzyme leucine aminopeptidase (Kiselev *et al.*, 1977). It is a protein of molecular weight 328 000, composed of six subunits. Images of the molecule [Fig. 31(a)] in one projection are hexagons of symmetry $3m$ with sides of 90Å and 30–40 Å. Within the hexagon near the middle of its long sides there are "structural units" forming an internal triangle. The side projection is a rectangle with dimensions of 65 Å × 90 Å. Images were obtained also from crystals of leucine aminopeptidase [Fig. 31(c), (d)]. One projection has symmetry $p6m$. The picture is formed by triads corresponding in size and details to internal triangles of three structural subunits as seen in the individual particles. From the analysis of these and some other types of image, a model of the quaternary structure of leucine aminopeptidase has been proposed [Fig. 31(e)]. In this model six subunits are arranged with symmetry 32 at the vertices of a distorted three-faced prism. The triangles with subunits situated at the vertices and along the sides are rotated with respect to each other through 30°, the subunits being elongated along the sides. Each of the six subunits has a long "outgrowth", the ends

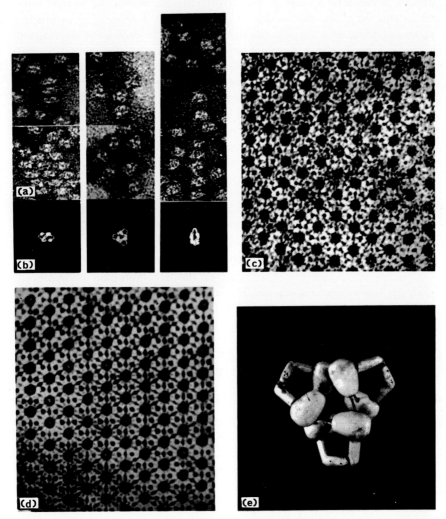

Fig. 31. Leucine aminopeptidase. (a) Individual molecules and (b) the model in different orientations; (c), (d) a crystal in projection along the major axis and its filtered image; (e) a model of the molecule.

of the subunits being joined in pairs. Actually, these projecting parts form outlines of the external hexagon in one projection of the particles and sharp prominences in their side images.

It should be noted that as a result of the numerous photographic operations, the appearance of the protein molecules in their filtered images carries excess contrast. The human eye also adds "contrast" to individual images of the kind shown in Fig. 31(a), (b). Therefore, the models built up in this way, e.g. the models of phosphorylase b [Fig. 7(f)] or leucine aminopeptidase show mainly the distribution of the protein in the internal zones of subunits. Such a model reflects, in the main, the general scheme of the subunits and their packing, but it appears to be more skeletal than it should be on account of the real distribution of the protein.

By the method of semiquantitative molecular model building just described, a large number of proteins has been studied.* Hoppe *et al.* (1975) applied the method of three-dimensional reconstruction to the structual study of negatively stained molecules of fatty acid synthetase. As the shape of this molecule is asymmetric, the set of its projections was collected with different inclinations of the specimen to the beam. In this case there arises the problem of a common origin for different projections. It has been solved using cross-convolution functions (Hoppe, 1974). As a result, the shape of the molecule for the protein mentioned has been found at 20 Å resolution.

B. *Study of Catalase*

Catalase is an enzyme that catalyzes the decomposition of hydrogen peroxide into water and oxygen. The molecular weight of catalase is about 250 000. From biochemical studies it is known that it can be dissociated into two and then four subunits. This protein is easily crystallized to form three- or two-dimensional crystals and tubes. The hexagonal modification of catalase from ox liver has been studied. Electron-microscopic and X-ray studies (Vainshtein *et al.*, 1968, 1969; Barynin and Vainshtein, 1971, 1972) made it possible to determine the unit cell dimensions of wet and electron-microscopically studied crystals. In the first case, these dimensions are $a = 173$ Å, $c = 237$ Å, in the second, $a = 160$ Å, $c = 235$ Å, with 6 molecules per cell in both cases. The space group is P3$_1$21. The volume Ω_m of the catalase molecule found from density measurements is 300 000 Å^3. Figure 32(a), (b) represents electron micrographs of the structure in orientations along [10$\bar{1}$0] and [0001]. Figure 32(c) is a contour plot of the values of $L(x, z)$ found from Fig. 32(a). Owing to the presence of the screw axis 3$_1$, this projection is equivalent to three projections. The algebraic methods of reconstruction [Eqn (61)] have been applied. Since the number of pro-

* See, for example, the reviews Finch (1975) and Vainshtein (1973a, b).

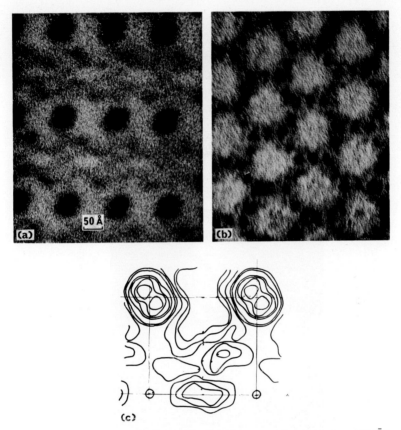

50 Å

(a)   (b)

(c)

FIG. 32. (a), (b) Electron micrographs of catalase crystals taken along [10$\bar{1}$0] and [0001]; (c) contour plot of asymmetrical unit of [10$\bar{1}$0] projection.

jections was insufficient, an additional sorting procedure for a set of solutisuo has been used which made it possible, on the ground of several criteria, to find the most probable solution. Figure 27 shows one of the cross-sections of the hexagonal unit cell. The three-dimensional model of catalase is shown in Fig. 33(a).

The molecules form an open packing; they seem to be threaded on the 2_1 axis. Their shape displays clearly two subunits of molecular weight 120 000. Examination of the arrangement of subunits and the shape of the molecule as a whole shows that it has the tetrahedral symmetry 222, which agrees with the existence of four subunits. The boundary between the smallest subunits of molecular weight 60 000 is marked as well. Figure 33(b) shows a model of the molecule as averaged over its intrinsic symmetry axes.

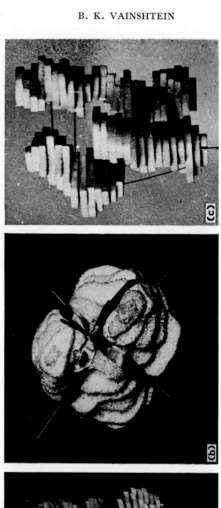

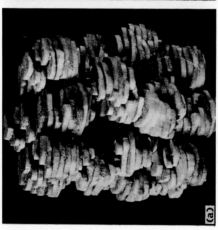

Fig. 33. (a) Three-dimensional reconstruction of the structure of catalase; (b) a catalase molecule; (c) the catalase molecule as obtained from the data of combined synthesis from $|\Phi_{exp,\,x}|$. For the sake of clarity, the subunits are drawn individually.

The dimensions of the molecule along its three axes are about 70, 80 and 95 Å. The coordinates of the centre of gravity of the molecule are $x = 0.64 \pm 0.06$, $y = 0.14 \pm 0.06$, $z = 0.05 \pm 0.03$. The subunits of molecular weight 60 000 have dimensions of about 55 Å $\times$ 47 Å $\times$ 40 Å, their centres of gravity forming a flattened tetrahedron of sides 55, 47 and 35 Å. The results obtained have been confirmed by a study of the tubular crystals of catalase (see below, p. 340). Electron microscope data for the crystalline hexagonal catalase were used further to combine them with the X-ray data (Gurskaya et al., 1971, 1972; Gurskaya, 1975) according to the scheme shown in Fig. 30, right. From the electron microscopical projection $\rho_{2,e}$ and from the three-dimensional reconstructed structure $\rho_{3,e}$ the phases ϕ_{h0e} and ϕ_{hkl} have been calculated; they have been assigned to $|\Phi_{exp., \, X\text{-ray}}|$ to calculate the combined Fourier synthesis [Eqn (26)].

To do this, one must be sure that ρ_e in the stained crystals studied in the electron microscope and ρ_x in the wet protein crystals studied by X-rays resemble one another. This resemblance has been established by comparison of the amplitudes $|\Phi_{hkl}|$ for the two distributions, using the optical diffraction pattern of the electron micrographs and the corresponding X-ray diffraction patterns. Figure 33(c) shows the catalase molecule as determined from the combined Fourier synthesis. It represents a refined version of the model shown in Fig. 33(b), both models being similar enough in their basic parameters.

C. Study of Purple Membranes

These membranes (Henderson and Unwin, 1975) are a specialized part of the cell membrane of *Halobacterium halobium* and serve as a "proton pump" in the processes of photosynthesis. They consist of protein molecules of molecular weight 26 000 (75% of the total mass) and of lipid (25%). To each protein molecule is linked a molecule of the visual pigment, retinal. The membranes appear as oval plates up to 10 000 Å in diameter; the thickness of one unit cell in the direction of the c axis is 45 Å. Such a two-dimensional unit cell is hexagonal, $a = 62$ Å, and the space group is P3 with three molecules of the protein. A single membrane contains up to 4×10^4 unit cells, i.e. 12×10^4 protein molecules. The preparations have been stabilized by 0.5% glucose. Electron diffraction patterns have been obtained with $d_{min} \simeq 7$ Å. Radiation damage has been minimized by short exposures. After insertion of PCF corrections [Eqns (24a, b)] to the images obtained, the phases have been calculated from these images, which along with $|\Phi_{exp}|$ have been used as Fourier terms for calculation of the three-dimensional map [Eqn (26)]. The procedure for obtaining the reconstructed two-dimensional image has been described above (p. 302) and is illustrated by Fig. 11.

In reciprocal space the Fourier transform of thin objects with two-dimensional periodicity can be represented as $\Phi(hkz)$, that is each lattice point hk is a thin rod extended along the z axis. The section through these rods at $z = 0$ gives the value $\Phi(hk0)$ of the transform for the projection $\rho_2(x, y)$ [Fig. 11(b)]. The values of $\Phi(hkz)$ have been obtained [Fig. 34(a)]

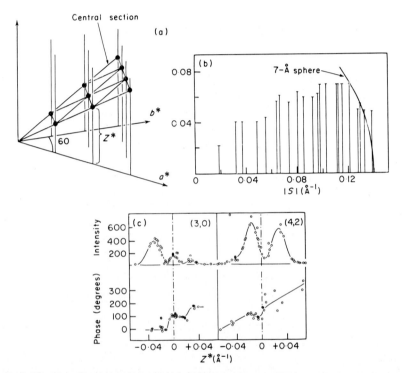

Fig. 34. Investigation of the three-dimensional structure of purple membranes. (a) Diagram of the section of reciprocal space at the inclination of the specimen; (b) diagram showing the region of reciprocal space contributing to Fourier synthesis; (c) examples of the determination of $|\Phi|$ and phases for reflections (3,0) and (4,2).

by tilting the specimens at angles up to 57°. These values correspond to the region shown in Fig. 34(b) confined along the z-axis up to the value of $d_{min} = 14$ Å. Then the phases have been calculated from the corresponding images. The plots $|\Phi|^2$ and the phases of reflections (3,0) and (4,2) are shown in Fig. 34(c). Although these Φ have not covered the whole reciprocal space, they made it possible to calculate the potential map, which gives a rough picture of the three-dimensional structure of the membrane. The structure of protein molecules inside the membrane so obtained is shown in Fig. 35. X-ray data for this protein strongly support the predominance of the α-helical secondary structure. Therefore, the rods in the model shown in Fig. 35, which are perpendicular to the plane of the membrane and packed about 12 Å apart, have been assumed to be the α-helices—their projections on the basic plane give peaks which can be seen in Fig. 11(d). There are

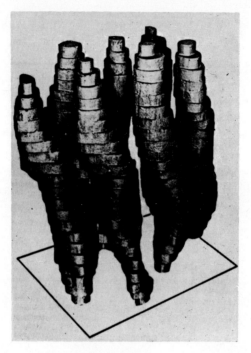

Fig. 35. Three-dimensional reconstruction of the protein molecules of the purple membrane.

$3 + 4 = 7$ such rods per molecule, the overall dimensions of the molecule being 25 Å × 35 Å × 45 Å. The molecules are grouped in threes around the threefold axis. The helices outermost with respect to this axis are interlocked, forming a left-handed screw. The assumption is that lipid forms a double layer inside the ring of the nine α-helices.

D. *Structures with Helical Symmetry*

Many different structures of biological origin exist which are built up in a helical manner; their symmetry G_1^3 is illustrated by Fig. 17. The particular packing of the molecules in such structures may be of differing character.

If the molecules are located approximately one above the other they form a "chain"-type structure [Fig. 36(a)]. If the slope of the helix formed by molecules is small, it leads to "rod-like" or "tubular" structures [Fig. 36(b), (c)]. In the first case, the elongated molecules fill up almost the whole space inside the rod, with a narrow channel near the axis. The tubular structures [Fig. 36(c)] may also be described as cylindrically rolled mono-

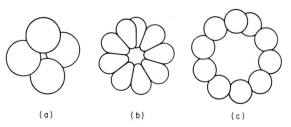

(a)   (b)   (c)

FIG. 36. Packing of the molecules into structures with helical symmetry. (a) Chain, (b) rod-like and (c) tubular structure.

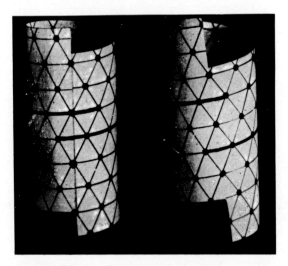

FIG. 37. Scheme of the structure of tubular crystals.

molecular layers with a large empty space inside (Fig. 37). All these structures can be characterized by the ratio of the diameter of the structure D to the radial dimensions d of the molecule; $g = D/d$. For chain structures, $g = 1$–2; actin filaments belong to this kind of structure. For rods, $g = 2$–3, as is observed in the case of the rod-like viruses. The tubular structures are examplified by the tubular crystals of globular proteins with $g = 5$–6. For the sheaths of bacteriophages, $g = 3$–4 (Vainshtein, 1972).

The structures with cylindrical (helical) symmetry are known to be conveniently described by their radial projection along the radii $r \perp Z$ onto the surface that "envelopes" the structure, with subsequent unwrapping of it onto the plane. The position of each molecule (or its centre) on the radial projection is denoted by a point, the packing of the molecules by a net [Fig. 17(b)]. The structure is described by its own symmetry $s_{p/q}N$ and its metrical parameters.

When considering the tubular structures, Erickson (1973) showed that geometrically they may be represented as the close packing of spherical bodies on the cylindrical surface. Giving successive numbers to the centres of spheres in the order of increase of their z-coordinates, one can describe any type of packing by the numbers of nearest molecules being in close

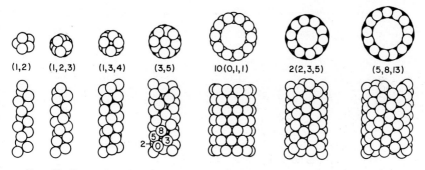

FIG. 38. Examples of the close-packing of spheres on a cylindrical surface.

contact. Some examples are given in Fig. 38. The digits before the brackets correspond to the rotational symmetry N, if such a symmetry does exist.

E. Tubular Crystals of Globular Proteins

Such crystals were first discovered in electron microscopic studies of catalase (many forms of ordinary three-dimensional crystals are also known to exist for this protein as well as plane two-dimensional layers). Later on, tubular crystals were found for phosphorylases b and a and glucose oxidase. Tubular crystals *in vivo* and *in vitro* are formed by the protein tubulin. The length of tubes for all these proteins reaches several thousand Ångström units. Sometimes ring fragments of tubes lying hole up are observed. Some details of tubular structures can be revealed by the method of optical diffraction and filtering, which allows one to refine the packing parameters and to show separately the "near" and "far" sides of the wall, giving, ultimately, an estimate of the size and shape of the molecules (Fig. 7). The formation of a monomolecular layer (wall) may be explained by the selective character of the interaction between protein molecules. These interactions are mainly electrostatic and depend upon the presence of some charged groups on the surface of the protein molecules (Fig. 39). The overall interaction can result in the attraction of certain "lateral" parts of the surface, while the "end" parts may not attract one another (or may even cause repulsion of the molecules [Fig. 39(a), (b)]. The shape of the molecules also can contribute, being appropriate for complementary packing in layers. The monomolecular layer formed in such a way may be plane in a particular case, but generally it appears to be curvilinear [Fig. 39 (b)].

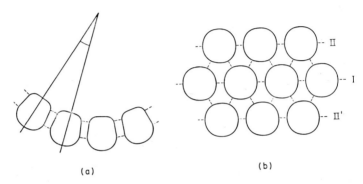

(a)   (b)

Fig. 39. Interaction between molecules leading to their packing in tubular crystals (strongest bonds are denoted by dashed lines). (a) View along the tube axis; (b) perpendicular to it.

It should be emphasized that Figs 37 and 39 serve only as a formal geometrical illustration of the relativeness of the tubular and planar net structures, and not as examples of how the formation (crystallization) of the tubes proceeds. They crystallize in different ways—by helical growth, strand by strand, or by piling of the "discs", and not by "rolling up" of a monomolecular layer already formed.

The parameters of some tubular crystals are given in Table I.

For catalase from erythrocytes and for phosphorylases *b* and *a* (Fig. 7), conclusions have been drawn about the symmetry of the molecules (it is tetrahedral, 222), and structural models have been proposed. The three-dimensional reconstruction has been performed for ox liver catalase, glucose oxidase and tubulin.

F. *Catalase from Ox Liver*

An electron micrograph is shown in Fig. 40(a). Owing to the symmetry 142/17, one projection of a catalase tube with the length of image equal to

TABLE I

Protein	d	D	l, c	$p/q, N$	D/d	Reference
Catalase from erythrocytes (m.w. 250 000)	65	420	80, 375	23/5, 2	6·4	Vainshtein *et al.* (1966), Kiselev *et al.* (1967), Kiselev *et al.* (1968)
Catalase from ox-liver (m.w. 250 000)	65	310	49, 544	142/17	4·8	Vainshtein *et al.* (1978)
Glucose oxidase	50	230	60	39/11	4·6	Vainshtein *et al.* (1973)
Tubulin from flagella	40	240	80, 80	13/4	6·0	Amos and Klug (1974)
Tubulin from ox brain	40	250	40, 40 (80)	13/3	6·1	Tsuprun *et al.* (1974)
Phosphorylase *b* (m.w. 350 000)	70	320	120/840	27/7, 2	4·6	Kiselev *et al.* (1971)
Phosphorylase *a*	70	350	110/1000	229/6, 3	5·0	Kiselev *et al.* (1974a)

Notation: m.w., molecular weight; d, thickness of tube wall; D, external diameter of tube; l, width of a turn in projection onto an axis of the helix; c, period of the helix; p, q, N, helical parameters.

one period c is equivalent to 142 projections. The "longer" image gives rise to a further increase in the effective number of projections, p, which was taken to be 150. The reconstruction was performed by the SMPF method, $d_{min} = 25$ Å. One section of the tube, as can be seen in the horizontal section of the radial projection [Fig. 40(b)], gives cross-sections of the molecule at different levels, the difference in height being $c/p = 5·9$ Å, revealing, in fact, the whole of the three-dimensional structure [Fig. 40(c)]. The cross-section maxima, separated by the angular distance of $\alpha = 2\pi q/p = 43°$, represent "slices" of the molecule. The maxima show clearly the structure of the molecule, which is distinctly revealed by the peaks above the level of $\rho = 60$ (relative scale). The radial maxima on most of the sections show a tangential splitting, revealing inside the molecule four peaks related by symmetry 222. The result of reconstruction of the tube is shown in Fig. 41(a).

To refine the structure, the density distribution of the molecule has been averaged over its own symmetry axes 2_P, 2_Q, 2_R. This averaged molecule is shown in Fig. 41(b). Along the 2_P-axis one can clearly see a region of lower

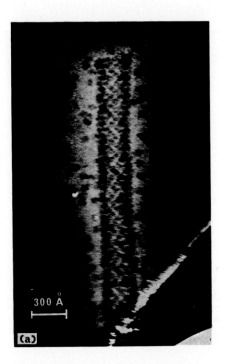

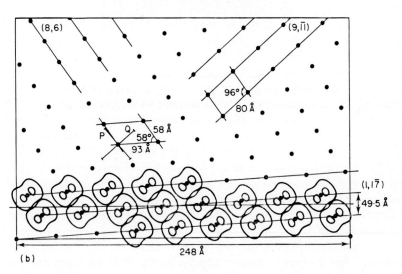

Fig. 40.

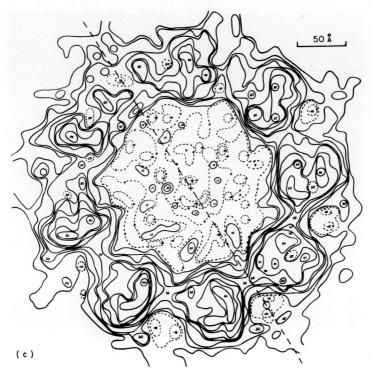

(c)

FIG. 40. (a) Electron micrograph of tubular crystals of ox liver catalase; (b) radial projection on which the molecules are shown schematically; (c) horizontal cross-section of the tube; its maxima correspond to cross-sections of the molecule that differ in height by 5·9 Å.

values of ρ, giving evidence of the presence of a channel in this part of the molecule. The centres of maxima corresponding to four subunits of catalase form a fairly flattened tetrahedron. The distances between the edges of the tetrahedron are the same along the axes 2_Q and 2_R and equal 24 Å. The edges perpendicular to the 2_P-axis stand apart about 8 Å.

The catalase molecule under the normalization conditions $\Omega_M = 300\,000\,\text{Å}^3$, has the dimensions 69 ± 8 Å along the 2_P-axis, 87 ± 8 Å along the 2_Q-axis and 92 ± 8 Å along the 2_R-axis.

A large number of contacts of subunits lying inside the tube makes the internal surface of the wall comparatively smooth, unlike the external surface on which helical "grooving" is clearly seen [Fig. 41(a), (c)].

The model of the molecule obtained from studies of tubular crystals is close to that obtained earlier from the study of the crystalline trigonal catalase [Fig. 33(b)].

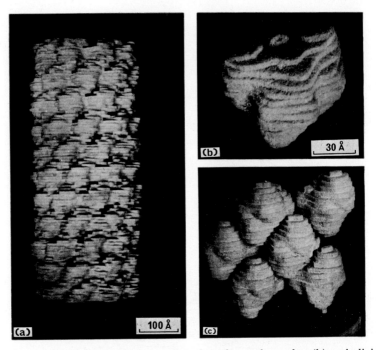

FIG. 41. (a) Three-dimensional reconstruction of a catalase tube; (b) an individual molecule of catalase from a tube [cf. Fig. 33(b), (c)]; (c) fragment of the wall, showing the mutual packing of molecules.

G. *Glucose Oxidase*

Glucose oxidase is one of many enzymes involved in the processes of biological oxidation; it catalyses the oxidation of glucose to glucolactone and hydrogen peroxide.

The enzyme isolated from various sources has a molecular weight of about 150 000 and contains two flavine prosthetic groups (FAD) per molecule as well as 10–16% of carbohydrates. From biochemical studies, glucose oxidase is known to be made up from subunits, but their actual number is a matter of controversy (2 or 4 subunits).

By electron microscopic studies of negatively stained preparations it has been established that the enzyme is crystallized in tubes [Fig. 42(a), (b)].

The three-dimensional reconstruction has been carried out by the SMPF method. The thickness of elementary discs calculated for the tubes of glucose oxidase proved to be equal to 8 Å. The model obtained from the reconstruction is presented in Fig. 42(c). The individual molecules [Fig. 43(d)] can be clearly seen in this model. Unlike catalase, the molecules of this

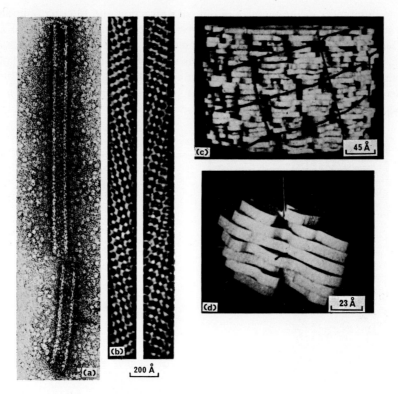

FIG. 42. (a) Electron micrograph of tubes of glucose oxidase; (b) its optical filtering; (c) three-dimensional reconstruction of the tube; (d) an individual molecule.

enzyme are elongated and lie with their long axes along a slowly sloping strand of the tube. In this direction, the molecules dissociate into two parts, each part showing two density peaks. Thus, the molecule of glucose oxidase is made of four subunits with symmetry 222. The molecular dimensions are about 60 Å × 58 Å × 85 Å, the volume is 290 000 Å^3.

H. *Studies of Microtubules*

Structural elements in the form of microtubules in some organisms take part in a variety of important cellular functions: the maintenance of the cell volume, movement of cilia and flagella, the transport of substances inside the cell. They are built from dimeric molecules of tubulin (molecular weight 110 000). Microtubules from a variety of sources have been investigated by electron microscopy with treatment of images by the methods of optical diffraction, filtering and three-dimensional reconstruction. There are some differences in the pictures of optical diffraction and filtering obtained in studies of microtubules from different sources, which also arise from different concepts of the quaternary structure of tubulin. From the work of Chasey (1972) with microtubules of cilia and from studies of Amos and Klug (1974), who applied the FSR-method in the investigation of flagellar microtubules, the molecule of tubulin at 40-Å resolution appears on filtered images as a dumb-belled particle with dimensions 80 Å × 40 Å [Fig. 43(a)].

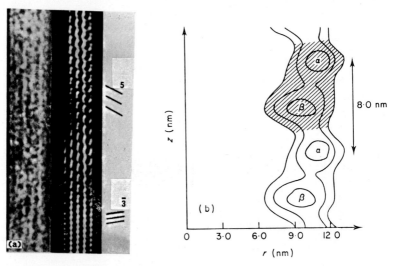

Fig. 43. Tubulin from flagellum. (a) Microphotograph of a part of the tube and a filtered image; (b) radial cross-section of protofilament.

The tubular structure is built from 13 vertical strands, staggered along the c-axis [Fig. 43(b)]. In the work of Tsuprun et al. (1974) the recrystallized layers and tubes of tubulin from ox brain cytoplasm have been studied. The three-dimensional reconstruction has been performed by the SMPF-method. These microtubules are also built from 13 strands, but with symmetry 13/4 instead of 13/3. An example of the layer image is given in Fig. 44(a). It can be seen that in this projection the packing units have the outlines of a distorted dumb-bell with dimensions of 80 Å × 40 Å. Sometimes the periodicity of 80 Å cannot be seen and in this case the "dumb-bell" molecule gives place to "rings".

The fragments of cytoplasmic microtubules are shown in Fig. 44(b), (c). On the filtered images of separate walls of microtubules, the packing units show the same appearance as in layers. A section of the microtubule is shown in Fig. 44(d), which clearly demonstrates the longitudinal splitting

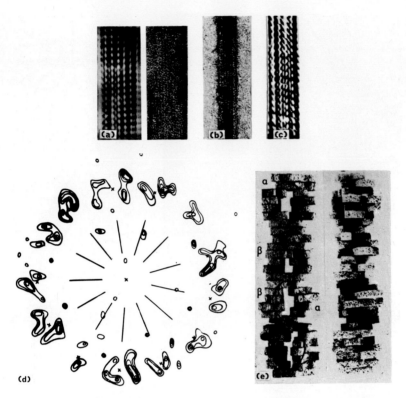

FIG. 44. Tubulin from ox brain. (a) Electron micrograph of a recrystallized layer of molecules; (b) fragments of microtubule and (c) their optical filtering; (d) tube cross-section; (e) three-dimensional reconstruction.

of the molecule. Figure 44(e) shows a model of the molecules of tubulin deduced from the three-dimensional reconstruction.

Let us now consider some examples of studies of rod-like structures.

I. *Tobacco Mosaic Virus*

Tobacco mosaic virus appears as a rod 3000 Å long with a diameter of 180 Å. From many X-ray and electron microscopical studies [Fig. 45(a)] TMV particles have been shown to be characterized by symmetry $p/q = 49/3$, with the pitch of the helix 23 Å and period $c = 69$ Å. A model of the molecular packing is given in Fig. 45(b). Recrystallization of TMV protein under certain conditions allows one to obtain discs which consist of two layers with 17 protein molecules per layer rotated through $2\pi/17$.

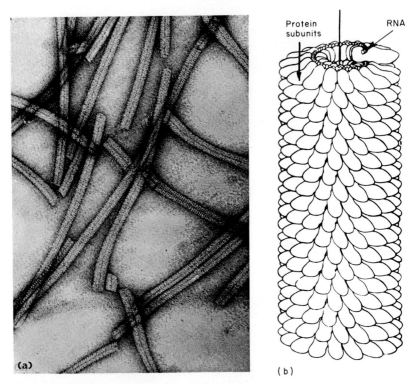

Fig. 45. Electron micrograph of tobacco mosaic virus (a) and a model of the virus (b).

The three-dimensional reconstruction of images from electron micrographs of negatively-stained stacked disc-aggregates of TMV has been carried out by Finch and Klug (1971) using the FSR-method. Figure 46 shows clearly the central channel and round holes which correspond to a weakly sloping RNA-containing channel in the native structure.

In the work of Unwin and Klug (1974) the electron micrographs [Fig. 47(a)] of negatively stained TMV rods from stacked discs have been obtained using the electrostatic phase plate. The FSR-algorithm has been used.

Figure 47(b), (c) shows the results of reconstruction at $d_{min} = 8.5$ Å. Figure 47(b) represents a section of the cylindrically averaged disc. One can see discrepancies in the appearance of the "upper" and "lower" layers, each containing 17 protein molecules, the upper molecules being elongated while the lower ones are seen to be bent into a zigzag. In a full picture of the structure [Fig. 47(c)], it manifests itself as a type of thread on the

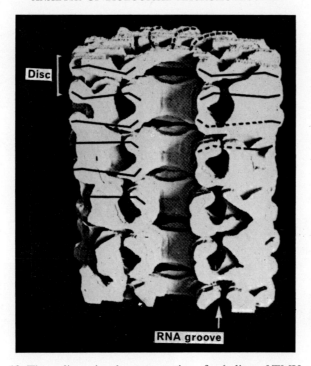

Fig. 46. Three-dimensional reconstruction of polydiscs of TMV.

external surface of the stacked disc rod. The discrepancies in two layers of the disc have been confirmed by X-ray analysis of this structure. It should be noted, however, that in native TMV particles (Fig. 45) possessing helical symmetry all the protein molecules are completely identical.

J. *Structure of Haemocyanin*

The molecules of the copper-containing protein, haemocyanin, are concerned with oxygen transport in the haemolymph of molluscs, crabs, snails, octopuses and other invertebrates. Figure 48 is an electron micrograph of gastropod haemocyanin. These molecules have a molecular weight of about 8×10^6; they are cylinders of height 360 Å, with a diameter of 300 Å, having a complex quaternary structure. The molecules dissociate into halves in a plane perpendicular to the cylinder axis (Bois d'Enghien *et al.*, 1971). Mellema and Klug (1972) have carried out three-dimensional reconstruction of the structure. The analysis of rotational symmetry shows that a half of the molecule has in projection a fivefold axis $(N = 5)$, but its outside part is more accurately characterized by a tenfold axis $(N = 10)$.

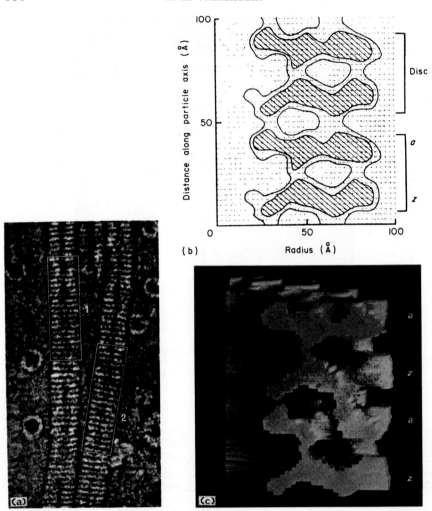

FIG. 47. Structure of polydiscs of TMV. (a) Electron micrograph obtained by the phase plate method; (b) cross-section of the cylindrically averaged structure; (c) three-dimensional reconstruction at a resolution 8·5 Å.

The whole particle has symmetry 52. Under appropriate conditions the molecules are crystallized end-to-end, forming rods with an axial repeat of about 1150 Å, successive particles being rotated by 120°. Thus, the effective number of projections of the molecule is equal to $3 \times 5 = 15$. This allowed the FSR-method to be applied, with $d_{\min} = 50$ Å in the radial direction and $d_{\min} = 30$ Å in the axial one. Figure 48(c) shows the cylindrically

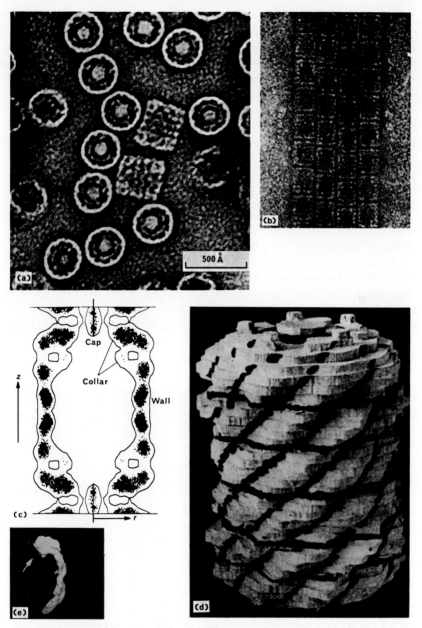

FIG. 48. Gastropod haemocyanin. (a) Electron micrographs of individual molecules and their halves; (b) piles of molecules; (c) cross-section of a cylindrically averaged molecule; (d) three-dimensional reconstruction; (e) structure of individual subunits.

averaged distribution of density in the molecule of haemocyanin. The model obtained by three-dimensional reconstruction is illustrated by Fig. 48(d). The molecule is hollow and narrowed in the upper and lower parts, forming a collar. The cylindrical part consists of 60 morphological subunits which are packed forming a clearly cut "thread" with symmetry $N = 10$, while the collar has symmetry $N = 5$. The conclusion can be drawn that the morphological unit is itself composed of two functional subunits related by a twofold axis. Thus there are, in fact, 120 subunits of molecular weight 60 000. Such functional subunits were actually isolated and observed in the work of Siezen and van Bruggen (1974) [Fig. 48(e)].

K. *Muscle Proteins*

It is well known that muscle is composed of two main protein systems: thin filaments of actin and thick fibres of myosin. In muscle these two kinds of filaments are parallel to each other, forming in cross-section a hexagonal packing. The process of muscle contraction may be described as the sliding of these two kinds of protein systems. From many electron microscopic and X-ray data for the whole muscle and its components, in isolated and reaggregated states, it has been established that each protein consists of globular molecules joined in chains and many details of their structure are now known. Here we shall consider the data obtained by the FSR-method.

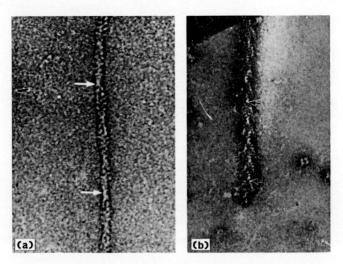

Fig. 49. Electron micrographs of (a) individual actin filaments and (b) filaments of the actin–myosin complex (the 715 Å period is arrowed).

The actin filaments can be isolated separately [Fig. 49(a)]. They are about 80 Å in diameter and are made of globular subunits (of molecular weight 45 000) arranged on a double helix having symmetry s_{13} with $c/p = 55$ Å. A purified specimen can also be prepared in the form of a "paracrystal" made up of these filaments. Figure 50(a) shows a reconstruction of the actin filament (Moore *et al.*, 1970) that reveals the globular subunits and the connections between them. Actin filaments isolated directly from muscle and "decorated" with the so-called subfragments of myosin have a more complex structure [Fig. 49(b)]. They show the same symmetry s_{13}. The subfragment molecule is about 45 Å thick and about

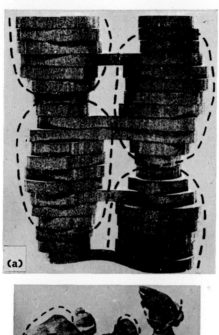

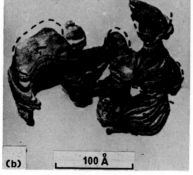

FIG. 50. (a) Reconstruction of an element of the actin filament; (b) reconstruction of an element of the actin–myosin complex.

150 Å long. The reconstruction is illustrated in Fig. 50(b). A fundamental feature is the inclination of the subfragments which implies a polarity or "arrowlike" nature of the structure. Fig. 51 shows the relative arrangement of the main components of the filaments in cross-section.

In the work of Wakabayashi *et al.* (1975) a three-dimensional reconstruction has been carried out of actin–tropomyosin $(A + Tm)$ complexes which are the active form of the thin filaments, and also of a more complicated inhibited complex actin–tropomyosin–troponin $(T + I)$:

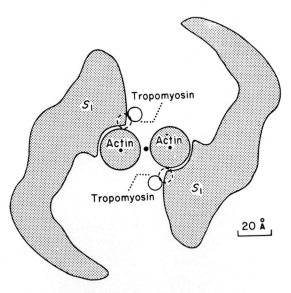

FIG. 51. Mutual arrangement of the main components of a thin filament in cross-section. The position of T_2 in the active state is represented by a solid circle and in the inhibited filament by a dashed circle.

$[A + Tm + Tr(T + I)]$. There is one globular molecule of troponin per 7 actin subunits, the distance between troponin molecules being 400 Å along a thin filament. Its function is the binding of the calcium involved in regulation of the muscle activity. The change in physical state of troponin induced by the calcium ions produces via tropomyosin the changes in the state of actin. The best micrographs of paracrystals were selected for analysis, the data obtained being averaged. Figure 52(a), (b) shows the two-dimensional computationally filtered image of the $A + T$ and $A + T + Tr(T+I)$ complexes. Parts of the reconstructed three-dimensional models are shown in Fig. 52(c), (d). The Fourier synthesis had the terms limited by $d_{\min}$ up to 45 Å in the axial direction and to 15 Å in the radial direction. So-called

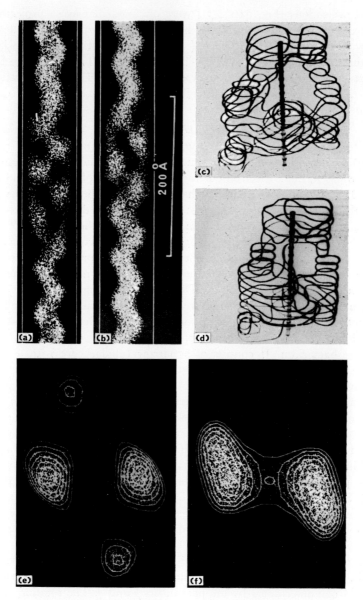

Fig. 52. The computationally filtered image of filaments of the complexes A + Tm (a) and A + Tm + Tr (b); (c), (d) sections of the three-dimensional reconstruction of these complexes; (e), (f) helical projections of corresponding structures. In (f) one can clearly see the A + Tm peaks becoming merged (see diagram in Fig. 51).

helical projections [Fig. 52(e), (f)] were obtained that are a projection of the structure along the continuous helical lines corresponding to the symmetry of the structure. Figure 52(e), (f) illustrates the difference in the structure of the complexes (A + Tm) and A + Tm + Tr(T + I). It consists in a shift of Tm in the presence of Tr(T + I) in the direction of actin. This shift is shown schematically in Fig. 51.

L. *Structure of Bacteriophages*

Bacteriophages belong to the group of complex viruses having a special apparatus for injection of the genetic material—nucleic acid—into the infected bacterium. Electron micrographs of some phages are shown in Fig. 53. The head of the bacteriophage is built of a protein coat that contains RNA. The main parts of the tail are the core, the sheath, baseplate and tail filaments. The different functional parts of the phage are built of some dozens of different proteins. A great amount of work has been devoted to the phage structure. Some of the bacteriophage proteins, e.g. proteins of the head coat, can be isolated and investigated in a crystallized state (see, for example, Poglazov, 1966; De Rosier and Klug, 1972).

Of much interest is the structure of the phage tails possessing helical symmetry and consisting of several sorts of protein molecules. In most of the bacteriophages the tail is an active organ which injects the nucleic acid into the host bacterium. It consists of a narrow tubular core with a central channel surrounded by a sheath. When the phage attaches to the bacterium, the sheath is seen to contract causing the core to penetrate the host cell wall and leading to the injection of the nucleic acid into the cell. Thus the sheath is one of the most primitive motility organs observed in nature.

At present the structure of the tails of a number of phages has been studied by the method of three-dimensional reconstruction. They are listed in Tables II and III. All these structures have helical symmetry.

The parameters p, q and N of the helix are determined by optical diffraction [Fig. 54(a)]. According to the selection rule [Eqn (40)] Bessel functions whose order is a multiple of the order N of the rotation axis of the object contribute to the reflections in the diffraction pattern. All of the studied tails have rotational symmetry, $N = 6$.

Thus these structures can be described as piles of stacked discs along the N-axis. The discs are laid on one another with a rotation with respect to the next one determined by the parameters p and q. The rotation angle is $\phi = 2\pi q/p$. Since the N-axis is available, a rotation may be presented by any angle $2\pi q/p \pm \dfrac{k2\pi}{N}$, $k = 1, 2, 3 \ldots$. For T-even phages it is $p/q = 7/2$ and the rotation of the disc is equal to 103°. For the phage Phi 5, $p/q = 7/3$

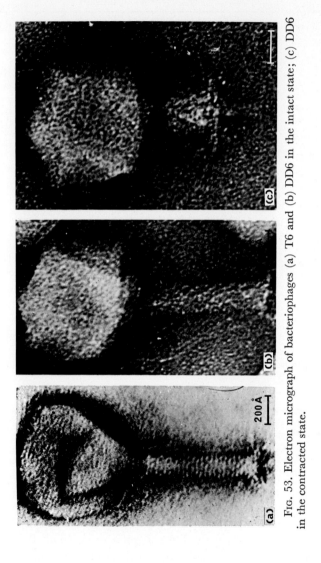

FIG. 53. Electron micrograph of bacteriophages (a) T6 and (b) DD6 in the intact state; (c) DD6 in the contracted state.

TABLE II

Geometrical parameters* of contractile tails of phages in the intact state
and of the tail of phage Butyricum

Parameter	T2	T6	H17	AR9	Phi5	Butyricum
N	6	6	6	6	6	6
p/q	7/2	7/2	17/6	11/3	7/3	$18/1 = 3/\frac{1}{6}$
c/p (Å)	40	38	39	40	36	35–40
Rotation of disc $2\pi q/p$ (degrees)	103°	103°	127°	98°	154°	20°
Length of tail (Å)	960	810		2000–2200	1100–1200	1100–1200
Outer diameter (Å)	170	170	210	300–360	180–210	120–160
Number of asymmetric units of the sheath	144	144		300–324		330
Number of elementary discs	24	24		50–54		55
Outer diameter of the tail core (Å)	70–80	85		100–150	75	
Diameter of axial channel of the core (Å)	20–25	25–30	30	40–65	25–30	60
Distance from the axis of the tail to the centre of the sheath units (Å)	70			110–135	75	
Diameter of helical channels	20	20–30	20–30		35	
Method	SPF	SPF	Convol.	SMPF	SMPF	SMPF

References: T2, Mikhailov and Vainshtein (1972); T6, Mikhailov and Vainshtein (1971a, b); H17, Edinzov *et al.* (1975); AR9, Vainshtein *et al.* (1976b); Phi5, Mikhailov *et al.* (1977); Butyricum, Mikhailov *et al.* (1976).

* In some cases, two extreme values of the parameters are indicated, due either to scatter of experimental data or data obtained by different methods.

and the disc is rotated at an angle of 154°. Every disc of number n is translationally equivalent to the disc of number $n + p$. That is, it lies exactly under (or over) the latter in the same angular orientation. In accordance with Eqn (33d), one projection of the tail is equivalent to $Np/2$ projections. For T-even phages this value is 21, which suffices for reconstruction. The diameters of the tails, their periods and some other data are given in Table II. Thus, determining the structure of one disc suffices for determining the spatial

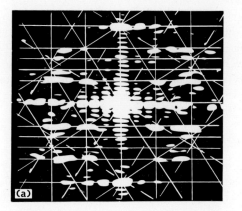

FIG. 54. (a) Optical diffraction pattern of the tail of the bacteriophage T6. The most important layer lines and the reciprocal lattice net are indicated; (b) optically filtered image.

structure of the tail segment. The thickness of a disc is about 40 Å. So to reconstruct its structure it is sufficient to calculate 3 or 4 planar cross-sections perpendicular to the tail axis. Examples are given in Figs 55(a) and 57. Since the outer radius of the phage is known, the value of the edge

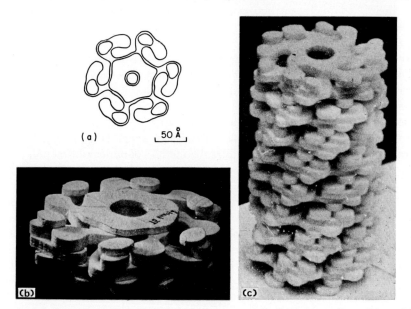

FIG. 55. Phage T6. (a) One of the cross-sections of the elementary discs; (b) model of an elementary disc; (c) the three-dimensional structure of the tail.

contour that marks the presence of protein in the object is also known. This (as well as the volume of the object being known) makes it possible to select the contour corresponding to the boundary of the protein.

It is appropriate to describe the "polypeptide substance" of the protein molecules with a quantity numerically equal to the ratio of the volume Ω (in Å^3) to its molecular weight M. For the protein subunits of the phages the following relationship holds well:

$$\Omega \text{ (Å)}/M \text{ (daltons)} = 1\cdot2-1\cdot3. \tag{69}$$

Superposing the discs on one another with an appropriate rotation gives the three-dimensional structure [Fig. 55(c)].

Let us consider the characteristic features of the structure of the tails, using the phage T6 as an example. Its diameter is equal to 170 Å. As has been already mentioned, the rotation of the disc as a whole is equal to 103°. But with $N = 6$, the subunits of the disc repeat themselves after 60°, and the minimal rotations of the nearest subunits of the neighbouring discs are $2 \times 60° - 103° = 17°$ and $60° - 103° = 43°$. Originating from these angles, two families of helical grooves are observed on the outer surface of the tail that seem to form "parallelograms" on the surface of a cylinder. There is a central cylindrical channel along the axis ($d \approx 30$–35 Å) and additionally six helical channels run between the subunits at some distance from the axis of the tail (see Tables II and III). Two density maxima are observed along the radii of the tails. One of them adjoins the axial channel and the other is on the periphery of the tail. The near-axis maxima correspond to the protein molecules (m.w. 20 000) that form the phage core, and the peripheral ones correspond to the protein molecules (m.w. 80 000) that form the sheath. Synthesis reveals clearly the elongated shape of asymmetric subunits of the sheath of the phage T6. Each of the six peripheral density maxima appears as a "dumb-bell" of irregular shape [Fig. 55(c)]. Micrographs of stained phages obtained by the method of optical diffraction have $d_{\min} \approx 25$–35 Å, giving an estimate of resolution of the models built in this way.

The phage Butyricum belongs to the group of phages with a long non-contractile tail. This type of bacteriophage is widespread among bacterial viruses. The tail is composed only of the sheath with $N = 6$, the rotation of the elementary discs being 20°. The size of the axial channel is 50–60 Å. This phage (unlike the phages with a contractile tail) has the sheath subunits, with dimensions of about 70 Å $\times$ 32 Å $\times$ 40 Å, arranged with their long axis along the radii (Fig. 56).

The dimeric structure of the sheath subunits has been revealed for the phage Phi 5 [Fig. 57(a), (b)].

TABLE III

Geometrical parameters of intact and contracted tails of phages DD6 and T4

Parameter	DD6		T4	
	intact	contracted	intact	sheath
N	6	6	6	6
p/q	7/2	11/1	7/2	11/1
c/p (Å)	40	15	41	17
Minimal rotation of a sheath unit	17°	33°	17°	33°
Length of tail (Å)	950–1000	360	812	
Outer diameter (Å)	180–210	240–300	236–250	270–340
Number of asymmetric units of the sheath	144	144	144	
Number of elementary discs	24	24	24	
Outer diameter of the tail core (Å)	90–100	80–90	90	
Diameter of axial channel (Å)	35–40	40	15–30	
Distance from the axis of the tail to the centre of the sheath units (Å)	80–90	100		
Distance from axis of tail to helical channels (Å)	60–65		65–70	
Diameter of helical channels	30		30	
Method	SPF	SMPF	FSR	FSR

References: DD6, Mikhailov and Vainshtein (1972), Vainshtein *et. al.* (1977a); T4, De Rosier and Klug (1968), Amos and Klug (1975).

The process of contraction of the tail deserves special consideration. The length of the tail is becoming shorter and its diameter increasing [Fig. 53(c)], apparently due to the rearrangement of protein subunits. The structure of the contracted tail has been studied for phages T4 (Amos and Klug, 1975) and DD6 (Vainshtein *et al.*, 1977)). In studying the phage T4, the tubular structure produced by recrystallization of the protein subunits of the sheath served as a model of the contracted sheath. The parameters of the tails of both phages in the intact and contracted state are given in Table III. In practice, due to the small value $c/p = 15$ Å for the contracted sheath, we managed to get only one plane cross-section of the structure (Fig. 58). However, it gives a good picture of the mutual packing of the

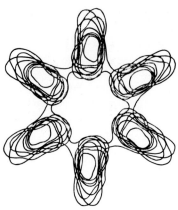

FIG. 56. The structure of an elementary disc of the phage Butyricum (super-position of cross-sections).

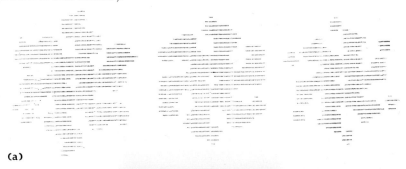

(a)

(b)

FIG. 57. Phage $\phi5$. (a) Cross-sections of the elementary disc; (b) three-dimensional reconstruction.

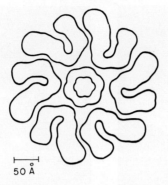

50 Å

FIG. 58. A cross-section of the tail of phage DD6 in the contracted state.

subunits: the latter have an elongated shape, their dimensions are 80 Å × 38 Å × 30 Å. The "height" of the subunits is 30 Å. Therefore, the cross-section of Fig. 58 comprises 12 cuts of the subunits. Six of them correspond to the cuts of the subunits of one disc, and the other six to those of the disc which lies under the first. In other words, the subunits of one disc enter the gaps between the subunits of the disc lying under (or over) the former. Figure 59(c), (d) shows models of the structure of the tail of phage DD6 in the intact and contracted state. In the intact structure the sheath subunits are arranged with their long axis approximately tangential to the circumference, whereas in the contracted state they are rotated in the horizontal plane at an angle of ∼40–50° and are found to be close to the radial direction. The centre of gravity of the subunits appears to be at a distance of 15 Å from the tail axis. A diagram of this rearrangement is given in Fig. 60 (a).

The rotation of the subunits and their penetration into the gaps between the subunits of the neighbouring "discs" occur simultaneously, the discs rotating with respect to each other as a single whole. In the intact state the angular displacements [Fig. 60(b)] are 17° and −43°, in the contracted state 33° and −27°. The geometrical scheme of the transition is shown in Fig. 60(b). Thus we observe the "unscrewing" of the structure starting from the baseplate with the neighbouring discs rotated through 16°. Taking into account the subunit rotations, the sheath diameter increases from 210 Å to 300 Å. This is accompanied by the decrease in the height of the sheath from 1000 Å down to 360 Å. The structure consists of 24 discs; hence, during contraction the rotation of the last disc with respect to the first one turns out to be 230°. Within the error limits, the shape and dimensions of the subunits in both states of the phage are found to be unchanged (Table III).

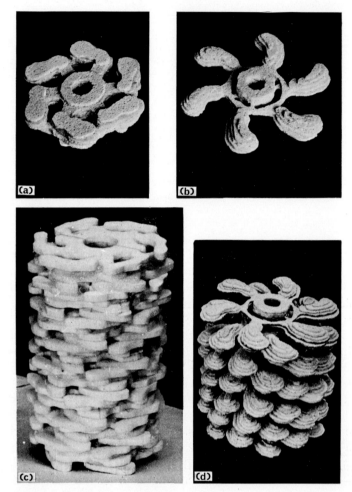

FIG. 59. Phage DD6. Three-dimensional reconstruction of the structure (a, b) of discs and (c, d) of the tail as a whole, in the intact (a, c) and contracted (b, d) state.

However, it may well be that during contraction a change in the structure of the subunits themselves occurs that has not so far been recorded.

Similar data on the rearrangement of the subunits in the intact-contracted state transition have been obtained in the work on phage T4* (Table III). As a model for the contracted structure the authors used a polysheath [Fig. 61(a)]. These structures are shown in Fig. 61(b)–(d). The

* Experimental studies of the contracted tail of phage T4 were carried out by Moody (1973).

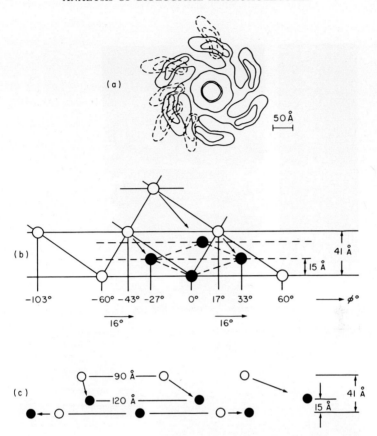

Fig. 60. (a) Diagram of the rearrangement of protein units of the DD6 phage sheath in the process of contraction; (b) the radial projection of the sheath in the intact (white circles) and contracted (black circles) state; displacement of the units being contracted is shown by arrows; (c) diagram of the rearrangement on the dimensional radial projection (the distances between the centres of gravity of the subunits are indicated).

reconstruction of the contracted tail of the phage DD6 made it possible to reveal the tail core, while in the T4 polysheath it is, naturally, lacking. On calculation of the dimensions of the structure, the authors pointed out that in negative staining the radial shrinkage coefficients for the extended tail is 1·18, whereas for the polysheath it is 1·38 on the basis of measurements of freeze-etched specimens.

One can make the assumption that the structure of the tail in the intact phage is tense, ready for contraction when coming into contact with the

366   B. K. VAINSHTEIN

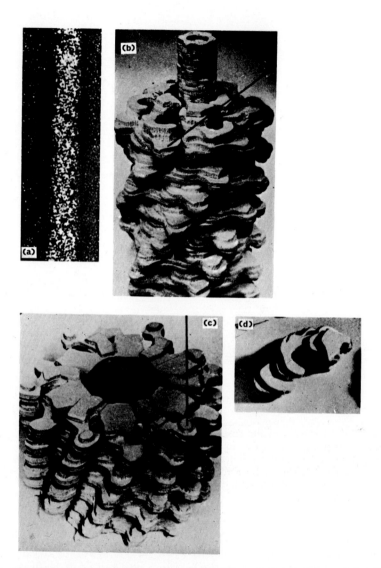

Fig. 61. Phage T4. (a) Electron micrograph of the polysheath. Three-dimensional reconstruction of the structure of the intact tail (b) and polysheath (c); (d) an individual unit of the sheath.

host bacterium. The contracted state is consequently stable; this is confirmed by the evidence that during recrystallization the subunits form a polysheath whose structure corresponds to the contracted structure.

A very tempting object for three-dimensional reconstruction appears to be the ribosomes—the particles involved in a synthesis of protein inside the cell. However, in studying them we come up against certain experimental difficulties. At present a semiquantitative model for ribosomes has been constructed (Nonomura *et al.*, 1971; Kiselev *et al.*, 1974b). Lake (1972) and Lake and Slayter (1972) have investigated the particle packing in the so-called chromatoid "braids", using the method of three-dimensional reconstruction.

M. *Spherical Viruses*

The method of three-dimensional reconstruction has been successfully applied in studying the structure of spherical viruses of animals and plants. The viruses, e.g. viruses of herpes, polyoma, polyomyelitis, turnip yellow mosaic virus, are made up of a protein coat and the RNA, the carrier of the genetic information, which is located inside the coat. It is this RNA that enters the host cell and causes the informational-synthesizing system of the latter to reproduce the virus, instead of the proteins needed by the cell itself.

The closed protein coat is built of a monomolecular layer of protein morphological units which in first approximation can be represented by spheres [see Fig. 62(a), (b)]. This coat seems to be built of a close-packed layer of these units. The most economical principle of construction of a coat requires the maximal ratio of the inner volume to the surface. Close-packing of morphological units on the surface of a sphere is impossible, but the best solution in this sense is icosahedral packing. The icosahedral point-group symmetry has the symbol 532 (Fig. 63). Symmetry planes are impossible here, just as in any biological structures made of "left-handed" amino acids.

An individual protein globule (subunit) is always asymmetric. Hence a morphological protein unit, which is provisionally depicted as a sphere in Fig. 62(b), must consist of six protein molecules in the "planar" regions of the coat and on the edges, i.e. it is a so-called hexamer. At the same time, in order to permit building a closed icosahedral coat, we must assume that the morphological subunits lying on the fivefold axis are associations of the subunit molecules into pentamers. The possible number M of morphological units in icosahedral viruses and the number P of protein subunits in the coats are determined by the formulae (Klug and Caspar, 1960):

$$M = 12_{\text{(pent)}} + 10(T - 1)_{\text{(hex)}}; \; P = 60T + 6(M - 12). \quad (70)$$

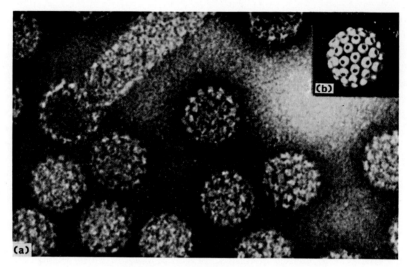

FIG. 62. Human wart virus (a) and its model (b).

Here the "triangulation number" T can take on certain integer values: $T = 1, 3, 4$ or 7. Thus, for phage ϕ, $T = 1$, i.e. $M = 12$ and $P = 60$ (the simplest case). For turnip yellow mosaic virus $T = 3$, $M = 32$ and $P = 180$, and for viruses of herpes and varicella $T = 16$, $M = 162$ and $P = 1500$. However, the protein subunits may associate not only into pentamers and hexamers, but also into dimers or trimers, then:

$$M_{\text{dimers}} = P/2 \text{ or } M_{\text{trimers}} = P/3. \tag{71}$$

Before performing a three-dimensional reconstruction, the orientation of a virus particle on the substrate must be determined. To do this, one must

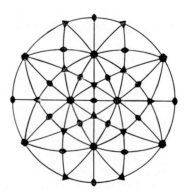

FIG. 63. Stereographic projection of the point group 532.

obtain on a computer a simulated image of virus projections for different orientations and compare the observed picture with the calculated one. Figure 64 shows the different projections of a polyoma-type virus [such as the human wart virus (see Fig. 62) which is built of 72 morphological units] as calculated by a computer and as they appear on the screen. These projections simulate well the corresponding photographs. Analysis of the Fourier transforms (Crowther, 1971) allows us to select the undistorted

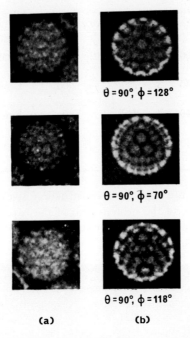

$\theta = 90°, \phi = 128°$

$\theta = 90°, \phi = 70°$

$\theta = 90°, \phi = 118°$

(a)   (b)

FIG. 64. (a) Electron micrographs of particles of polyoma-type virus; (b) the computationally obtained simulation of particle projections in corresponding orientations.

particles and define their orientation more accurately. The reconstruction was carried out in cylindrical coordinates using the FSR method. Here the most advantageous position of the particles on the substrate had the five-fold axis parallel to the latter. This is equivalent to observing $p = 10$ projections. Actually, in order to expand the set of Ψ_i in Eqn (33b) other particles were selected, also with the fivefold axis parallel to the substrate, but in different azimuthal orientations. As a result, the effective number of projections was increased.

The results of the calculations are averaged according to the icosahedral symmetry.

Table IV contains the principal data on the viruses studied. It should be noted that since the stain envelopes only the surface of a virus without

TABLE IV

Virus	Diameter Å	T	P	M	Reference
Human wart virus	550	7	420	$12p+60h=72$	Crowther *et al.* (1970b), Crowther and Amos (1971b)
Turnip yellow mosaic virus	300	3	180	$12p+20h=32$	Mellema and Amos (1972)
Tomato bushy stunt virus	330	3	180	90d	Crowther *et al.* (1970b)
Nudaurelia capensis β virus	340	4	240	80t	Finch *et al.* (1974)
Cowpea mosaic virus	240	3	60+60	$12p+20t$	Crowther *et al.* (1974)

penetrating into the interior, the reconstruction gives information only on the extrinsic structure of the protein coat of the capsule without providing any data on the structure of its inner surface, to say nothing of the nucleic acid core of the virus.

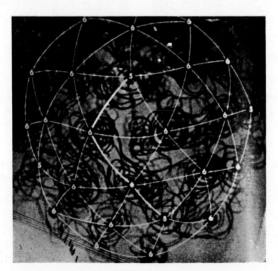

FIG. 65. Reconstruction of human wart virus.

One of the objects studied was human wart virus (HWV). The result of reconstruction by the FSR method (Fig. 65) distinctly reveals the icosahedral symmetry and nature of the packing of the particles. At a resolution as good as 40 Å, the hexamers appear as "rings" of protein globules. The polyoma virus has an analogous structure. The pattern of HWV obtained by the SMPF method is shown in Fig. 26.

In the case of tomato bushy stunt virus (TBSV) the grouping into pentamers and hexamers was not observed, but dimers were present. Their

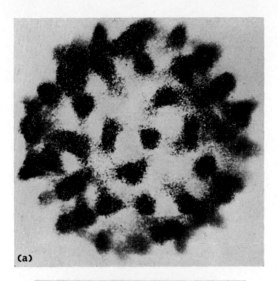

(a)

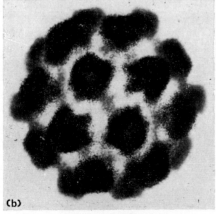

(b)

FIG. 66. Reconstruction of (a) TBSV and (b) TYMV represented as spacial blobs of density. The difference in structure of morphological units is clearly revealed.

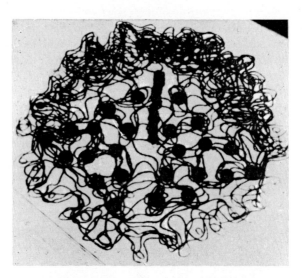

FIG. 67. Reconstruction of the structure of *Nudaurelia capensis β* virus.

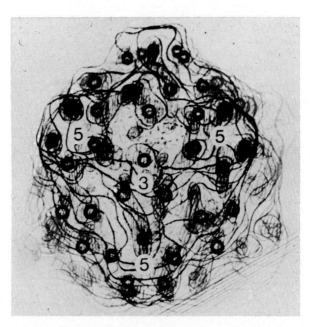

FIG. 68. Reconstruction of cowpea mosaic virus.

number is 90. Figure 66(a) shows the reconstruction at a resolution of
~30 Å. Blobs of density corresponding to dimers stand out clearly. Some
of them lie on the twofold axes. These dimers seem to be more massive, their
radius being greater by 10 Å. The dimeric units are grouped in fives around
the fivefold axes, but they also enter into sixes around the threefold axes.

The reconstruction of turnip yellow mosaic virus (TYMV) has been
performed by reference to five images ($d_{min} \approx 40$ Å). The result is displayed
in Fig. 66(b). Pentamers and hexamers show up quite distinctly.

A rare case, $T = 4$, is realized in *Nudaurelia capensis* β (NCβV); here the
protein molecules manifest clustering into trimers (Fig. 67). Four trimers
are located at each triangular face of an icosahedron.

The capsule of cowpea mosaic virus is built of two sorts of protein molecules with molecular weights of 49 000 and 27 500. The surface of the
capsule displays prominences on the fivefold axes (Fig. 68). Deeper under
the surface there are five density peaks around the fivefold axis, and three
peaks around the threefold axis. The authors suggest that the large protein
forms 12 pentamers, and the small one 20 trimers.

VI. Conclusion

As a result of the development of experimental techniques, the ideas of
diffraction optics and methods of three-dimensional reconstruction, electron
microscopy has now become, along with X-ray diffraction and other
diffraction methods, an independent method of structure analysis of biological objects.

As we have seen, many valuable results in studying biological macromolecules, crystals, viruses, phages and other objects have been obtained
with the aid of this method.

Electron microscopy has not yet achieved the level of 1·5 Å resolution
inherent in X-ray diffraction. However, establishing a structure at the
atomic level by X-ray analysis is very time-consuming, and high resolution work requires good crystals. Electron microscopical methods are
simpler and require considerably less time.

For the time being, however, electron microscopy is seriously inferior in
resolution to diffraction methods. In studying stained objects it reaches
30–20 Å, and only in rare cases with unstained specimens has a better
resolution been achieved.

On the other hand, electron microscopy has the advantage of investigation not only of crystals, but also individual molecules or their micro-
associations, e.g. viruses, etc. The X-ray analysis of such objects, e.g.
individual molecules in solution, by the small-angle scattering technique
gives much less information as compared with electron microscopy.

It goes without saying that these methods should not be opposed against each other. On the contrary, they complement each other very well both in studying biological structures and in general in the investigation of any other materials, and may be applied simultaneously.

There is no doubt that further development of the theory, experimental technique and methods of image interpretation will permit new advances in electron microscopy as a method for analysis of the three-dimensional structure of matter and of biological objects in particular.

REFERENCES

Amos, L. A. and Klug, A. (1974). *J. Cell Sci.* **14**, 523.
Amos, L. A. and Klug, A. (1975). *J. molec. Biol.* **99**, 51.
Barynin, V. V. and Vainshtein, B. K. (1971). *Kristallografiya* **16**, 751.
Barynin, V. V. and Vainshtein, B. K. (1972). *Sov. Phys. Crystallogr.* **16**, 653.
Berry, M. V. and Gibbs, D. F. (1970). *Proc. R. Soc. A* **314**, 143.
Birch, K. G. (1972). *Rep. Progr. Phys.* **35**, 1265.
Bois d'Enghien, A. P., Elliott, F. G., Bartels, W. J. and van Bruggen, E. F. J. (1971). *Comp. Biochem. Physiol. B* **40**, 1045.
Bracewell, R. N. (1956). *Aust. J. Phys.* **9**, 198.
Bracewell, R. N. and Riddle, A. C. (1967). *Astrophys. J.* **150**, 427.
Chang, S. K. (1971). *Communs Assoc. Comput. Mach.* **14**, 21.
Chang, S. K. and Shelton, G. L. (1971). *Instn elect. electron. Engrs Trans. Systems Man Cybernet.* **1**, 90.
Chasey, D. (1972). *Exptl Cell Res.* **74**, 140.
Cochran, W., Crick, F. H. C. and Vand, V. (1952). *Acta crystallogr.* **5**, 581.
Cormack, A. M. (1963). *J. appl. Phys.* **34**, 2722.
Cormack, A. M. (1964). *J. appl. Phys.* **35**, 2908.
Cosslett, V. E. (1972). *Proc. Manchester lit. philos. Soc.* **115**, 1.
Crowther, R. A. (1971). *Philos. Trans. R. Soc. B* **261**, 221.
Crowther, R. A. and Amos, L. A. (1971a). *J. molec. Biol.* **60**, 123.
Crowther, R. A. and Amos, L. A. (1971b). *Cold Spring Harbor Symp. quant. Biol.* **36**, 489.
Crowther, R. A. and Klug, A. (1975). *A. Rev. Biochem.* **44**, 161–182.
Crowther, R. A. De Rosier, D. J. and Klug, A. (1970a). *Proc. R. Soc. A* **317**, 319.
Crowther, R. A., Geelen, J. L. M. C. and Mellema, J. E. (1974). *Virology* **57**, 20.
Crowther, R. A., Amos, L. A., Finch, J. T., De Rosier, D. J. and Klug, A. (1970b). *Nature, Lond.* **226**, 421.
De Rosier, D. J. and Klug, A. (1968). *Nature, Lond.* **217**, 130.
De Rosier, D. J. and Klug, A. (1972). *J. molec. Biol.* **65**, 469–488.
De Rosier, D. J. and Moore, P. B. (1970). *J. molec. Biol.* **52**, 355.
Dorset, D. L. and Parsons, D. F. (1975). *Acta crystallogr. A* **31**, 210.
Edinzov, I. M., Ivanizkiy, G. R. and Kuniskiy, A. C. (1975). *Dokl. Akad. Nauk SSSR* **224**, 704.
Erickson, H. P. and Klug, A. (1970). *Ber. Bunsen-Ges. phys. Chem.* **74**, 1129.
Erickson, R. O. (1973). *Science, N.Y.* **181**, 705–716.
Finch, J. T. (1975). *In* "The Proteins" (3rd ed), Vol. 1, p. 413. Academic Press, London and New York.

Finch, J. T. and Klug, A. (1971). *Philos. Trans. R. Soc. B* **261,** 211.
Finch, J. T., Crowther, R. A., Hendry, D. A. and Struthers, J. K. (1974). *J. gen. Virol.* **24,** 191.
Frieder, G. and Herman, G. T. (1971). *J. theor. Biol.* **33,** 189.
Gabor, D. (1949). *Proc. R. Soc. A* **197,** 545.
Gabor, D. (1951). *Proc. R. Soc. B* **64,** 449.
Gel'fand, I. M. and Shilov, G. E. (1964). "Generalized Functions". Academic Press, London and New York. Vol. 1.
Gel'fand, I. M., Graew, H. N. and Shapiro, Z. Ya (1967). *Funkzion. Anal.* **1,** 15–31.
Gilbert, P. C. F. (1972a) *Proc. R. Soc. B.* **182,** 89.
Gilbert, P. C. F. (1972b). *J. theor. Biol.* **36,** 105.
Gordon, R. Bender, R. and Herman, G. T. (1970). *J. theor. Biol.* **29,** 471.
Gordon, R. and Herman, G. T. (1971). *Center theor. Biol. quart. Bull.* **4,** 71.
Gurskaya, G. V. (1975). *Kristallografiya* **20,** 516–523.
Gurskaya, G. V., Lobanova, G. M. and Vainshtein, B. K. (1971). *Kristallografiya* **16,** 764–773.
Gurskaya, G. V., Lobanova, G. M. and Vainshtein, B. K. (1972). *Sov. Phys. Crystallogr.* **16,** 662–669.
Hanszen, K. J. (1969). *Z. Naturf.* **24a,** 1849.
Henderson, R. and Unwin, P. N. T. (1975). *Nature, Lond.* **257,** 28.
Herman, G. T. and Rowland, S. W. (1971). *J. theor. Biol.* **33,** 213.
Herman, G. T. and Rowland, S. W. (1973). *Comput. Graphics Image Process.* **2,** 151.
Herman, G. T., Lent, A. and Rowland, S. W. (1973). *J. theor. Biol.* **42,** 1.
Hoppe, W. (1969). *Optik* **29,** 617.
Hoppe, W. (1970). *Acta crystallogr. A* **26,** 414.
Hoppe, W. (1971). *Philos. Trans. R. Soc. B* **261,** 71–94.
Hoppe, W. (1974). *Naturwissenschaften* **61,** 534.
Hoppe, W., Langer, K. and Thon, F. (1970). *Optik* **30,** 538.
Hoppe, W., Hunsmann, N., Grassmann, J., Schramm, H. J., Sturm, M. and Grill, B. (1975). *Coll. Abstr. 10th int. Congr. Crytallogr.* 289.
Kiselev, N. A., De Rosier, D. J. and Klug, A. (1968). *J. molec. Biol.* **35,** 561–566.
Kiselev, N. A., Lerner, F. Ya and Livanova, N. B. (1971). *J. molec. Biol.* **62,** 537–549.
Kiselev, N. A., Lerner, F. Ya and Livanova, N. B. (1974a). *J. molec. Biol.* **86,** 587–589.
Kiselev, N. A., Spitzberg, C. L. and Vainshtein, B. K. (1967). *J. molec. Biol.* **25,** 433–441.
Kiselev, N. A., Stel'mashuk, V. Ya, Lerman, M. I. and Abakumova, O. Yu (1974b). *J. molec. Biol.* **86,** 577–586.
Kiselev, N. A., Stel'mashuk, V. Ya, Tsuprun, V. L., Ludewig, M. and Hansen, G. (1977). *J. Molec. Biol.,* **115,** 33.
Klug, A. and Berger, J. E. (1964). *J. molec. Biol.* **10,** 565.
Klug, A. and Caspar, D. L. D. (1960). *Adv. Virus Res.* **7,** 225.
Klug, A. and Crowther, R. A. (1972). *Nature, Lond.* **238,** 435–440.
Klug, A. and De Rosier, D. J. (1966). *Nature, Lond.* **212,** 29.
Klug, A., Crick, F. H. C. and Wyckoff, H. W. (1958). *Acta crystallogr.* **11,** 199.
Lake, J. A. (1972). *J. molec. Biol.* **66,** 255.
Lake, J. A. and Slayter, H. S. (1972). *J. molec. Biol.* **66,** 271.
Markham, R., Frey, S. and Hills, G. J. (1963). *Virology* **20,** 88.
Marr, R. B. (Ed.) (1974). "Techniques of Three-dimensional Reconstruction. Proceedings of an International Workshop". Brookhaven National Laboratory, Brookhaven.

376 B. K. VAINSHTEIN

Mellema, J. E. and Amos, L. (1972). *J. molec. Biol.* **72**, 819–822.
Mellema, J. E. and Klug, A. (1972). *Nature, Lond.* **239**, 146.
Merserau, R. M. and Oppenheim, A. V. (1974). *Proc. Instn elect. electron. Engrs* **62**, 1319–1338.
Mikhailov, A. M. and Vainshtein, B. K. (1971a). *Kristallografiya* **16**, 505.
Mikhailov, A. M. and Vainshtein, B. K. (1971b). *Sov. Phys. Crystallogr.* **16**, 428.
Mikhailov, A. M. and Vainshtein, B. K. (1972). *Dokl. Akad. Nauk SSSR* **203**, 253.
Mikhailov, A. M., Vainshtein, B. K., Kaftanova, A. S., Petrovsky, G. V. and Andiashvili, I. A. (1977). *Dokl. Akad. Nauk SSSR.* **234**, 699.
Mikhailov, A. M., Vainshtein, B. K., Kaftanova, A. S., Somogyi, P. A., Grigorgev, V. B. and Petrovsky, G. V. (1976). *Dokl. Akad. Nauk SSSR* **231**, 1472.
Moody, M. F. (1973). *J. molec. Biol.* **80**, 613–635.
Moore, P. B., Huxley, H. E. and De Rosier, D. J. (1970). *J. molec. Biol.* **50**, 279.
Nonomura, Y., Blobel, G. and Sabatini, D. (1971). *J. molec. Biol.* **60**, 303–323.
Orlov, S. S. (1975). *Kristallografiya* **20**, 701–708.
Poglazov, B. F. (1966). "Structure and Functions of Contractile Proteins". Academic Press, London and New York.
Radon, J. (1917). *Ber. Verhandl. Sachs ges. Math. Phys.* **69**, 262–277.
Ramachandran, C. N. and Lakshminarayanan, A. V. (1971). *Proc. natn. Acad. Sci. USA* **68**, 2236–2240.
Scherzer, O. (1949). *J. appl. Phys.* **20**, 20.
Siezen, R. I. and van Bruggen, E. F. J. (1974). *J. molec. Biol.* **90**, 77, 113.
Smith, R. R., Peters, T. M. and Bates, P. H. T. (1973). *J. Phys. A, math. nucl. gen.* **6**, 361.
Stoyanova, I. G. and Anaskin, I. F. (1972). "Fizicheskie Osnovy Prosvechivayushchie Elektronnoi Mikroskopii" ("Physical Fundamentals of Transmission Electron Microscopy"). Nauka, Moscow.
Stroke, G. W. (1971). *New Scient.* **51**, 671.
Thon, F. (1966). *Z. Naturf.* **21a**, 476.
Tsuprun, V. L., Stel'mashuk, V. Ya, Kiselev, N. A., Gel'fand, V. I. and Rosenblatt, V. A. (1974). *Molekularnaya Biologiya.* **10**, 445.
Unwin, P. N. T. (1971). *Philos. Trans. R. Soc. B* **261**, 95–104.
Unwin, P. N. T. (1972). *Proc. R. Soc. A* **329**, 327.
Unwin, P. N. T. (1974a). *J. molec. Biol.* **87**, 657.
Unwin, P. N. T. (1974b). *Z. Naturf.* **29a**, 158.
Unwin, P. N. T. and Henderson, R. (1975). *J. molec. Biol.* **94**, 425.
Unwin, P. N. T. and Klug, A. (1974). *J. molec. Biol.* **87**, 641.
Vainshtein, B. K. (1964). "Structure Analysis by Electron Diffraction". Pergamon Press, Oxford.
Vainshtein, B. K. (1970). *Kristallografiya* **15**, 894.
Vainshtein, B. K. (1971a). *Sov. Phys.-Cryst.* **15**, 781.
Vainshtein, B. K. (1971b). *Dokl. Akad. Nauk SSSR* **196**, 1072.
Vainshtein, B. K. (1971c). *Sov. Phys. Dokl.* **16**, 66.
Vainshtein, B. K. (1972). *Mat. Res. Bull.* **7**, 1347.
Vainshtein, B. K. (1973a). *Usp. Fiz. Nauk* **109**, 445.
Vainshtein, B. K. (1973b). *Sov. Phys. Usp.* **16**, 185.
Vainshtein, B. K. and Orlov, S. S. (1972a). *Kristallografiya* **17**, 253.
Vainshtein, B. K. and Orlov, S. S. (1972b). *Sov. Phys. Crystallogr.* **17**, 213.

Vainshtein, B. K. and Orlov, S. S. (1974). *In* "Techniques of Three-dimensional Reconstruction. Proceedings of an International Workshop". (R. B. Marr, ed.), p. 158. Brookhaven National Laboratory, Brookhaven.

Vainshtein, B. K., Barynin, V. V. and Gurskaya, G. V. (1968). *Dokl. Akad. Nauk SSSR* **182,** 569.

Vainshtein, B. K., Barynin, V. V. and Gurskaya, G. V. (1969). *Sov. Phys. Dokl.* **13,** 838.

Vainshtein, B. K., Kiselev, N. A. and Spitzberg, C. L. (1966). *Dokl. Akad. Nauk SSSR* **167,** 212.

Vainshtein, B. K., Mikhailov, A. M. and Kaftanova, A. S. (1977). *Kristallografiya.* **22,** 287.

Vainshtein, B. K., Sherman, M. B. and Barynin, V. V. (1976a). *Kristallografiya* **21,** 520.

Vainshtein, B. K., Barynin, V. V., Zograff, O. N. and Karpuchina, S. Ya (1978). *Molekularnaya Biologiya.* In press.

Vainshtein, B. K., Mikhailov, A. M., Tichonenko, A. S. and Belyaeva, N. N. (1976b). *Dokl. Akad. Nauk SSSR* **228,** 1456.

Vainshtein, B. K., Kiselev, N. A., Kaftanova, A. S., Orlova, E. V., Bogdanov, V. P., Morozkin, A. D. and Degtyar, N. A. (1973). *Dokl. Akad. Nauk SSSR* **213,** 217.

Wakabayashi, T., Huxley, H. E., Amos, L. A. and Klug, A. (1975). *J. molec. Biol.* **93,** 477.

Zaitsev, V. N., Vainshtein, B. K. and Kosourov, G. I. (1968). *Kristallografiya* **13,** 594.

Zaitsev, V. N., Vainshtein, B. K. and Kosourov, G. I. (1969). *Sov. Phys. Crystallogr.* **13,** 507.

Author Index

(Numbers in italics refer to pages in the References at the end of each chapter)

A

Abakumova, O. Yu., 341, 367, *375*
Abbe, E., 17, 18, 29, *69*
Ade, G., 121, 145, 147, 151, 156, 158, 168, 169, *173, 174, 178*
Adler, J., 1, 6, 8, *13, 14*
Allegra, G., 245, 274, *276*
Allen, R. D., 65, *69*
American Society for Testing and Materials, *69*
Amos, L. A., 303, 312, 324, 328, 341, 346, 354, 361, 370, *374, 376, 377*
Anaskin, I. F., 165, *165, 174, 183*, 302, *376*
Anderson, R. A., 7, *13*
Andiashvili, I. A., 358, *376*
Ansley, D. A., 190, 220, 227, *276*
Anstis, G. R., 138, *174*
Arsenault, H., 159, *174*
Asakura, T., 162, *174, 177*
Asano, M., 93, 96, *99*
Ast, D., 148, 156, *177, 180*
Atkins, A. J., 122, 136, *181*

B

Badde, H. G., 217, *276*
Bagchi, S. N., 191, 208, 275, *278*
Baltes, H. P., 112, *174*
Barnes, F. S., *15*
Barnett, M. E., 142, 143, 145, *174*
Barrett, A. N., 191, 246, 274, *276*
Barrington Leigh, J., 191, 246, 274, *276*
Bartell, L. S., 249, *276*
Bartels, W. J., 349, *374*
Barth, J. E., 106, *181*
Barus, C., 164, *174*
Barynin, V. V., 299, 304, 324, 332, 341, *374, 377*
Basler, A., 74, 96, *99*
Bastiaans, M. J., 112, *174*

Basuray, A., 156, *175*
Bates, P. H. T., 304, 319, *376*
Bates, R. H. T., 168, *174*, 243, 244, 245, 274, *276, 278*
Baumeister, W., 253, *276*
Beadle, C., 65, *69*
Beck, V., 145, *174*
Beer, M., 138, *174*, 186, 191, 192, 257, 258, *276*
Bellarminoff, L., 74, 96, *99*
Belvaux, Y., 220, 228, *276*
Belyaeva, N. N., 358, *377*
Bénard, C. M., 172, *174*
Bender, R., 325, 326, *375*
Beorchia, A., 129, 131, 136, 159, *174, 175*, 260, 262, *276*
Beran, M. J., 103, 122, *174*
Berg, H. C., 1, 2, 3, 5, 6, 7, 8, 9, 11, 12, 13, *13, 14*
Berger, J. E., 293, *375*
Berry, M. V., 319, *374*
Billingsley, F. C., 65, *69*
Birch, K. G., 293, 304, *374*
Blobel, G., 367, *376*
Boersch, H., 160, 167, *174*
Bogdanov, V. P., 341, *377*
Bois d'Enghien, A. P., 349, *374*
Bond, R. L., 65, *69*
Bonhomme, P., 129, 131, 136, 159, *174, 175*, 260, 262, *276*
Bonnet, N., 129, 131, *175*
Born, M., 102, 103, 105, 108, 110, 111, 113, 114, 120, 158, *175*
Bostrom, R. C., 65, *70*
Böttcher, W., 96, *99*
Bowring, I. M., 172, *175*
Boyce, J. F., 245, 275, *276*
Bracewell, R. N., *69*, 310, 321, *374*
Brandt, G. B., 168, *175*
Branemark, P-I., 93, 96, *99*
Brault, J. W., 65, *69*
Brokaw, C. J., 6, *14*
Brown, D. A., 5, 9, *14*

Subject Index

A

Absorption of radiation from biological macromolecules, 282

Actin
electron micrographs, 352
filament, three-dimensional reconstruction, 353
myosin complex, reconstruction, 353
tropomyosin complex, reconstruction, 354

Aerial photography, stripe photomicrography, 81, 82

Algebraic reconstruction three-dimensional images, 324–327

Analysis, optical transforms, 55–62

Andesite, 37

Angle of illumination, phase object approximation, 194

Annular detector, size, in STEM, 271

Area microkymography, 76, 79
object display, 89
quantitative evaluation, 89
registration principles and techniques, 78

ASTM Plate 1, E112–68, optical transforms, 39

ASTM Plate III, E112–68, optical transforms, 40

Autocorrelation function, 108

B

Bacteria
manipulation on tracking microscope, 5–8
movement, 5
tracking microscope and, 1, 12

Bacteriophage DD6
electron micrograph, 357
protein units, rearrangement, 365
structure, 364
tails, geometrical parameters, 361
structure, 363

Bacteriophage ϕ, three-dimensional reconstruction, 368

Bacteriophage $\Phi 5$, elementary disc, three dimensional reconstruction, 362
sheath sub units, structure, 360

Bacteriophage T_4
base plates, electron micrographs, 303
polysheath, electron micrograph, 366
tails, contraction, 361
electron micrograph, 313
geometrical parameters, 361

Bacteriophage T_6
electron micrograph, 357
tail, optical diffraction pattern, 359
three-dimensional reconstruction, 359

Bacteriophages
half plane image, 233
negative staining, 288
sheaths, three-dimensional structure, 338
tails, three dimensional structure, 295, 356
three-dimensional structure, 356–367
tubes, three dimensional structure, 295

Bandwidth estimation, 160

Biotite, oligoclase porphyroblast in, 37

Blood cells
flow rate, 90
movement, speed determination, 13, 74
by stripe microkymography, 96

Blood flow studies, 96

Boersch effect, 160

Bright field images, phase problem solution and, 227, 228

Bright field microscopy
complementary half plane objective apertures, 251–252
phase problem and, 239–242, 247–249
tilted illumination 249